A
NATION OF
SHEPHERDS

A Novel Based On A True Story

by

Donald L. Lucero

SUNSTONE
PRESS

SANTA FE

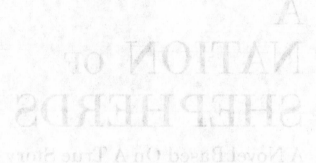

Sunstone books may be purchased for educational, business, or sales promotional use. For information please write: Special Markets Department, Sunstone Press, P.O. Box 2321, Santa Fe, New Mexico 87504-2321.

Library of Congress Cataloging-in-Publication Data:

Lucero, Donald L., 1935-
   A nation of shepherds : a novel / Donald L. Lucero.
     p. cm.
   "Based on a true story."
   ISBN 0-86534-436-1 (pbk.)
1. New Mexico—History—To 1848—Fiction. 2. Spanish Americans—Fiction. 3. Colonies—Fiction. I. Title.
PS3612.U255N38 2005
813'.6—dc22

2004012747

Published in
Santa Fe

WWW.SUNSTONEPRESS.COM
SUNSTONE PRESS / POST OFFICE BOX 2321 / SANTA FE, NM 87504-2321 /USA
(505) 988-4418 / *ORDERS ONLY* (800) 243-5644 / FAX (505) 988-1025

A
NATION OF
SHEPHERDS

IN MEMORY OF PEDRO ROBLEDO and CATALINA LOPEZ
who were the parents of

Lucia Lopez Robledo
who bore

Ana Robledo
who bore

Matias Romero
who begat

Andres Gomez Robledo
who begat

Francisco Romero de Pedraza
who begat

Margarita Gomez Robledo
who bore

Antonio Romero de Pedraza
who begat

Maria Pelaez
who bore

Domingo Romero
who begat

Teodora Fernandez de la Pedrera
who bore

Juan Jose Romero I
who begat

Diego Pedro Manuel Baca
who begat
the brothers

Jose Rafael Narcisco Romero
who begat

Jose Joaquin Baca & Jose Rafael Albino Baca
who begat   who begat

Juan Jose Romero II
who begat

Maria Martina Baca
who bore

Celso Baca
who begat

Maria Estephana Rael
who bore

Maria Juliana Romero
who bore

Maria Ana Baca   Jose Placido Baca
who bore   who begat

Maria Sinforiana Baca II

Edmundo Margarito Lucero

who are the parents of
the author

The pure Spaniard has always been
an agriculturalist by necessity,
and a shepherd by choice,
when he was not a soldier.

—Miguel de Unamuno

Spain was essentially
a nation of shepherds.

—John A. Crow
Spain: The Root and the Flower

PROLOGUE

On April 30, 1598, nine years before the founding of Jamestown, Virginia, and the Popham Colony of Maine, and 22 years before the Pilgrims anchored in Cape Cod Bay, Spain established a permanent colony in the high country of New Mexico. *A Nation of Shepherds*, which was inspired by this historic event, commemorates the lives of the 129 soldier-colonists and their families who were among the members of this first successful colonizing expedition.

No one portrayal of a historic event can be completely accurate. History is inevitably compromised in any telling. This is especially true when the author is attempting to compensate for things that have been told badly or, as in the present case, to offer a point of view not included in the previous tellings.

Despite the loss of documents in Mexico City and in New Mexico, during the Pueblo Indian Revolt of 1680, we have a surprising amount of factual information regarding the settlement of New Mexico. Among the major sources there are the documents published by Herbert E. Bolton and Charles W. Hackett; the incredible archival research conducted by George P. Hammond and Agapito Rey; a tract on the *entrada* written by *Fray* Juan de Torquemada; and notes on the archaeology of San Gabriel, New Mexico's first capital. Although this information does not rival that provided by the works of William Bradford, John Winthrop, John Eliot, or Cotton and Increase Mather regarding the settlement of the New England frontier, the information is sufficient to both inspire one's imagination and to prevent wild and arbitrary speculation regarding the

7

colonization. While these sources reflect a Spanish colonial bias, they seem to record the facts, both favorable and unfavorable, allowing one to draw his/her own conclusions from the information presented. The gap in the documentation, of course, is the total absence of Indian sources. The Indians of New Mexico did not have a written language, and their oral histories regarding some key events appear to be either lacking or of very recent interpretation. This makes the reconstruction of this history from an Indian perspective a very difficult, if not impossible, endeavor.

The task I set for myself was to take an amazing story about real people and, as accurately as possible, tell it in a blend of fact and fiction. My obligation to history was to remain true to the facts, and to 'get it right.' In recounting the story, however, I was forced to fill a complete void in my knowledge regarding the lives of the Robledo family in Spain and in New Spain. In building the lives of these people, and in providing a hypothesis for their emigration to the New World, I tethered my imagination to what is known about the social and economic conditions of the historic period.

The narrative, which is written in a semi-documentary style, is divided into three acts or periods similar to the manner in which a Spanish play would have been presented. Except for two people, each of the individuals depicted in Period III, "*The Kingdom of New Mexico*," was a member of the New Mexico colony. Antonio de Godoy, fictional chronicler of the expedition, replaces Juan Perez de Donis and Juan Gutierrez Bocanegra who were the actual secretaries of the mission. Godoy is patterned after Diego de Godoy, the Royal Notary who served in a similar capacity with Hernando Cortes. The fictional Godoy is charged with keeping the diary, and acts as cosmographer, and as mapmaker for the New Mexico expedition. These were written, described, and drawn by him in this story for the purpose of promoting Spain's most remote Northern Kingdom.

Although this narrative is based on fact, I have used fictional elements to add drama, detail and explanation. The following will clarify which is which:

King Philip II and Hernando Cortes are historical figures whose actions were as described. Elvira del Campo is historical.

Her crime, torture and testimony were as presented.

The religious facts are historical. Brother Joaquin Rodriguez, *Senor* Mattos, and Teo Machado are fictional.

Statements regarding the beginnings of Marranism, Inquisitional procedures, and the religion of the Marranos are from *A History of the Marronos* by Cecil Roth.

The journals attributed to Pedro Robledo the elder, are fictional. To my knowledge, no private diaries, letters, journals, or notebooks from the ordinary colonists survive from this period except for the epic poem, *A History of New Mexico*, published by Gaspar Perez de Villagra at Henares, Spain, in 1610, the letter from Alonso Sanchez to Rodrigo del Rio de Losa, and the letter from the officials of the royal army in New Mexico to the king.

The Indian attack on the train of 60 wagons carrying $30,000 worth of cloth actually happened. The plague of 1544 and 1555 recurred in 1575 and continued through a part of 1577. The deaths from hunger, thirst, and the effects of the cruel disease, are said to have exceeded 2,000,000, and occurred as presented.

Lucia's *carta de arras*, which in this story is said to survive among the archives at the church in Valladolid, is fictional. The names of Catalina's parents are unknown.

The geological, meteorological, calendrical, and astrometrical events were pretty much as described. The 'march across the sky' referred to when Onate leaves San Gabriel for his 'expedition toward the east,' pertains to George A. Custer and occurred in 1876.

The letters and reports attributed to Juan de Onate are historical. However, some of the descriptions of New Mexico and of its native peoples, are from the reports of Antonio de Espejo.

The reports attributed to Antonio de Godoy are historical, although the author is unknown.

The building of the *acequia*, or irrigation canal, mills, and church at San Juan are conjectured, although based on archaeological evidence, the needs of the village, and the engineering involved in their construction.

The building of the outpost north of San Juan and of the *finca de San Pedro* are supported by vague references among historical documents.

The unearthing of the dinosaur fossil, although historical, did not occur until 1947.

Certain words in the text regarding "a newer world," "knowledge," and "the quest" are from *Ulysses* by Alfred, Lord Tennyson. Quotations regarding the gypsies are from *The Gypsies* by Angus Fraser. The poem, *The Snow Man*, is by Wallace Stevens. Each of the entries in the Epilogue is historic.

The information and characterizations made regarding the leaders of the New Mexico expedition are as accurate as can be determined from archival records. Although this is a work of fiction, the thoughts and dialogues I have attributed to figures in the narrative are based on research and on my understanding of the relevant people, places and events. There are certain scenes in which I have used my imagination, based on research, to create a thought process or even a conversation in order to give the scene its full expression. This seems totally legitimate as one can infer a thought process from a record of behavior. Archival records, however, are insufficient for helping us know New Mexico's ordinary colonists. We have little information about them beyond their origins, and the physical description of the men and of their participation in some the colony's leading events. Therefore, I have drawn New Mexico's colonists to represent individuals from all aspects of Spain's Third Estate, its ordinary people.

In many respects, the questions posed in this narrative echo questions about contemporary life. The year 1598, like 1998, was a banner year of optimism and confidence, the staging period for entree into a new century. Yet, despite this unbridled optimism and confidence, the apparent initial results of the colonial enterprise were abject failure, disintegration, and abandonment. I hope that the characterizations I have made regarding the colonists in respect to their participation in and contribution to this debacle have done no one a disservice. It is unfortunate that some of the colonists' behaviors appear aberrational, startling, or even criminal, but they seem to be supported by research.

In the final analysis, may I say that I have the utmost respect and admiration for the achievements of these colonists. In individual drive, stubborn will, and indefatigable courage, they were the match of any people, and this is their story.

—Donald L. Lucero de Godoy
Dartmouth, Massachusetts

PERIOD I
THE KINGDOM OF CASTILE

The Tribunal

March 28, 1577

The sound was merely that of a hurried tap made with the butt of the knife he carried to raise the occupants of the small house but no one else. There was no answer.

The windowless house, which faced a stonewalled lane, looked like little more than a heap of puddled stone all gathered together. The man who had come up the cobblestone path stepped away from the doorway and looked up to see a whisper of white smoke, the remnant of a cooking fire, which rose from the stone chimney. He returned to the doorway, pressed his ear against the upper hinge and listened with every fiber of his being before continuing.

"Pedro," he whispered as he slapped at the door with an open palm, his knife now replaced in its leather sheath beneath his dark clothing. "It's Adan," he said. "I pray I'm in time."

Within the house, Luis, who had been sleeping before the open hearth, rose and moved to the poor bed where his aunt and uncle slept. Gently, he touched his uncle's shoulder. "*Tio*," he said, "there's someone at the door."

Pedro stirred, ran his fingers through his matted hair, and, dressed only in a nightshirt, rolled out of bed. Both he and his nephew appeared at the door where they were confronted by Pedro's workmate.

"Pedro," Adan said breathlessly as he stepped over the stone threshold, "they're coming to get you. At first light, Pedro," he warned, "they're coming for you."

"Who?" Pedro asked as he peered around the open door before closing it. "Who?" he asked again, as he struggled to put on his trousers and his boots.

"The Holy Office," Adan answered as he assisted in closing the heavy door, the three of them lifting it so that it would clear the threshold. "They blame you for the prisoner's escape and now he's been killed."

"Killed!" Pedro asked incredulously. "How? By whom?"

"A posse sent looking for him by the Inquisition trailed him to a robber's cave, and he was killed by them before he could reveal his secrets regarding additional backsliders. They say you ruined years of work by allowing him to escape."

"How could he be responsible?" asked Catalina, who was now standing behind her husband in the candlelit room. "Pedro is a scribe only," she defended in her peculiarly soft and sweet voice. "He's not responsible for prisoners."

"The prisoner was de los Santos," Pedro replied as a way of explanation, "one of those betrayed to the Holy Office by the wife of Alonso de Maya. She was the one I told you about, Catalina. What is it now . . . eight years ago? Elvira del Campo, who was charged with practicing Judaism in secret . . . not eating pork and with putting on clean clothes on Saturday. The Edict of Grace[1] had been published, and the Term of Grace[2] had passed, and the poor woman was being required to confess. You should have heard her, Catalina," Pedro said. "I was working in the room next to the chamber where she had been taken and where she was being told to tell the truth. She was subjected to the *jarra* (jug)[3] and then to the tying of the arms. '*Senores*,' she screamed, over and over again 'remind me of what I have to say for I don't know it!' A cord was applied to her arms and twisted and she was being admonished to tell the truth. 'I did it!' she screamed over and over again. 'I did what the witnesses say. I don't know how to tell it.' I went next door to plead for leniency, but they wouldn't allow me to enter. It was obvious that they wanted her to confess and that there was some proper way for her to say it. She was given 16 turns of the cord until it broke. She would have done anything—

14

said anything—to end her torture," Pedro said, "denouncing and perhaps even inventing the names of others whom she claimed were guilty of lighting special lamps on Friday evening, observing the Day of Atonement, or some other trivial action performed absent mindedly or by mere force of habit. Who knows of what, if anything, de los Santos was guilty!" he exclaimed. "I was merely being asked to escort him to the old Castle of Maqueda. We were within sight of the towers, Catalina. I could see them in the mist—four towers, plain and severe. We were almost there when his mule tumbled over the side of a ravine and he was gone!"

"It doesn't matter, Pedro," Adan said. "Someone's got to be the scape-goat and this time it's you. The *calificadores* will find ample justification for further action, and your punishment will be severe: the frame, the funnel and the water, Pedro. If you survive the torture and are convicted, you'll be sent to the galleys. You're done here, Pedro," Adan said in resignation. "Perhaps you can make your plea to authorities in Toledo, but in Torrijos and Carmena, you're done. We must go!"

"How go, Adan?" Pedro asked while looking at his wife as though seeking an answer. "Carmena has been our home for generations. How can I be made to leave?"

"You have no choice, *Tio*," Luis said, as he gathered his uncle's cloak from its place on the wall. "Go with Adan, *Tio*, go!"

"They're right, Pero," Catalina added using his pet name. "You can go to my papa's home in Toledo. He'll hide you. We can join you there."

Adan, who had been standing before the open hearth, now moved to the oaken table where he sought to help Pedro gather his belongings. "That may work for awhile, *dona* Catalina," he said, "and it's good that you have a place to go. But they'll follow you and compel Pedro's return. He has a few days—perhaps a few weeks at most. Maybe your father can help you get to the coast where you can make use of the license for overseas travel you obtained a few years ago. That license may be your ticket to freedom. Anyhow," Adan said, "we've no time to talk. They'll be here at first light. Take only what's required."

"Go, Pero," Catalina begged. "We'll follow you."

"They won't let you," Pedro replied. "That's how they'll get me to return."

"We'll find a way to get them out," Adan promised. "We've done it before, and we can do it again. I've got mules waiting below the walls."

"Go, *Tio*," Luis urged while putting a comforting arm around his aunt's shoulder. "We'll meet you in Toledo. Two days only. *Mi Tia*, Ana, Diego, *mi tocayo*, Luis and Lucia. We'll meet you in two days!"

"At the *Pena del Rio*," replied Pedro who was at his best when designing and executing a plan, "you'll have to avoid the Moorish bridges and the river is the most shallow there. I'll have lines strung across the Tagus at the great rock. We'll use them to steady the cart and to pull you across. Look for the towers of Malpica, Luis. Use them to guide you," he stated emphatically as he held and kissed his wife for the final time. "Day after tomorrow, Luis," he said as he stuffed several items including his journal into a leather bag. "Wait for light, Luis," he added as he and Adan moved though the open doorway. "Wait for light."

As Catalina and Luis approached the river, they traversed the barren slopes of the Castilian *meseta*, a high tableland of fertile plains, broken here and there by a lone olive tree, piled gray stones, sparse scrub, and a tangle of undergrowth all dusty-gray but excellent cover for game. As they rode in the darkness, Catalina confirmed what Luis had been hearing for some period—hounds in full cry apparently in pursuit of game. They tried to assure themselves that these were the sounds of an early hunting party, but both knew this to be unlikely. They were, they feared, the ones being hunted.

Catalina and Luis had for some period been picking their way through a riverine forest of tamarisk and willow in their attempt to reach the river. Luis, who was holding his three-year-old cousin of the same name, flailed at the oxen with his right hand. The cart, which was filled with the two adults and a locust of children, rose and fell with great jolts as it bumped and rocked its way towards the steep bank.

Suddenly—almost miraculously—they emerged from the tangle and were at the water's edge where they were confronted by a raging torrent now swollen with rain. Luis dismounted and entered the slower water that flowed near the bank, testing its depth with his oaken pole.

"Here, *Tia*," he said urgently. "We can enter the water here."

"How do you know this is the right place, Luis?" his aunt asked in a whispered tone as he reentered the cart. "Your *Tio* said to wait for light, and we don't have the towers to guide us."

"It will be all right, *Tia*," Luis replied. "We may be a little above the rock, but the current will carry us downstream where the lines will stop us."

"No, Luis," his aunt said, holding her son Luis and his four-year-old sister Lucia to her side. "Let's wait. It will only be a short time till light. Then we can see."

"We have no choice, *Tia*," Luis replied as he prodded the oxen with the point of his long goad. "They're behind us. We've got to go!"

The oxen were balky. The sound and the smell of the muddy water, which carried a river of debris, frightened them. They required the whip to compel them to enter the raging stream, a dark swirling torrent which they could now also feel, taste and see . . . and it was terrible. Luis immediately realized he had made the wrong decision, that he had chosen the wrong time and place which was more than two *harquebus* shots above the spot suggested to him by his uncle. His frightened beasts, tethered to an oaken shaft that was but an extension of the framework of the cart's body, plunged into a deep hole. His beasts, with only their horns and eyes visible, bellowed with fright as they sought firm ground. Luis again entered the water where, holding on to the horns of the nearest beast, he attempted to turn his team toward shore. Momentarily, the docile animals quieted and began to turn with the current. The cart, however, snagged on an obstruction, lurched forward, and then overturned, dragging its massive beasts below the surface. The wooden frame and the bows of their harness, which had assured their bondage and servitude, now guaranteed their death.

As the cart overturned in the intense current—with the frame yet bumping and reeling as it dragged along the ragged bottom—Diego was thrown into the turgid stream. He was pressed against one of the wheels, a solid barrier of three pieces, which was attached to the one axle. He struggled to remain upright as he held onto his five-year-old sister, Ana, who had entered the water on his side of the cart.

"My babies! My babies!" His mother cried as she desperately flailed in the raging water. Diego could not see her for both she and Lucia were on the other side of the second wheel.

"I've got Ana, Mama," he cried as he fought to hold on to her. "I've got Ana."

"And Luis?" she screamed.

"I don't know, Mama," he cried as he searched the water around him. "I don't see them."

Diego, six-years-old, and the oldest of the four children, held Ana around her waist as the water worked to tear her from his grasp. In an instant, the rushing water pulled her thin body from beneath his arm.

"Diego," she said quietly. Just his name. Nothing else.

"Hold on to my neck, Ana!" he cried as he tried to work his way around the wheel, his move encumbered by his hold on her wrist. "Hold on to me, Ana!" he yelled in desperation. "Don't let go!" he cried as the first light of dawn came up on his face.

As he inched his way around the ancient wheel, the Stygian water filled his mouth and nostrils with mud, and he feared that both he and Ana would also be swept away. It was beginning to become light now, and he thought he could see the distant shore, although the muddy water which cascaded over his back and shoulders made it difficult to see. Ana's thin arms encircled his neck while the cart reeled and groaned, turning this way and that as it moved down the streambed. In the dim light he could see the oxen's yoke. One of the two bow-shaped pieces of wood which had been inserted from beneath the neck of one of the oxen had broken. Its occupant was now gone, and hanging from below the horizontal bar was a hook to which a draw line was still attached. He released his grip on Ana's wrist and reached for it, hoping to put it to some use. "Hold on, Ana," he begged. "papa will get us."

As he reached for the rope, Ana began to lose her hold on him. He could feel her small hands grasping and tearing at him as she slowly slid from her place on his back. And when he turned, he could see her, a beautiful elfin doll, who appeared to be suspended on a cushion of air, the cold black water revealing a deep gash on her forehead. He reached for her. She looked back at him with eyes seemingly filled with wonder, said nothing, and then she was gone.

18

Pedro stood with his father-in-law's overseer, Tonio, on the south bank of the river as the sun came up shining on the red of his hair and beard. He was distressed by what he saw. The lines which he and Tonio's men had strung across the water the previous evening were now largely submerged by the flood waters, their ends only apparent where they emerged from the angry waves and were tethered to a tree. *It was a bad plan*, he said to himself, his blue eyes searching the far bank. He realized that these floodwaters should have been anticipated. They might be coming from as far away as the *Sierra de Albarracin*. The river, which cut into limestone rocks there, flowed through narrow, sinuous valleys with deep canyons and abundant ravines and was often in flood from unseen storms. *It runs more peacefully here*, Pedro said to himself. But above—and also below Toledo where it again flows through narrow, steep-edged trenches formed by quartzites and shales—the river could be deadly. "I should have anticipated this," he said to Tonio as they surveyed the far bank. "We must signal them and tell them not to cross."

Pedro pulled at his beard in apprehension as he searched the far bank in the early light. He was concerned that his family had not yet arrived. He could see various items of flood debris—logs, a market basket, an unshorn lamb—as they moved downstream. He had not taken notice of a circular shaped object that now broke the surface, but as the object moved slowly down the streambed and lodged on a rock directly across from him, he realized that it was a segmented wheel, and that it was attached to a cart. Pedro immediately entered the water but then retreated, reaching back with his right hand at the rope being offered him by Tonio. He then again entered the water as did Tonio and two of Tonio's men, pressing their lean, muscular bodies against the tow ropes but unable to move forward due to the tumble of the water.

Eventually, the men were able to attach a rope to the upturned cart and to drag it ashore. Ana's body lay but a short distance below the great rock, and was found later that morning. The roots of a tree had snagged her body and that of a fallow deer. However, despite extensive searches, which were conducted on both banks of the river, they were unable to find the bodies of the two Luises.

_____

Although a cart had been offered to carry Ana from where she had been found, Pedro refused to relinquish her care to another. Accompanied by black-robed men, whose mumbled prayers seemed to lack both rhyme and reason, he carried her from the bank of the river to the home of his father-in-law, Alonso Lopez, where Catalina, Diego and Lucia had been taken. Here Catalina and the children were lodged in their mother's old bedroom, the room in which Ana and each of the children had been born. Surrounded by a throng of black-robed men, Ana was placed on her mother's bed, which had been draped in black. In the flickering light of the priests' candles, Diego and Lucia could see Ana wrapped in a small cotton blanket and cradled in their mother's arms as if asleep. Outside the room, Pedro's grief exploded in angry words regarding the unwelcome procession from the river. In his anguish, he likened it to "the pagan observance of the *Robigalia*," the procession through fields of corn to pray for the preservation of the crops from mildew. "My God," he exclaimed to his father-in-law who had attempted to console him, "have they nothing better to do? God save us from them!" He later apologized to the priests for his outburst, but they often had to deal with the peoples' anger as they provided for their spiritual needs and had been little put off by his display.

Catalina, ordinarily frail-looking, gentle, and perhaps a bit hesitant in her manner, had inevitably begun to crumble. Her conduct, if not yet that of one insane, was certainly that of an individual laboring under extreme distress. Mute and benumbed, she first lay with Ana in her room until the child was taken from her to prepare her for her burial. She then sat alone in her cell, an alcove which opened onto the *zaguan*, or vestibule, but which was completely dark and had previously served only for sleeping. There, draped in black, she sat with her head seemingly nailed to her hand and appeared to be involved in a battle to retain her senses. Asking repeatedly for Luis, she seemingly did not comprehend the responses she received. She sat like this through the day, refusing to leave Ana who had now been returned to her in a small pine box. Before Ana was removed from her room to the church, Catalina required that Pedro pry open the pine shell in which she had been placed. Then, with no alteration of demeanor, she looked at, and even put her hands on, Ana's body, which was now wrapped in a white linen shroud, perfectly white and clean. Afterward, Catalina became totally closed off and listless.

The coffin was placed on a poor catafalque before the great cathedral, a vast edifice of marble and granite, where the coffin was opened again, the box of wood pried apart, and her cerements again revealed. The grief stricken observers, among whom were Catalina's children, were required to affirm that the body was truly Ana's. Then the coffin was closed again and draped in black.

Night was coming on by the time a cart was provided and the grim cortege was arranged in the cobbled street before the cathedral. There King Ferdinand and Queen Isabel had prayed before the tomb of their great- great-grandfather exactly a hundred years before. Catalina, supported by Pedro and followed by her two surviving children, walked barefoot behind the cart with a crush of priests chanting prayers for the dead as they began to wind their way toward the river.

An opacous cloud of fog hugged the earth, "the heaviest cloud in the world," noted Diego, and soon it became so dense that they were barely able to move along the road. They pushed on, however, stopping seven times along their route of desolation until Catalina, whose strength had been ebbing, was unable to walk any further. She was placed in the cart with Ana, and again they went forward.

The procession continued along the river until the mourners arrived at an ancient and beautiful stone bridge across from which was the burial place. There the coffin was opened for a final time. Catalina kissed Ana's hands and feet. And then, for what seemed like hours, the small group, wrapped in their plain trappings, huddled around the small coffin, their wax torches guttering in the wind. The service, like the procession itself, was the essence of simplicity and equality. "God is the true judge," said one of the priests. "May her death be an atonement for all sins she may have committed, and may she come to her place in peace."

Pedro felt they were speaking of him and not of Ana. *For what sins could this child have possibly committed?* he asked himself.

With the final words of the priest now spoken, they tore their garments to put the mark of a broken heart upon their clothing. Then, with the dark of night nearly upon them, they picked up the small box and lowered it into the virgin ground, the sound of the first fall of earth on the coffin providing an air of finality

_____

That evening after their return from the burial ground, Pedro and his father-in-law walked through the entire house making an inventory of its contents.

"You'll take whatever you need Pedro," his father-in-law said.

"I'll repay you, *don* Alonso," Pedro responded quietly as they made their way from room to room.

"We're not going to worry about that now," the older man said. "You'll take what you need. And when you get to *Sevilla*, the cargo there will also be yours."

"I can't repay you for that, *don* Alonso," Pedro said. "I don't think we can accept it."

"You'll accept it, damn it!" his father-in-law said with a brief display of anger. "It'll be your nest egg. It was to go to your cousin, Miguel de Sandoval, God rest his soul. But with him dead now, and with his wife, Catalina Sanchez now returned from New Spain, it'll go to you."

"But if I go, *don* Alonso," Pedro said emphatically, continuing the conversation in which they had been engaged, "it won't be as a fugitive."

"However you go, Pedro," his father-in-law responded as he closed the door to the storeroom they were leaving, "your days here are numbered."

"But as a free man," *don* Alonso, Pedro said, "never as a renegade."

"Oh, your pride, Pedro," Catalina's father responded in exasperation, his lips tightening as though he was trying to control some emotion. "Your pride kept you from working for me, Pedro, and it's going to get you killed."

"It wasn't my pride that killed my children, *don* Alonso," Pedro responded. "It was my fear . . . and my stupidity."

"What stupidity?" the older man asked as they ascended the worn stairs from the *zaguan*. "No one could have known the river would be in flood, Pedro. Do you think God is under an obligation to give notice of a coming misfortune? No one could have known," he continued softly, his anguish now spent. "It was just an accident, Pedro," he said while turning away from his son-in-law so that Pedro would not see the tears. He was silent before going on. "It was a tragic accident, that's all," he said quietly as he continued covering mirrors and emptying standing water throughout the house.

Pedro sat on a stool that stood on one side of *don* Alonso's *estrado de cumplimiento*, or state salon. From there he could see the pictures, the heavy, carved wooden chests, the delicate chests of drawers and the sideboards inside the room, as well as the salon's balcony which stood outside its full length windows whose silken curtains now billowed in the wind. The balcony of forged iron, the angles of which were decorated with balls of copper, overlooked the towers and spires of the city and faced the damnable river, a sullen dark thing without obvious movement. As he looked at the balcony through the open windows, a rush of emotion seized him as he thought of the memories the balcony evoked. It was here that he had first held Diego and each of his children.

"She was the most perfect child," Pedro said of Ana, speaking more to himself than to Catalina's father as he rose and moved toward the windows. "So bright and eager to learn. Nose to everything. If it was there, she had to know what and why. Questions all through the day," he said of his five-year-old. "And Luis," he continued with a catch in his throat, "he was just a baby. My poor innocent lambs," he said. "There's been such suffering and I alone am responsible."

He stood for a moment, lost in his own thoughts, and then continued as though trying to provide an explanation to himself. "I ran because I believed it to be the right thing to do," he said. "The Inquisitors would have trumped up some charge against me. You know how they are. They might even have tried me for heresy. Perhaps I would have been acquitted," he said, "but who can take the chance? Persons have been known to languish in prison for as long as 14 years before they might be pronounced free of guilt or blame. I couldn't risk it, *don* Alonso," he said in resignation.

23

The old man was silent for a long time, and when he responded, it was with a voice full of sadness. "I never wanted you to work for the Inquisition," said *don* Alonso, pulling his cloak about his shoulders. "I felt it unseemly, Pedro. Baptism has done little more than convert a considerable proportion of our people from infidels outside the Church to heretics inside it. And these searching inquiries into our conduct, and the punishments meted out for those of us found guilty of backsliding, are not only unseemly but criminal," he said. "I didn't want you to have anything to do with it."

"And I thought of my job as only that of a scrivener," Pedro said. "I was lying to myself, *don* Alonso," he said sadly. "Now I feel like *La Susanna*, carrying on an intrigue with a Christian, disclosing our secrets, and bringing all to ruin. My interests were only in manuscripts and the law," he said. "What have I done?"

"You've done nothing," his father-law stated emphatically. "You give yourself more blame than you're due. But I know your value, Pedro" he said. "You can do whatever you put your mind to. You'll start on a new course and we'll be partners."

"But passage, *don* Alonso. How do we gain passage?"

"Everything's for sale here," his father-in-law responded as he joined Pedro at the balcony's entrance, "titles of nobility, the offices of *regidor* and *jurado*, letters of legitimization for the sons of priests. Everything. The crown needs our money," he said gesturing with his hand as though holding a fistful of coins. "My God, Pedro," he said, "what does *don* Felipe owe, 37,000,000 *duats*? All grants have been suspended, Pedro. He can't pay his bills. *Don* Felipe needs our money. It won't be difficult to gain your passage," he said with the air of one who has learned how to deal successfully and shrewdly in the world of commerce and politics.

For a few moments they stood looking at each other before Pedro's father-in-law continued. "You'll leave tomorrow, Pedro, and Tonio will see you to the coast."

"I don't see how we can go, *don* Alonso," Pedro responded. "Catalina . . . Catalina can't travel."

"You're right, of course," his father-in-law said as he held back the curtain to get a better view of the night. "And under ordinary circumstances she'd remain with me until she was better. But she's like her mother, Pedro," his father-in-law said regarding his daughter, "seemingly fragile, but strong when it comes to her family. Her place," he said, "is with you. You must try to distract her from her melancholy. Stay away from the towns and villages as much as you can, Pedro, and buy your provisions along the road. Avoid the *milliones*," he said, referring to the taxes which were imposed upon everything one ate. "You should be able to buy everything you need along the way. I'm going to the corrals now," he said, throwing the skirt of his cloak over his shoulders. "I must see to the mules."

"I'll go with you," Pedro said, gathering his cloak about him.

"No," his father-in-law responded, while taking his broad brimmed hat from its place near the glass doors. "You must get ready for tomorrow and there must not be too much noise about it," said this shrewd and careful man. "You're a good man, Pedro," he continued, with the tears again welling in his eyes. "You must not grieve," he said as he began to provide the advice which a father must give to his son. "You must look for happiness," he said placing his hand on Pedro's shoulder. "You must accept your lot, Pedro. You must say to yourself, 'Perhaps it was for the best.' I hope and pray that all goes well with you," he said as he readied himself to leave the salon. "You'll always be as my own to me, Pedro, and I want only for your safety."

Pedro entered the gallery and watched his father-in-law as he closed the street door below him. As he stood on Catalina's balcony of joys and sorrows, he recalled with an effusion of emotion that moment in which he had sat there with Diego looking over the tiled rooftops and spires of the ancient city and toward the Tagusian moat. He had often sat there with his father-in-law, listening to the music being sung at the cathedral, but on that particular evening with Diego there had been no music, the hushed village seemingly awaiting a momentous event.

The sky had been a ghostly rose and violet in color, lilac shadowed with majestic serenity. Pedro and Diego had been sitting there quietly while Pedro engaged in the long process of filling the bowl of his pipe with tobacco he had taken from a pouch in the pocket of his shirt. Then, suddenly, without warning, an incredible flock of perhaps a hundred or more swallows, swooped down out of the sky to the top of the balcony and then off again into the amethyst heavens. They flew in a line, one after another. At times, the swallows came within inches of their faces, the glossy blue-black on their upper parts contrasting beautifully with the white on their outer tail quills. They continued in this manner, swooping down with a delicate grace, flicking the pools of street water with their dark wings and then, with a shrill twitter, returning to the open sky. They continued like this for many minutes during which Diego and his father seemed to be members of the flock, participants in their aerial display.

"Papa, Papa! Look at them, look at them!" Diego had squealed. "Where'd they come from?" he asked, as he peered into the heavens, hoping that by some miracle they would return.

"They're coming home, Diego," his father had replied as he returned to the task of filling his pipe. "Home from the wilderness where they nest during the winter. I've not seen it, Diego," he said, "but it's called *Las Marismas*—the tidelands—and it's a place where millions of land, water, and shore birds go to find food during our long winters. Birds come there from Asia and Africa and from all over Europe. Geese from Denmark, starlings from Germany, and the beautiful white egret from West Africa, among many, many others. It's said they have purple herons, and bee-eaters and hoopes without number. Someday, perhaps you'll see it, Diego," he had said, not realizing the prophecy of his words. "It's near *Sevilla*, but my travels aren't likely to take me there.

"Birds, Diego!" he had exclaimed. "It's all about birds. Each town and village is watched over by a guardian bird which, according to the day and hour, renders the town pleasing, ravishing, or disquieting. I'm not sure what bird guards your grandfather's home, but Carmena is watched over by a dove. Adam is said to have named them and perhaps this is true, for they're ancient auguries of that which is favorable or unfavorable," he had said, beginning one of those tales for which he was justly famous.

"When Noah's ark landed at Mount Ararat after the great flood, he let loose a raven which flew off into a blackened sky. For countless days, he awaited its arrival, but it did not return. He then sent out a dove, and it returned because it couldn't find a place to land. Later," he had continued, "he sent out the same dove two more times. On the second flight, it returned with an olive branch in its mouth. It was a sign, Diego, a sign to Noah that he, his family, and all the animals could come out of the ark and begin a new life.

"Good old Noah," he had continued. "He was the only righteous person of his time. And he took enough birds and animals aboard his ark to re-populate the earth. He knew, as we've all come to know, that birds are the best indication of a good climate and country. And now it's said that the birds of the monsoon are seen as messengers of hope, for if they come, they foretell a year of plenty. If they don't come, people know that there'll be famine throughout the land. They're symbols of all things wild and free and are a blessing. We've only to read their signs, Diego. We've only to read their signs.

"Over there, *mi ijiko*," he had said, gesturing towards the northwest, "beyond Carmena and Avila, that's where your *abuelo* and I saw an enormous flock of stilts coming from the north, from France where they're said to nest. You should have seen them, Diego," he had said with enthusiasm. "There were hundreds of them, the most beautiful things I've ever seen. Their necks were long, and their bills were, too, thin and very straight. They flew with their endless legs trailing behind them. I'd seen them before. On the Alberche below the walls at Escalona, their legs so long that they had to tilt their bodies to reach the ground. But when they fly, Diego," he had continued, "they're majestic. White with black wings and with a call like the yelp of a small dog. Your *abuelo* and I were on our way to Salamanca to visit the university. 'Following knowledge endlessly like stars sinking below the horizon,' is how my papa described it."

"Stars, how stars, Papa?"

"Well, not stars, exactly" he had said, peering into the fading light and pulling his collar about his neck. "At least not the kind we see in the sky. But hopes and dreams. Salamanca is where your grandpa and I went in search of my education."

"Further than Carmena, Papa?" Diego had asked. "Maybe we can go someday, Papa," he had said, emphasizing the "we."

"Perhaps, Diego," his father had answered as though considering the possibility. "We'll see, Diego," he had said. "'We'll see."

Pedro leaned against the wrought iron rail and thought of the sentiment expressed by his father-in-law, a sentiment he wished his father had also held: that it's better to dare mighty things than to count oneself among those that neither enjoy much nor suffer much. "You must not grieve," his father-in-law had said. "You must look for happiness, for to do otherwise is to live in a gray twilight and know neither success nor failure."

We've suffered much, Pedro said to himself, *and Ana, Luis and my poor nephew paid the ultimate price.* The joy of his existence had been rooted in Castile and now God who had given these children to him had also taken then away. "I'll keep you in my heart," he said aloud to his beloved dead. And with no further time to contemplate their loss, left the balcony.

This Crag of Sorrow

"I can go by myself, Papa," Lucia pleaded in her small voice as she stood beside her hooded mule, the hem of her nightdress trailing in the mud. "Like Diego," she said. "I can go by myself."

"Shh," her father responded as he put his finger to her lips. He then placed her astride her mule, the scent of her—of angel water and sleep—sweet in the damp cool air. "We'll see, *ijika*," her father promised as he placed her in her saddle. "You'll go with Tonio for now," he said, "but we'll see. We'll see how it goes."

Lucia, appearing spare and wan, held her thin arms tightly across her chest refusing to touch the withers or mane of her beast. The corners of her budded lips drooped slightly at their edges as she observed the remainder of her family waiting in the darkness. While she sat there, her father so close she could have reached out and touched him, she looked down into her mother's sedan chair and could, she thought, make out her mother's knees and her clasped hands which were folded in her lap.

It was one of those moments, however, when one did not know whether what one was experiencing was real or imagined. She knew that her mother's face and neck were hidden from her view, and that it would have been impossible for her to see the auburn hair, long, white throat or those blue-green eyes which she wished were her own. But would she have been able to see her mother's hands? she asked herself. Or was this just the way she knew her mother would be seated? She did not know. What she did know was that she could see or sense movement within the sedan chair as her mother rearranged her seating.

Within the chair, Catalina felt for the correct placement of her feet on top of the Moroccan cushion which she had asked to take from her mother's parlor. She had, until this moment, been brooding and immobile, locked in a deep trance from which she could not seem to escape. However, with the realization that she had to provide for the welfare of her remaining children, she had broken through her passivity, and assumed an active role in the preparations, even seeking to take some precious objects from her parents' home to which she would likely never return. The darkness, as well as the haunches of her lead mule, obscured her view forward, although she knew that her position in the train, as in life, was immediately behind her husband who now sat on his mule ahead of her. As she settled back within her enclosed settee, which rested on the haunches and shoulders of her mule team, she could, through the dark clothing and the black shawl that she wore, feel the cold leather of the sedan's seat and back as they pressed against her frail body. Additional mules, coughing and wheezing in protest, carried the trunks and valises containing the meager clothing and household goods they had obtained from her father. Once mounted, the family waited in silence.

The stars and the moonlight cast shadows against the walls of the tortuous passageway, a street so narrow that the overhanging roofs of the adjacent homes nearly touched. The normal qualities of the stones of this passageway were unrecognizable in the veiled light. The sky, reflected in the family's tears and in the pools of moisture that had collected from the evening's heavy dew, had a timeless quality about it that did not identify it as either a day or night sky. In the darkness, Lucia could barely distinguish one silhouette from another as additional muleteers came up the cobbled path. She tried to tell whether or not any of them were men who worked for her grandfather. One of them—whom she identified by his 'limp of Lepanto'—was Tonio, her grandfather's *mayordomo* or overseer. It was unlikely she knew any of the others. Still, she wondered who these men were who were about to lead them into the night. The light had the cast of sadness. The sounds were those of anxious hooves. And the smells those of working men, leather, and mules.

In the darkness, Tonio and his head packer, or *cargador*, rechecked the seating of every load, each of them walking down his own side of the mule train, the clack of their double-soled boots resounding in the darkness. Tonio, who was responsible for the safety of his charges, his men, and his beasts, wanted to assure himself that his muleteers had done their work well as he felt for the correct placement and security of each item. Saddle clothes, grass stuffed pads, grass cinch, straw mat coverings—nothing was overlooked in his inspection. Once the examination was completed, he mounted his own mule which stood at the front of the train. Then with the *cargador's* "*Adios!*" and Tonio's response of "*Vaya!*" the mules, led by a bellmare and divided into four strings, began to inch their way down the steep cobblestoned corridor and away from the house on one of Toledo's highest hills. Then, although admonished by his father not to look back, Diego glanced one final time at his grandfather's home which now appeared empty, dark, and desolate, and at its exterior balcony as he rode beneath it. He searched in vain for the spot in the wall where he had hidden his white stone as a prayer to assure their return and worried that it would not be able to work its magic. However, his attention was quickly diverted to more pressing matters when one of his mother's mules slid into his as they exited the corridor.

Through shadowed, Moorish streets like dark ravines, the family moved along steep, narrow corridors paved with cobbles taken from the muddy, red bed of the Tagus. They rode past crowded whitewashed houses, which faced terraced streets, the corridors overhung by glazed verandas or by wrought-iron balustrades enclosing narrow passages. The silence was broken only by the sound of hooves and of water splashing into stone basins.

As they neared the river, they rode through the ancient Jewish quarter of Toledo, virtually a town in itself, situated in the southwestern portion of the city. The southern section of the district sloped down an incline to the bank of the Tagus and included a fortress once known as the 'Jew's Citadel.' Here, with the clatter of their mules the only sound to be heard they passed through the battle-scarred walls of the fortress, away from the roofs, towers, and domes of the ancient city and began their steep descent to the river.

Galiana's Palace

A few plain trees and Spanish poplars marked the road the Robledo party traveled. There were many rocks, and the fields, which at winter's end had been a broad stretch of parched meadows, were now covered with the emerald grasses of an early spring. The hollows of dry waterbeds were choked with tamarisk, their fine, feathery branches and minute scale-like leaves now moving in the pristine air. A gentle breeze sprang up along the deeply etched bed of the Tagus, bearing the scent of mud and dry leaves and, incongruously, the faint odor of animal dung, the remains of a previous passage.

As they rode alongside the river, which was bordered by white-trunked poplars and giant tamarisks, the sun began to tip the horizon, and the landscape in all directions became clearer. While riding, they began to see the harsh uplands long-celebrated in the annals of Spanish history. Streams interlaced the area of scrubby brush, rock rose, heather, and cork oaks, while in the heights, deer, foxes, lynx, wolves, and wild boar were to be found. A single cloud, like tufted cotton, was ridged against the sky as they headed toward a distant hill.

Riding through the area, Pedro thought of how, during visits to their grandfather's home, the children had begged to be taken to see the local wonders. Scattered throughout the area were numerous prehistoric sites, all boasting megalithic ruins composed of huge stone monuments and tombs. Also in the area was an ancient ghost town once protected by a fortress, while odd stone boars or bulls—*verracos*—decorated nearby castles. Each of these sites had presented the possibility for an excursion and a chance to enjoy life in the open air but would have required a long day's ride. Therefore, instead of visiting one of these, he had last taken them to Galiana's Palace and the *clypsedra*, or water clock, which had been one of the wonders of the Moorish world. The water clock, which lay among the ruins of a Moorish palace, or *alcazar*, on the banks of the Tagus River, had once consisted of two large stone basins that filled and emptied themselves of water every lunar month in time with the waxing and waning of the moon. It was said that in 1085, some 50 years after the Christian re-conquest of Toledo by Alfonso VI, Alfonso VII, his grandson, curious to learn how the clock worked, had it taken apart. Unfortunately, his craftsmen, as skilled as they were, had been unable to reconstruct it. Pedro had presented the story to them as an allegory. "Sometimes," he had said to his children, his blue eyes seemingly reflecting the late winter sky, "it's best to accept things as they are, to enjoy them, to marvel at them, or to suffer the pains of their sorrows without question. However, at other times, it's best to search for meaning."

To accept things as they are, he thought to himself as they rode by the palatial ruin. His hallmark had always been his cheerful acceptance of life in its simplest and most sublime terms—with all its tragedy and all its enveloping mystery. Now, however, he, too, searched for meaning in the family's recent tragic events and could find none.

* * *

As the members of the mule train rode to the brow of a rounded hill, a little beyond where they had once dismounted for their walk to Galiana's Palace, Pedro reined in his mule. Here he turned to look back for the last time at the city of high walls which ascend and descend and enclose the small hill ringed by the river. On their right was the deeply carved bed of the Tagus still veiled in drifting mists and shadows. On their left were hills, rocks, and low scrub, all of which were half-shrouded in a dusty gray. The southern mountains under the early April sky were dimly visible in the distance. Toledo, its neutral tones broken only by shadows cast within its gigantic walls, its roofs dominated by the magnificent towers of its cathedral and its *alcazar*, was barely visible on the distant horizon. Without comment or command, Pedro took Diego and Lucia from their mules and lowered them to the ground. Catalina, however, asked to be left where she was. The children and their father then sat in the grass beside her litter while their train waited on the road above them.

The river was beautiful in the morning light with the sun glinting off the blue and yellow waters of the stream. Above them, just before the crest of the hill, Pedro and his children could see some crumbling walls. Below them, on the slope of the hill, were live oaks, ilex and olive trees. The olive trees' delicate, silver leaves parted to reveal clusters of small, black fruit that had refused to be beaten from the branches at harvest. Pedro, who refused to look at the river, sat there bareheaded and motionless as he strained to see the home of his father-in-law on the hill beside the cathedral. He imagined that he could see both the house and its exterior balcony. As they gazed, Pedro, Diego and Lucia were enclosed in their own thoughts of Alonso's home, the ancient city behind them, and all that they had lost, until Pedro decided that it was time to go. Again, without a word being spoken, for they had all learned to suffer in silence, Pedro placed the children upon their mules. Then, seemingly as an afterthought, he reached into one of the panniers that were slung across the croup of his mule, took out a leather-clad book, and returned to his seat on the hillside. With a final look at Toledo, which was but a smear on the distant horizon, and a last search for the balcony, he began to write.

> *The first week of April has been filled with such sadness that I have pushed aside my journal and can, now, only cobble it together from memory. It might seem meaningless that I do so. However, I follow the dictates of my teacher who made me believe that who we are and what we experience as a family— and as a people—are important and deserve to be preserved. The dates now seem unimportant. Suffice it to say that this has been the most tragic period of our lives.*

He stood up, re-wrapped the journal in its oilskin, and, with a brief prayer rendered to St. Tobit, patron of travelers, said, "We must go."

To Newer Lands

The plan, as Pedro had outlined in his journal before the family's departure from Toledo, was for the family to follow the swift-flowing Tagus to Puebla del Mont. Here, they were to ascend the Rio Torcon to the village of Navahermosa. From this point, they were to follow an ancient track across the southward-looking slopes of the *Sierra de Guadalupe*, to Puerto de San Vicente, Logrosan, and, finally Merida. This track would take them overland through broken, mountainous country whose twisted trees and undergrowth of flowering gorze, blackberry and bilberry sheltered an assortment of wild animals. Here, the woods would be full of animals of every description even if they did not see them. It was this portion of the trip through the mountains of Central Spain that most concerned them. They would be at the mercy of the weather and of the bandits who preyed upon small parties such as theirs. At Merida, they would turn south towards Seville, and from there, they would reach the sea. With luck, and barring any unforeseen circumstances, they would reach the banks of the olive-bordered Guadalquivir River at Seville within three weeks.

Pedro had much on his mind as he let his beast select its own route up the forested trail. He followed the lead mules of their mule train as they slipped and stumbled in mire and muck from melting snow and on the stones and boulders that defined the thorny track. They were following a narrow valley of wood and cork trees with small villages scattered here and there along the way.

* * *

As they passed their days in travel Pedro worried abut what lay ahead. Although there were *ventas*, or inns, along much of the route, it was impossible to find one that provided both board and lodging. Despite the fact that the inns were filthy, especially the kitchens, which belched thick, black smoke, Pedro and his family continued to stay in them when the opportunity presented itself, for their only other recourse was to set up housekeeping in the fields. The general good appearance of the family often resulted in their being given the best room, but, although they often had the room to themselves, the children's parents refused to allow them to sleep on the beds, which were little more than lumpy quilts infested with fleas and bedbugs. Instead, and in a guestroom with a chamber pot as their only luxury, they slept on mud floors and on bedding that they carried with them. While the family was accommodated within the inns, however, their muleteers, in the rude manner of the day, slept in the stables on nothing but the panniers and the coverings of their mules all thrown in a heap.

Although the initial portion of their trip was not very difficult, Catalina and Pedro had suffered a catastrophic blow in the deaths of their two children and of their nephew and would have had to be harder than diamonds not to have been brought to their knees. As a wife, aunt, and mother, Catalina had been vitally stricken and was to wear mourning much of her life. As for Pedro, the wound would always be there. But suffering is the essence of being Spanish, and rest a commodity they could ill afford.

For the children, at least, the journey provided distraction. Sleeping each night in a different place and sharing a room and candle with their parents as they had at their home in Carmena, made the trip seem like a grand adventure. That sense of adventure ended when they arrived at the forest.

*   *   *

Generally, the mountains of Spain have a harsh and lonely appearance. Many are rough, craggy, steeply sloped and forbidding. They have surprisingly few trees and are very sparsely populated. Mercifully, the mountains, or *monts*, through which the Robledos traveled were small and covered with trees. Although they were also sparsely settled, they served as common pasturage for village cooperatives for the small and infrequent hamlets, which the family came across. However, the Robledos sometimes rode for a whole day without seeing a living creature, except perhaps a cork-stripper with his long-handled hatchet cutting long, oblong sections of bark from the bottom of a tree.

One evening, as it was approaching dark, Pedro and his muletrain spied an inn beside a sluggish creek. They decided to make their lodging there, but the inn was full. The last room had been sold to an odd gentleman, the innkeeper told them, who appeared to be a 'Romero,' one of those pilgrims who had gained his name by traveling from the Western

Empire (Roman) through the Eastern Empire (Byzantine) on his way to the Holy Land. This man in question, however, was on his way to Santiago de Compostella and he was standing in the courtyard.

The gentleman, a shabby-looking man in what appeared to be penitent's garb, was standing ankle-deep in mud in his trail-worn sandals. His clothing was most strange. He wore a rude cloak of the coarsest cloth, a short cape, and a flexible hat, and carried a staff to which he had attached a *calabaza*, or gourd, containing the food he ate. His name, he told them, was Teodore del Torre and he was not actually a pilgrim. "I wear these clothes only to deter thieves on the road," he said. And his ruse had apparently worked, for he still had all he had come with, which was to say—nothing. Nothing, that is, but a worn book regarding heraldry.

"I'll be honored to share my room with you," the strange man said, "and the *senora* and children can share my bed. It will be a good arrangement," he said with enthusiasm. "All I ask is that you share the food you've brought, for I've not come with any."

The arrangement was not to Pedro's liking, but he agreed, knowing that Catalina on this night, at least, had to sleep in a bed. The five of them entered the inn and drew up chairs at a rude table that stood near the door. They sat at the table inspecting the hare, which the *ventore* had placed before them, sniffing at wine stinking of hide and pitch being poured from a ragged goatskin into stone cups, and speaking about this and that. Pedro's decided to keep the man busy in conversation through the night, leaving the room and bed to Catalina and the children. This appeared to be of no difficulty for Teodore was full of talk. He was planning to submit a petition to become an *hidalgo*,[1] he said, and he was busy designing a coat of arms complete with quartering, crowns and coronets of rank.

"It's beautiful," Pedro said of the drawing placed before them expressing more enthusiasm than he felt, "but how does it relate to your name or to your house?"

"The tower, of course, is for Torre," the man said, "and the mountain is symbolic of my mother's name which is Montes. This is a little ray of sunshine," he said, pointing to a yellow slash mark on his drawing, "and the horse is just because I like horses.

36

"In reality," he told the family, "my father's name is Rodriguez, but how does one draw it? The world is full of Rodriguezes," he said with disdain. "Descendant of Rodrigo! What's that? I might as well be a Perez, or a Ruiz, or a Martinez . . . a descendant of Pero, Ruy, or Martin . . . one can't draw those either!"

"Oh, I don't know," Pedro said, while holding the drawing up to the candle light and examining the document. "I wouldn't give that up too quickly, *Senor*. For example, Martin, or *Martinus*, derives from Mars or Martis, the Roman god of fertility and war. And, ultimately, Martis derives from the root 'mar' which means 'gleam.' One could certainly use that. Perhaps you could further search your origins. There's a Martinez in every wood pile!"

The man looked at him reviewing his red hair and beard and the blue of his eyes in an attempt to determine with whom among their ancestors to place him. Was he Celt, Iberian, Roman or was he one of those Visigoths with their strange un-Spanish names?

"And your name is Robledo, is that right?" the strange man asked with deliberation, a wry smile sliding across his face. "At least that's what the *ventore* told me," he said as though expecting a denial.

"Yes, Robledo. Pedro Robledo," he responded while looking at Catalina.

"And your father?" the traveler asked, his open mouth revealing acorn stained teeth. "Of what name may we give him?"

"Alejo," Pedro said, while working at the carcass of their hare with his bare hands.

"Ah. Alejo . . . Alejandro. That's Greek, you know?"

"Yes," Pedro responded. "The derivation's Greek, but we're Spaniards like yourself."

"Ro-ble-do," he said again, drawing out the syllables. "Oak grove, isn't that what it means? That's very different from most names and much better than Rodriguez."

"Thank you," Pedro responded, knowing that this man now knew more about him than he had cared to share. "Perhaps it's a place name like Robledo de Chavela or Robledo del Buey."

"Perhaps," the man responded while tearing a leg off the rabbit they were eating. "But is it not also like Carvajal, which means 'oak field,' or even Zarate, an Arabic word which means essentially the same thing?"

Pedro said nothing, and the man seemed not to notice as he continued with his naming.

"My mother—God rest her soul—said that I should have been a Marquez for my ambitions to become a marquis," the man continued, his thin lips working but silent. "But my father reminded her that the name may also designate one who works as a servant in house of a marquis. He judged me to be one of the latter," he said, demonstrating that he could still laugh at himself. "You know, Robledo," the man went on while requesting another cup of wine. "I would have preferred to have been named Bustillo, or Jaramillo, or Losada, or even Serrano. Preferred to have been named for a pasture for bullocks, a field of orach, an area paved with flagstones, or one who lives on a saw-toothed mountain."

"Or how about Hinojosa, Vasquez, or Pedroso?" asked Pedro, growing weary of the name game. "A field of fennel, a shepherd, or a place of stones could also be drawn. Those are strong names which conjure up pictures of glory . . . although *de hinojos* could also refer to kneeling."

"And you could draw them?" the odd man questioned.

"And you could draw them," Pedro responded.

Senor Torre and Pedro stood as Catalina excused herself from the table to take the children, Diego and Lucia, and retire to their room. As the man stood there speaking to Catalina who looked pale and worn from their day of travel, Pedro had his first opportunity to really examine him. Pedro made him out to be about 40-years-old, perhaps no older than himself, a serious man of medium stature, earnest but full of pretensions. His pride, he had said, was in being a gentleman and a Catholic, a gentleman as a descendant of those who had re-won the land from the Moors, and a Catholic, in sharp distinction to the New Christians of Moorish blood. He demonstrated the incredible combination of poverty and pride, which, in Pedro's mind, were so characteristically Castilian. He had nothing, yet he conducted himself with such a comely grace that one unacquainted with him would have taken him for the kinsman of a count. He lived a life of semi-starvation, however, sharing the bread of travelers such as Pedro, probably inhabiting a house of indescribable poverty and squalor and just surviving. Yet here he was with his cloak and his staff, searching for a sword and speaking grandly of his honor and of the estates he would obtain once he became an *hidalgo*.

After kissing Catalina's hand and bidding her a good night, the odd man returned to the table in front of the open door that he shared with Pedro. There, they continued their review of Iberian patronymics, place names, and ornamentals from Arechuleta to Zaldivar.

"You'll notice," the odd man said, "that neither of us spoke of Herrera or Ferrer, the only two names I'm aware of which designate an occupation."

"Well there's Varela, also," Pedro replied, "even if it is a nickname. It designates a keeper of animals and the rod with which he works."

"Ah *Senor* Robledo," the odd man said, his eyes glazing over from his third cup of wine. "There you have it! If I were to be named Varela, it would be for the *varra* which I carried as a symbol of my office, or, more importantly, for the rod I take to bed."

They both laughed at this latter designation, and Pedro reconciled himself to the fact that it was going to be a long night.

* * *

The mule train carrying Pedro, Catalina, and the children rode through a sunlit forest amid fragrant gray shrubs with, here and there, massive boulders draped in luminous foliage. They continued in shadowed silence as they listened for the sounds of horsemen, not knowing who, if anyone, might be pursuing them. However, the only sound they heard was the creak of leather against leather and the heavy breathing of their beasts as they plodded the flinty paths.

After they left the forest, the valley widened and became lush and more fertile. The vale and hillsides, which were awakening from winter's sleep, were replete with fruit trees now coming to bud. After a day of travel along the ridge of this valley, the mule train crowned the top of a hill in brilliant sunshine, and they could see the village of Punto Llano that lay in a green hollow below them. The houses, which gave the appearance of ancient rocks thrown together under a blazing sun, were shuttered and the doors, over which small family shields had been carved, were locked. Not a soul was to be seen, although the village reeked of tannic acid from cork bark, which was boiling in unattended vats. A lone cow, strangely hobbled by a rope tied to its horns and to one leg, and a small herd of goats wandered in the fields alone, their neck bells ringing in the stillness.

The Robledo party searched the village and could find no one until they came upon an old woman hiding in a hayloft. The woman, whom Pedro referred to as "a woman with a hundred weight of years"— that is a centenarian—told them that the village had been attacked by a group of bandits who had driven off their sheep. Although she was only armed with a thick staff made from the wood of the holly, she had refused to leave with the villagers. The villagers, she told them, were hiding in the hills and would return by nightfall. Although the Robledos were reluctant to leave her there, she insisted they do so, and they hurried away.

Below the village of Punto Llano, the Robledos were overtaken by a small party of two families who, following the same road, were coming along behind them. They were, they said, escaping the village they had left behind and asked to join the Robledos for the trip to Merida. Two of the men in this party carried matchlocks with which to protect themselves. With the safety provided by numbers and with the worn but serviceable arms the party carried, they felt a safe passage would be assured.

From Punto Llano they rode to Logrosan and then down a wide valley, generally following the course of the Rio Ruecas. This route took them through Medellin, formerly the home of Hernando Cortes who had opened the West Indies to colonization. In a bleak landscape commanded by a low hill, they found a crumbling castle with nothing to protect but a string of poor houses fronting a filthy street. Although Cortes had brought the riches of the Aztec Empire to the country of his birth, little of it had remained there, and none of it had stuck to his poor village of Medellin.

From Medellin to Merida was a fine journey of eight days through hills of gray boulders, regal stands of majestic pines, and enormous flocks of partridges, quail, and doves that filled each afternoon's sky.

* * *

Merida was an ancient city. The Romans, who were later to establish it as the capital of their vast and powerful province of Lusitania, had, in 25 BCE, founded it as Augusta Emerita (Augustus' Veteran Colony). These were the meritorious veterans of his fifth and tenth legions that had asked to retire from active service and take farms in the area.

The ride was beautiful. Now and then, the travelers saw an ancient *noria* or hydraulic water wheel with buckets attached. Burros were pulling them around. There were frequent rectangular storage bins of stone or wood, raised off the ground to keep the grain away from rodents. They also found along the trail, shrines and holy places, cowled with a mantle of stone and looking very much like enormous animal burrows. Occasionally, they came across ancient walls and the traces of an ancient Roman road, but, as they neared the city, Roman roads appeared more frequently.

They may have known that in the early history of the church, a young girl, St. Eulalia, the celebrated virgin-martyr of Spain, had, by the use of these roads, trudged into Merida eager for martyrdom. During the Diocletian persecutions (c 304 AD), she had presented herself to the judge, Dacian, and had reproached him for attempting to destroy souls by compelling them to renounce what she considered to be the one true God. Dacian at first tried to flatter and bribe her into withdrawing her words and into observing the edicts. He then threatened her, showing her instruments of torture, and saying, "These you shall escape if you will but touch a little salt and incense with the tip of your finger." Instead of acceding to his wishes, however, she trampled on the cake that was being laid for the sacrifice, and spat on the judge. Thereupon, two executioners tore at her body with iron hooks, and lighted torches were applied to her wounds. The fire caught her hair and she was burned alive. Legend has it that, following her death, her spirit, as a white dove, flew out of her mouth and soared into heaven.

The Robledo party also saw Roman ruins, including an immense circus formerly seating 30,000 people, and an amphitheater of 14,000 seats. They eventually came upon the Milagros Aqueduct, made of stones shaped and finished so skillfully as to require no mortar. Over 1,000 years old, at the time they saw it, it was doubtlessly good for a thousand more.

The Robledos also saw the 81-arched Roman bridge built across two arms of the wide valley of the Guadiana, a river celebrated for its underground course. The bridge, a half-mile long and the longest ever built in Spain, was repaired by the Visigoths in 686 AD. The members of the mule train knew that these structures were very old, and, although they did not identify them as Roman, they marveled at their construction.

On the morning of 14 April 1577, the mule train set off again with, as the Robledo journal states, "the sound of a distant bell carried by the wind." They were unaccompanied now but on a road heavy with traffic. Along this road, which was little more than a muddy track scattered with rocks, there were relay stages for the royal mail placed approximately two to four leagues apart. By the use of these stages, the riders of the royal mail could cover up to 30 leagues a day. It was by the use of roads such as these that the king's letters and special dispatches were carried from Madrid to Seville and to the principal towns of the kingdom. The Robledos made use of the corrals, draw wells and stone troughs of these stage stops to refresh their mules on two occasions, but otherwise stayed at various *ventas* or slept in makeshift shelters which they built for themselves along the road.

As they neared Almendralejo, they came upon a site recently abandoned by a band of gypsies usually called *gitanos bravios*, meaning wild or nomadic. The gypsies had camped alongside a stream in the valley below the road the mule train traveled. From the top of the trail, the members of the mule train could see a large wooden wash tub and piggin. They were to find these poorly constructed, their staves of white oak loose and rattly. There were, in addition, a number of other items strewn about which suggested that the encampment had been abandoned with some urgency. Although Pedro told his family that they would not have had anything to fear from these people in terms of their lives, he would have recommended that they remain clear of them because the gypsies were known for stealing and might have made off with their property.

"The gypsies," Pedro told his family, "entered Europe about 150 years ago and at first posed as pilgrims. The tale they told," Pedro said, "was that they were from 'Little Egypt' and were on a seven-year odyssey to pay for the sins of their forefathers who had turned away the Blessed Virgin with the Child Jesus. Now they've dropped this pose and call themselves Greek, but they refuse to go home. That, in fact, is the rub. They don't have a home, nor do they seem to want one. Their language," he continued, "is not like ours. It's said to be Indian, although they've apparently lived in Hungary for many years. They're intelligent and incredibly clever. They learn the language of the people among whom they travel so as to enter their homes, their stores, and their markets. I hate to make generalizations about a people for most often there are as many who don't fit the label as those who do. However, in this instance, the generalizations are largely true. They make their living by telling fortunes and by predicting what will occur in a person's life, and then, after they've lured you with their psychic 'gifts,' they steal from you. Women who've gone among them—my mother included—have even had pieces of their dresses cut off.

"When they first entered our country," he continued, mopping his brow with a well-used linen, "they were given offers of safe conduct and were even provided with alms. However, it wasn't long before they, and the people with whom they ran, were being paid to stay away.[2] It's unfortunate," he said with a shrug, "for they have skills as smiths, musicians, and soldiers. However, they're not to be trusted. No," he repeated, "best to stay clear of them. We may camp here now that they're gone, but, should they return for their washtub or these other things, we'll abandon this camp."

They took the camp the gypsies had deserted and Catalina, who had begun to brighten in her general demeanor, made use of the tub to disinfect the few items of clothing they had found, some of which fit the children. As she worked at her washtub, she assured herself that every fold and seam was thoroughly scrubbed in the boiling water. Looking over their encampment as the sun slowly sank behind the valley's western wall, she examined the sky and watched a bird circling at great height in the cloudless heavens. There was something about the evening, perhaps the color of the light as it filtered through the pines, that reminded her of home. She thought back to the bathing time they had been forced to keep secret and to a conversation she had had with Pedro.

It was at their home in Carmena and she had been helping Pedro as he secured their house prior to taking their forbidden baths. How was one to deal with such a concept, that warm baths were illegal? These were not ritual baths or baths of purification such as those that must be taken in the water of a rushing stream. These were only baths which created and intensified a sense of cleanliness and self-respect and the Cortes had decreed them illegal!

Surely, Catalina had insisted to anyone who would listen, that law of 1567 was intended for the *Moriscos*—the name given to converted Moors—and had nothing to do with them. Some of these followers of Mohammed were still wearing their shapeless pants, turbans, and white linen trappings, were still speaking Arabic, and were probably still Muslims beneath their forced conversions. The *Moriscos* were calling attention to themselves, she feared, and, like the dreaded gypsies, might not survive until this law, as with most laws in Spain, became a dead letter. In any event, she had insisted, if any Spaniard followed these insane laws, citizens could easily revert to a time when it was illegal to sit on the wall of a house and dangle one's feet, or to lead an animal to water by chains. Clothes left hanging outside their home might still be confiscated, but no one was going to decree that here behind her own walls she could not give her children a bath!

Pedro and Catalina talked as they completed preparations for the family's bathtime.

"'I'm glad she's gone," Catalina said, in reference to their housekeeper, Ama. "God help me, Pero there are times when she drives me crazy, absolutely crazy," she added, displaying the frustration she experienced at dealing with the 12-year-old.

"What'd she do now?" Pedro asked, steeling himself to hear a new absurdity while taking a caldron of water from the wrought iron rod of their stone hearth, the floor of which extended into their firelit room. He held it by its bail, placed it on top of an old hearth stool whose seat had been blackened by similar objects, and replaced it with another as she had continued with her lamentations.

"Oh the things she comes up with!" Catalina had said while wrapping her hair in a turban, her auburn curls revealed at its edge. "The things she tells the children, Pero," she said. "She scares them half to death. Last week she told them that this past fall while she was helping us pick corn from the fields below the walls, she saw a person's shadow without its head! Can you even imagine that, Pero?" she had asked in frustration. "A person's shadow without its head? She told them that her grandmother had told her that if a person sees her shadow without its head on the seventh day of the autumn festival, that she'll die during the year. Then, later, she told me that it wasn't her own shadow she'd seen, but someone else's . . . you know . . . in that way she has of speaking as though she has a secret known only to herself. *Porquerias*, Pero, that's all her secrets are. Useless trifles! I know that she wanted me to ask whose shadow she'd seen, but I refused. I wasn't going to encourage her foolishness. Thank God, she went to see her mother and won't be back till Tuesday. Anyhow, we couldn't be taking our baths outside if she was here."

Ama, Catalina's housekeeper, was a soot-splattered young urchin whom Catalina's father had rescued from the mills where she had worked with her mother amid the stale and sour smell of millions of silkworms. Catalina and Pedro had spoken with Ama's mother who seemed to be a sensible woman, but this ancient grandmother whom they had yet to meet, was constantly filling Ama's head with nonsense.

Catalina had tried to tame her—this mysterious and wild thing— providing clothing and shoes for her as replacements for the rags that she wore. But Ama refused to be tamed. She reluctantly wore the clothes they provided, but refused to wear the shoes which remained hidden beneath her bed. Catalina had wondered what had happened to them and had discovered them while searching for one of Luis's toys.

The shoes, *alpargatas* of the Basque region, tiny sandals of coarse canvas soled with hemp, just sat there, idle and abandoned, their toes curling toward the ceiling. There, too, hidden beneath her bed, were a tattered blanket, a sack of dried bread, several ears of corn, and, unaccountably, what appeared to be weeds from their garden—the latter with tufted roots the soil of which was still attached. Catalina recalled looking around her uncomfortably as she had halted her search, feeling that she had invaded a private space, the coop of a starving and frightened chicken. She left the items where they lay and retreated, never to speak of them to Ama, and, although Ama continued to sleep beneath the bed they provided, she spent most weekends with her own family, which gave Catalina a brief but needed respite from her.

Pedro, of course, was first as he walked across the cold stones with his final pail of water. Now clad in a sheet and clutching a bar of Neapolitan soap (made of wheat bran, milk of poppies, goat's milk, marrow of deer, bitter almonds and sugar), he moved quickly across the cold stones of the *plazuela*. Then, without taking off his mantle, which he wore as a barber's cape that encircled both shoulders, he sat in the water that he had poured for himself. His bath would be a short one, for there were two to go.

Diego and Luis were next, and their baths were also short as they sat in the water used by their father and washed with the soap and rag he had provided them. However, Diego, at least, seemed more interested in cleaning the beautiful white stone he had brought with him than caring for his own needs. Catalina had admonished the boys to wash here and there while she poured water over them with a copper cup. Diego though, continued to play with the stone he had found, noting that, with a cross seemingly etched across one of its surfaces, it looked like a *cruzado*. His father had told him that a white stone meant good luck and that this was a stone to cherish. Clutching it beneath the sheet his mother had provided him after the bath, he took the stone with him as he later ran into the house.

With their basin newly filled, and in the shadowed light of their open *plazuela*, Catalina placed Lucia and Ana within the water. Then, uncharacteristically, for she was excessively modest, she kicked off her *alpargatas*, let her robe slip from her slim, white shoulders and stepped in behind them.

Their bath, which now contained angel water, was a special treat. The angel water was a cosmetic made from the distillation of red and white roses, trefoil, red poppies, lavender root, honeysuckle, orange blossoms, white lilies, thyme, carnations and orange rinds which the three of them had made during the previous summer. It was a bath within which to soak. Therefore, with their knees tucked neatly beneath their chins, and with the warmth of bared flesh connecting them as they pressed one against another, they observed a small group of swifts and black martins as they flew in tight semicircles far above their heads. Then, with the flecks of orange rinds floating lazily about them, they watched as the late afternoon sun sank behind the wall of their *plazuela*.

Was that only a week ago? Catalina thought. Standing alone in the small clearing, she gazed past their mules tethered beyond the small fire of their encampment, and into the shadows of the forested slopes. The sky continued to lose its light and she again became closed off and enveloped in darkness.

* * *

Their journey continued as they rode through the mountains of Toledo, through Almendralejo, Zafra, and Fuente de Cantos. Days later, as they rode by the stone markers of the Castilian/Andalusian border, Pedro told the members of his mule train that many hundreds of years before, these rich pasturelands had been stud farms for the breeding of cavalry horses. Although the number of beautiful Arab-bred Andalusians in the valley was now greatly diminished, the rich pasturelands remained. And on 23 April 1577, through a forest of olive, orange, and cypress trees which spread out before them, they arrived at the 'City of Reflections.' They had been on the road for 20 days. This was several days longer than they had anticipated. However, the muleteers had found Catalina's swinging litter, the era's utmost form of comfort, extremely cumbersome, bumping and lurching on the difficult tracks. The Robledos promised themselves that should they be required to make a similar trip in the future, each member of the family would be mounted on his or her own mule.

The Robledos had planned to arrive in Seville for the May sailing of the merchant fleet from that city to Vera Cruz. Prior to 1492, Spain's trade center had resided in Catalonia on the Mediterranean coast, with Barcelona being the richest and most celebrated port in the world. However, with the discovery of America, trade switched from Catalonia to Seville leaving Catalan merchants and vessels high and dry. Now, Seville and Vera Cruz held the monopolies for all traffic with the West Indies. Seville was Spain's assigned point of departure, while Vera Cruz was the only seaport through which both New Spain and the other parts of Spanish America got their materials. The Robledos knew there would be a second sailing in September. This second fleet, known as the *Terra Firma*,[3] would be going to Porto Bello on the Isthmus of Panama. After crossing the Isthmus, the cargo of the *Terra Firma* vessels would be placed upon ships bound for trade in the South Sea. This, however, was not the Robledos' destination. They were going to Vera Cruz.

* * *

In 1577, Seville, formerly the site of the small Roman acropolis of Hispalis, and now a city of 150,000 inhabitants, was Spain's largest city. It was composed of two urban centers on either bank of the Guadalquivir River linked by a pontoon bridge. Seville was on the east bank while Triana, a *gitaneria* or home to a colony of gypsies, was on the west. Gigantic walls, which forced the meandering river into a new channel, separated the two sections of the city. The walls, which had served to bring the river closer to the city, also served as quays, which facilitated the rigging and provisioning of ships. Together, the two cities reflected the two main motivations for overseas travel, religion and commerce.

The mark of Christianity was clearly demonstrated by the number and size of Seville's religious buildings. These included many monasteries and convents, innumerable churches, chapels, and oratorios, and Seville's grand cathedral. Cheek by jowl with these were Seville's Customs' House, its mint, its marvelous Merchants' Hall (a magnificent structure of stone and brick close to the cathedral), and its House of Trade, or *Casa de Contratacion*. These represented Seville's position as a financial hub for Spain and New Spain. With shopkeepers from England, Flanders, France, Greece, Italy, and Portugal, it was a veritable Babel. These two entities, religion and commerce, dominated life in Seville in the late 16th century, and it was this world in which the Robledos immersed themselves while awaiting departure.

The city was indeed a marvel. As the only repository for all exchange and business with the West Indies, it was literally bursting at the seams. As Spain's American colonies had only a small number of industries apart from the development of mineral deposits and certain unrefined resources, they were reliant upon imports from Europe for a considerable variety of goods. With Seville's warehouses bulging, the overflow lay on the strand waiting for inspection. The Robledos had arrived too late to observe the off-loading of precious metals coming from the West Indies, but, they were told that there had been 257 cartloads of silver, gold and pearls of great value.[4] Since there was no room within the *Casa de Contratacion*, large quantities of bar gold and chests full of precious metals remained outside the building in its well-guarded courtyard. These, as well as cocoa, cochineal, leather and skins, sugar, and timber all coming from the West Indies were piled in heaps across the strand. Here, among an incredible array of goods, the Robledos placed their baggage to be watched over by their muleteers.

The strand, or *arenal,* on which cargo was stored, had the appearance of a colorful and unending bazaar that stretched from the battlement enclosing the city to the left bank of the Guadalquivir River. It was said that one could find bird's milk here if one wished to have it. There were Moorish *azulejos,* the distinctive blue and green picture tiles dating from the 14th century that were the preferred decoration for the finest palaces and monasteries. There were hats and caps, shirts and socks, cloth, ironware, oil, silk, soap, tools, wine, and even mercury, the latter destined for the mines of New Spain where it was to be used in the extraction of silver. The cargoes of many foreign nations also littered the strand. The presence of these foreign ships and their cargoes was largely due to the poor quality of cloth then available in Spain and New Spain, and an insufficient quantity of a whole range of exports which might have been provided by Spain itself. Ships had come from Rouen and St. Malo loaded with cloth from Normandy. Italian ships brought fine brocades, while ships from the German cities of Hamburg and Lubek carried lumber and hempen cord and ropes, each essential in the construction of ships. Also on the strand were the foodstuffs needed for the ocean passage. For the three-month voyage (though actually the duration was uncertain and could be longer) the novice sailors would need biscuits and dried meat, cheese, butter, rice, beans, vinegar, oil, salted cod and herring, fruits, vegetables, and red wine. Among the inviting aromas of stews and garlic, one could find the world on the strand.

* * *

On the morning following their arrival, Pedro donned his 'city clothes' in preparation for his excursion into the city. His clothing, much of which had been provided him by his father-in-law, consisted of a tight-fitting jacket, with a high stiff collar, short pantaloons, stockings, and a classic

Spanish cape. Although the clothes fit him well, except for the pantaloons, which were decidedly too short for him, he was uneasy in them. His well-shaped legs and average height body might have been appropriate to elegant suits and the finest clothes. Although he was a man who preferred wearing clothing for the road, this dress was required for a man of distinction. Pedro, Diego and their agent, Enrique Enriquez, who was to assist them in gaining passage, then set out on their walk to the commercial center of the city.

Their agent's home and place of business, Catalina's father had told them, were on the *Calle de la Frontera* near the tower of St. Mary (formerly known as '*La Giralda*' or 'The Weathervane'). This was a 20-story bell tower—now the steeple of the cathedral—built as the minaret for the ancient Grand Mosque that had hugged the walls of the *alcazar* in the old *aljama* or Jewish Quarter of the city. Because of the prominence of the tower which rose more than 300 feet above the city's walls, Pedro and his family had used it as a beacon in their search for their agent's home.[5]

After leaving their agent's house and walking with him through a beautiful walled-in garden cloister at the cathedral, they visited the *gradas*. These were the steps that led to the Orangery, the ruins of an old mosque that flanked the north side of the Victory-topped cathedral, the third largest church in the world. Here, on the worn steps, the business of arranging overseas travel and trade was being conducted.

On the steps, appearing *muy donoso*, and perfumed at that, were merchants, ship-owners, bankers and courtiers dressed in short capes, hats with plumes of many colors and with daggers hanging at their sides. They were discussing the value of gold and silver, rates of interest and exchange and the cost of commodities in the West Indies.

Also on the steps, and moving in and out of the milling crowd, were beautifully dressed women carrying embroidered handbags and wearing high-heeled shoes. They were attired in long-sleeved gowns of every color and either high-collared cloaks, vast sleeveless capes, or *mantas* of tulle or transparent silk which they drew across their faces to reveal just one eye. Diego watched in fascination as these women drifted in and out of the crowd. Occasionally, he could see a cheek painted with scarlet, lips covered with a thin layer of wax to make them gleam, or a long, white,

50

delicate hand to which its owner had applied either a special almond paste, an ointment made from bacon fat, or *vinagrillo* (vinegar water), a cosmetic lotion composed of vinegar, eggs, sweet limes and honey. And the scent of these women in the blaze of the Andalusian sun was overwhelming, for their maids, in droplets projected between beautiful white teeth, had spat ambergris, rosewater, and civet upon them.

It was at the Orangery that Pedro got his first glimpse of the manner in which the overseas business was conducted. He felt like a small fish in a pond of piranhas and wondered if he could learn to swim among them. This was not his way of doing business and the cacophony and odors he experienced were overwhelming. However, he could not escape Seville yet, for his agent told him that he had to meet with officials at the *Casa de la Contratacion*. They would obtain information regarding his character and confirm his license to travel overseas. His agent and his agent's wife were to be his only witnesses.

* * *

"They'll be asking you many questions, *Senor* Robledo," his agent said as they stood in the shade of one of the cathedral's soaring portals. "There'll be questions regarding your age, your community of residence, your marriage, the legitimacy of your children and whether either of them is committed to a religious order or to marriage. They'll want to have information regarding your parents and those of *Senora* Robledo, whether you're an old or a new Christian, everything. You're incredibly fortunate in one regard, at least," he said. "The prohibition against emigration was just this year suspended. And then we can hope that they'll not have been instructed to detain you, and that your answers mirror those you provided when you made your initial petition—the one you made three years ago. Are your circumstances the same?" he asked.

"No," Pedro responded. "Much has changed. The initial petition was made for my wife and for our four children, and also for my nephew, Luis, whom I raised as my own. Also, we were going to live with my cousins, Miguel de Sandoval and Catalina Sanchez who were residents of Mexico. My cousin Miguel, God rest his soul, died from a fall from his horse, and his wife returned here. And you know of my children and of Luis," he said sadly. "Things have changed enormously, *Senor* Enriquez. The initial

51

petition was made to provide us with a back-up plan. Now we're forced to go."

"I was sorry to hear of your children, *don* Pedro," his agent responded while crossing himself with his right hand. "Your loss is beyond measure. However, I'm sure they're in a better place, God save and keep them," he added in a guarded tone while he persisted with the task at hand. "Regarding the license, *don* Pedro," he continued. "We'll be truthful, but only as thorough as required, and it'll be best not to have anyone else there whom they might question—if you know what I mean. You do know what I mean?" he asked while again hitching his short cape about his shoulders.

"Yes, I understand," Pedro answered.

"Your wife and children might yet have to appear," he said, "but perhaps our testimony will be sufficient. We'll leave Diego in the garden. It can only be entered from the cathedral. Ordinarily, it's closed off to the laity, but I've received permission for him to stay there."

*　*　*

Diego would have preferred to be left on the *gradas* where he could have watched the people on the steps. Instead, he now sat in a little sunken garden at a corner of the cloister where shrubs and trees bordered a covered walk-way that ran along the inside walls. The little garden was cool and well-hidden, sheltered by copious orange trees and tall, downy palms motionless in the still air. The floor of the recessed garden was set with small, flat stones and ringed with a tangle of roses and stork's bill, red and white. The roses of this early spring perfumed the air and the splash of water into a moss-green pool made the speech of those around him unintelligible except for that of a small group of novitiates who were at his elbow.

Black-robed men in twos and threes made a circuit of the cloister. Each of these men was dressed in a long black tunic with winged sleeves, belts, scapulas and hoods. The look of them reminded him of the priests at the cathedral in Toledo and of the priests' procession up the stone corridor to his grandfather's home. That walk, however, had been conducted at night and had been lit by candles. As Diego watched the priests, he, too, placed his hands before his face in the manner of rendering a prayer.

The novitiates—children, really—wore the dress of their order and were seated around their superior discussing the nature and most important qualities of prayer. "Prayer," their superior said, "is an art to be learned, and may be one of four kinds: adoration, thanksgiving, penitence or petition." They nodded in apparent understanding of his words and he continued. "Our practice of praying for the dead," he said, "falls into the category of prayers of petition, and is based on our belief that those of our Church who have died, but not yet arrived at the Beatific Vision, the final destiny of the redeemed, can be helped by the prayers of those still alive."

"Members of our Church only?" questioned one. "What of the others, Father?"

"Heaven is the dwelling place of God, and the angels," their superior said, "and only His faithful disciples, members of our Church, will reign with Him in His glory. The rest? Well, they're lost."

"No matter their innocence, Father?"

"Well," he responded, "if they have a positive disbelief in the Christian faith can they really be said to be innocent?" he asked of the children as he looked quizzically from one to another. "No, my sons," he said with finality, "if they don't believe in our Catholic faith, they're infidels and can't be saved."

Diego listened to all of this and understood it as babble. Members of the Church? Beatific Vision? These were concepts that were beyond his comprehension. Leaving the sunken garden, he wandered into the cathedral and was overwhelmed by its majesty. He watched as others dipped the tips of their fingers into the holy font and did the same. He then sat in a pew beside a tier of votive candles and again assumed the posture of one in prayer.

He had been brought up a Catholic, and had only been introduced by osmosis to the secrets of his faith, for his family's beliefs were, to a large extent, rules of life, rather than a creed. He knew but one prayer— The Lord's Prayer—and he had no idea where among the four categories it belonged. He wondered whether he should have washed his hands before entering the cathedral, and thought how, at home, his parents' one candle ("the candle of the Lord," his mother pronounced it) would have been placed within a pitcher to conceal it from prying eyes.

His prayer was not one of those presented by the priest but was more in the form of a question. "Why? Why Ana and Luis?" he asked, as he began to sob quietly to himself, the tears of regret running down his cheeks. He could not reconcile himself to the fact that he had lived while they had died, and he would forever be haunted by the look in Ana's eyes as she slipped from his grasp, for she too appeared to be asking a question: "Why Diego? Why?"

"I don't know, Ana," he said aloud, startling those who sat around him. '"Why did I let go?"

Who Does Not Venture Forth Does Not Cross the Sea

The Passage

The fleet within which the Robledos were to sail was made up of several dozen vessels, merchantmen, and armed galleons. These were berthed at the docks alongside the river where cargo was being loaded into their holds. One of these ships, the *Morning Star*, on which the Robledos had gained passage, was a fully rigged sailing vessel carrying broadsides of brass and iron pieces, both ship- and man-killers, some of great weight. On this ship, and on the many others that lined the stone quay, a representative of the *Casa de la Contratacion* was inspecting *registros* or bills of lading.

Also on board were commissioners from the Office of the Inquisition who arrived to see that no books forbidden by the Holy Office were smuggled aboard. Pedro had made a decision regarding the Holy Office and hoped it would serve him well. His fear of the Office had resulted in tragedy and he was no longer going to conduct himself as a fugitive, hiding in the shadows and living in fear. If the Office had been commanded to detain him, so be it. He would return to accept whatever fate was presented him. If not, however, he would conduct himself as would any free Spanish citizen.

Among the books given to Pedro by his father-in-law was *The Works of Charles V* which was bound in parchment. He had also received the libretto of a long musical work published that year which preserved several folk tunes, and two curious works about the Jews. The Holy Office apparently had no instructions regarding him. Since the possession of Jewish works even in translation might have exposed him to persecution, however, these were left with his agent. The additional literary works in Pedro's possession were deemed not to contain anything contrary to good morals or to the Catholic faith. They were not among those written by heretical authors or listed in the *Index of Prohibited Books*. They were, therefore, not confiscated and with a payment of an *obol*, he was free to proceed.

* * *

Amid a chorus of pealing bells and the boom of cannons being fired as a salute from Seville's beautiful *alcazar*, everyone massed on the banks of the Guadalquivir River to watch the ships put to sea. With the Robledos' ship armed and outfitted, and with the last cask stored, the *Morning Star* slid into the irresistible current of the river and began its journey to the sea.

Traveling with the merchant fleet for the initial portion of the 20-league-trip to the mouth of the Guadalquivir were many fast and armed cruisers, the *zabras*, *fragatas*, and *patajes* of Spain's Mediterranean fleet. These vessels, which could be rowed, were used for scouting and for pursuit. They were low in the water, faster, and hardier than were the bigger ships and would have less difficulty at the mouth of the river where beyond the roadstead, the protected place near the shore where ships could anchor, there was a *syrtis*, the name given by the ancients to shoals or sandbars in the sea. After successfully crossing the sandbar, which was now a fury of white water, the Mediterranean fleet turned south toward Cadiz and the transatlantic fleet entered the open sea.

The immediate plan was for the fleet to drop down to the Canaries, a group of 13 islands in the Atlantic Ocean about 60 miles off the coast of Northwest Africa. From there, they would be borne across the Atlantic Ocean to the West Indies by southwest trade winds. It was a voyage that had been accomplished many times. This passage, however, would prove to be anything but routine.

* * *

The Robledos, like the other passengers of the *Morning Star*, were appalled by the area below deck where they were to spend the next three months. Led down the ladder of an aft hatchway when they first boarded the vessel, they were escorted to a gloomy and grimy space between decks. Across this area was strewn a hopeless clutter of kegs and barrels which encroached upon their living space. Their living 'quarters,' such as they were, extended from the forehatch of their vessel to the stern immediately below the main deck. The Robledo journal perhaps best describes it:

> *Under the maindeck someone had built stalls for the horses of a previous passage. The manger in front is still packed with hay. On*

*the other side of the ship are stalls for more horses, their feed
mangers worn down from incessant rubbing. We put our baggage
inside one of these and made it our home. I love horses, but I'm
glad they're not here!*

Although theoretically cleaned, fumigated, and sweetened, their
stall still held the strong scent of rot and mildew, of horse and unwashed
bodies, and of the flux with which many of its previous passengers had
been afflicted. Also in the hold were the vermin of its former occupants
waiting in the dark, eager to move onto new hosts. In these dismal
surroundings, the Robledos were placed with 30 other passengers, each
adult of whom presented two square yards of skin upon which the vermin
could graze, each child only slightly less.

The Vermin

Grazing upon the extensive fields of unwashed passengers, were fungi,
viruses, fleas, bedbugs, body and head lice, ticks, bacteria, and itch mites.
Some of these organisms carried diseases which could kill: fleas with
bubonic plague, body lice with epidemic typhus, and ticks with
encephalitis and other tick-borne diseases. And while the itch mites might
not kill people, they caused such torture that many wished they had. The
scabies mite, tunneling across the back of an afflicted person's hand like
a mole burrowing in a soggy field, used its skin-melting enzymes to help
it invade to lay eggs. Their feces and saliva caused terrible itching that
worsened when scratched. Itching from secondary lesions, which occurred
predominantly upon the male genitals, between the fingers, on the lower
buttocks, and about the areola of the breasts in women, was,
unaccountably, most intense at night.

Ever-present was a species of rodent called a 'black rat' which,
like the dreaded gypsies, had originally lived in India. These rats were
skilled climbers and found it easy to both ascend and descend sailing
ships by their mooring ropes. These creatures were the most hated and
also the most feared for they carried plague. You could treat head lice
with a shampoo of olive oil, but there was no defense against the plague.

The Passage

The habitable area of the Robledo family's room was totally dark and had no ventilation. They had been told that their cargo in crates and casks would be placed in the hold and would not under any circumstances be available to them during their passage. Therefore, whatever they needed for the next three months had to be in this 'room.' It was suggested that they cleat their trunks to the floor to prevent their movement in heavy seas, but when the room was packed, no floor was visible. There was no place to sit and little to stand. There was only one solid layer of baggage, one piece upon the other. Pedro likened this to Dante's hell, a horrible pit, shaped like a stall, deep in the bowels of their vessel. By placing bedding on top of their personal luggage, they attempted to establish a niche for themselves. Head to head, toe to toe, their hell seemed to have all nine circles.

* * *

By all accounts, the ocean passage of 12 weeks was a nightmare. It was a voyage that Pedro Robledo was to describe as "a seeming lifetime of tedium and vomitus." The assault was immediate, with the wind blowing hard off the sea at their exit from the Guadalquivir. It went on blowing furiously as they beat toward the Canaries, one gale after another, more like December than May. Then, two days out of port, they encountered a violent storm and considered turning back. It was a day of disaster, Robledo wrote.

> From sunset last night the wind grew quickly. It blew with severity, and the sea took on an ominous appearance. Soon we were pitching heavily and taking water over the rail. Crates and barrels began to rip loose from their lashings. The men and boys were required to work below deck, re-lashing them as well as we were able under desperate and dangerous conditions. The women and children were sent to the deck where the waters crashed over them. They had to hold on to whatever was available to keep from being swept into the sea. I told Catalina to stand with Lucia at the top of the

ladder and not to enter the deck, but the crew would not allow them to remain there and required them also to go above.

Throughout the night the wind blew furiously. A severe wind and an uncertain sea. Awoke to much motion, swaying, continually to the plunging of the ship as it pitched and rolled in the heavy seas. If one could have seen us through a hole in the deck, one would have seen a mass of miserable humanity rising up on one side together, while those on the other side swung down. Lucia is suffering badly from seasickness. Last night she drank a little— threw up—then drank a little more.

It was as though the sea harbored monsters that sought to devour them. Mountainous waves surged like wild beasts while the winds crawled like living creatures through the sails. Decks trembled and quaked relentlessly testing the soundness of their craft. Some of the passengers gathered on deck, but their position there was unenviable. The water repeatedly broke over the railing, hurling sheets of soaring spray on to everyone who huddled there. They sat with their backs to this breaking water filled with cold and despair.

The night wore on, and the sea appeared higher than ever. It came over the rail in a solid sheet of green, curling water. Although their vessel was not taking much water through open seams, a great quantity of the deluge cascading across the overlying deck was finding its way below so that the floors were soon gushing in rivulets. Below decks, the water rushed over the ribs of the ship in a frightening manner. The men and boys worked a bucket brigade carrying full pails to the deck only to have the water blown back in their faces as they attempted to throw it into the wind.

"Thank God," Robledo says in his journal some hours later, "the storm is waning. The waters are still monstrously high, but our vessel is not straining as badly as she was." The initial storm was followed by an evening's calm and a red-skied dawn that only warned that additional storms awaited them.

The first storm caused incredible damage, straining the seams of a number of the vessels and eventually sinking one. The doomed merchantman, whose seams had been opened, was leaking like a sieve, its well filling with water. Her captain had passed cables beneath her keel to support and strengthen her in a futile attempt to keep his ship from falling apart. Then, under the escort of an armed galleon, the waterlogged vessel made for the rock of Lisbon where it later sank in the harbor. The remainder of the badly strained vessels, some with fresh spars, caulking, cordage, and canvas, made repairs under rudder and continued.

Battered by contrary gales in an ocean pregnant with storms, the *Morning Star*, a three-masted vessel, seemed to be in imminent peril from ill winds and heavy seas. To add to the misery of the passengers (and some of the sailors, though most of them were able deep-water seamen), everyone was sick. Their symptoms of dizziness and cold sweats were followed by cyclic bouts of nausea and vomiting with incessant retching long after there was anything to lose. They felt better above deck, whatever the weather, and experienced the wind and rain there as blessings.

The passengers were required to remain on deck during most of the day while the ship was cleaned and rummaged and readied for the next bout of sickness that all knew would come. Unaccountably, the nausea seemed to subside with darkness, and sleep, too, brought blessed relief.

For the first few days they ate little—mostly biscuits and water— since they could not retain it. After a week of this sickness, during which many of the passengers spoke of killing themselves, they were able to eat slightly more. Lucia, though, could not ingest or retain the salted fish, carrots, potatoes, or any of the other solids available to her. Her world was made up of water, broth (which they made over the coals of a portable brazier such as that used in soldering), and dried fruit until this was exhausted.

Although more vulnerable to gunfire, the galleys had long keels in proportion to their beam. They rode lower in the water and were subject to less motion than were the merchantmen whose towering castles only exacerbated their rolling. In contrast to the galleys, the merchantmen, with shorter keels and broader beams, quaked and trembled, pitched and rolled in the peak and trough of every wave. Seemingly, the misery experienced by the passengers would not end—it could not end—until their ships were swamped or came apart. In the end, the passengers of the fleet were convinced their ships would kill them.

During the initial weeks of the voyage, the passengers huddled on deck as though in a stupor, captives of an unfriendly sea. They were crushed by the wretched conditions of their vessel and had the appearance of individuals who had been damned. Slowly, some began to recover only to be brought to nausea again by the next storm. Day after seemingly unending day, they sat or lay on the deck probably looking for an English or perhaps a French privateer to come and end their misery. None came, however, and their hell seemed to have become eternal.

* * *

For purposes of safety from attack, the ships attempted to maintain a spacing of a half-*culverin* shot of 300 yards between vessels. During the day, they were able to maintain this spacing without great effort, but at night, and often running before a storm, the fleet was scattered and at dawn had to be rejoined. Primarily, the members of the fleet were on the alert for three sea bandits, and it was possible that at least two of them would appear together.

The first of these bandits was the French Huguenot pirate, Jacques Soury. He had, in 1570, attacked a ship bound for Brazil. The captured passengers and crew of this ship had been dealt with most cruelly. Their heads had been split open. They had been bound and stabbed to death and then thrown into the sea. No less deadly were the English 'sea dogs,' Francis Drake, and his cousin, John Hawkins.[1] The pirates were out there somewhere, of this the members of the transatlantic fleet were sure, and, although the Spaniards could not see them, absence of evidence was not evidence of absence. Francis Drake, for one, was famous for his ability to find the exact spot in an endless sea where he could seize a particularly desirable prize. Undoubtedly, he was at this moment lurking on the high seas searching for more treasure and slaves and perhaps for the members of the transatlantic fleet.

* * *

In addition to enduring the wretched condition of the seas which daily plagued them, the passengers of the fleet also suffered miserably from fouled water and spoiled food. Many of the casks and butts were leaking and what water remained in them was green with slime and foul-smelling. Having no means of replenishing their supply from onshore resources, they consequently set to wringing rainwater from hanging sheets to replace their spoiled stores.[2]

Their having no control over what was happening to them and their inability to escape their ordeal intensified the misery of the passengers. However, a small group did what they could to bring order to the chaos. They sectioned off a small corner of the cabin for use as a latrine and organized the collection of the night's slops. They also helped to bring fresh water to those who were unable to rise from their beds. Although they could do nothing about their cramped and putrid quarters—the stench of which worsened daily—they urged that fouled bedding be cleaned and aired or even that it be thrown overboard. Eventually, however, the stench was so unbearable that a container in which incense was burned was put up—a *botafumeiro de Sant' Iago* it was called—to dull the odor and fumigate the air.

* * *

Each morning, at first light, Lucia's father would carry her to the open deck where she slipped in and out of consciousness. There he would cradle her racked body in his lap, and with his large cool hands attempt to soothe her distended stomach. Then, leaving her with Diego, who had become her guardian and nurse, he would return to their stall to retrieve his wife. This, unfortunately, became a daily routine, for Lucia was deathly ill. Whether the reason for this was seasickness, the unsanitary squalor, or simply an especially dangerous form of 'ship's fever,' (typhus) which was then virtually worldwide, Pedro's attempts to comfort Lucia seemed useless. He feared that if somehow their conditions did not improve, they would lose her.

While resting on deck, and with the ocean's spray washing over them, Robledo told stories to his family as a way of relieving their wretched condition. He told them the story of the shepherd and of his flock of 300 whom the shepherd was trying to have ferried across a stream. This was a counting story with infinite repetitions and it soon outlived its usefulness.

However, an additional story, and one he told more often, was the legend of the generous and noble Ulysses and the tale of his wanderings. This timeless story of man's struggle against great odds seemed to fit the occasion. Recited from memory, for the book was in the hold and unavailable to him, the beginning and end of the narrative remained the same. However, there was great variation in his narration of the remainder. In Pedro's version, Ulysses visited the land of the one-eyed giant, the Cyclops, the Lotus-Eaters, and the Kingdom of the Dead. He encountered Scylla and the Sirens and participated in the contest with the great bow. The differences in his telling were that Pedro focused on Ithaca, and, when alone with Diego, on the much-beloved Telemachus, to whom Ulysses had left his scepter and his kingdom. "And you, Diego," he would say in his great, sonorous voice, "are my Telemachus. We follow knowledge like a star sinking below the horizon. Remember Diego," he would add, his light blue eyes alive with excitement, "what we seek is a newer world, perhaps that of the fabled *Sobradisa* or *Micomicon*, and when we find it, it will be peaceful and grand! It's out there somewhere, Diego, beyond the horizon. We may not find it this year, in the next ten years, or perhaps in my lifetime. But it will be found. And when it is, Diego, you must hold on to it for you and for your children. Remember," he stated emphatically, "that the quest is as important as the discovery. To strive, to seek, to find and not to yield is our motto. If, in our quest, we don't find it, you must keep looking, for when I'm gone, Diego, your work will be mine."

* * *

The nights, Pedro wrote, were the most difficult. There was never a time when everyone in the cabin shared the same period of sleep. In his quarters in the family's minuscule living space, he would lie holding his wife spoon-like around her waist. There, amid the sounds of children crying, and of people coughing, moaning, and retching in new despair, Pedro awaited a new tomorrow. During these periods from sunset to dawn, although surrounded by a horde of humanity, he experienced profound bouts of loneliness. As he lay in the near-dark watching the cabin's lone candle-lamp swing in the creaking night, he thought of his beloved

Carmena, his children, Ana and Luis, and how Ana, especially, the quickest of the four children, would have been full of questions.

More often, though, when the weather allowed, he returned to the main deck after his family fell asleep. Here, from the high poop or from the taffrail of the embattled ship, he would watch the lanterns of the other vessels, the stars, and the cold, black waves like watered camlet as they flowed around his ship in the wake of its passage. Sometimes he thought he could see light coming from deep beneath the ocean's waves and wondered what this could be. More often, as the ship plowed through the peak and trough of every wave, he observed the bioluminescence of the tiny sea animals displaced by its wake. Perhaps the motion of the vessel as it plowed through the sea provided these sea creatures with the energy required to make this light, he thought to himself. He connected this with the round flash of St. Erasmus's light[3] that is seen around the masts of ships in a thunderstorm, although he did not know what caused either of these phenomena. Leaning on the taffrail at the stern of the ship, he often stood with his arms extended before him in the form of a cross. In this manner, he could gauge the hour by the position of the horn of Ursa Minor in relation to his arms as time passed before him. These considerations provided him with diversions until sleep came.

* * *

And so it went as, day after day, Spain's Atlantic fleet beat toward the West Indies. Coming together by day and dispersing at night, the individuals in these floating barracks watched for Drake and Hawkins and now, on the 92nd day, began looking for land.

Land

Lucia, through sunken eyes, now rimmed in black, saw them first. They were perched regally far above the deck, near the masthead, whose banner snapped in the wind, two scarlet macaws. They were predominantly red in color but with yellow, blue, and green plumage, each with an incredibly long, scarlet tail. There among the lines and ropes of the ship's mizzenmast, the birds allowed the wind to get beneath their wings and to

64

raise them majestically from their perch before they flew off. The crew, weakened and depleted by disease, identified them as land birds and speculated that they had been blown out to sea by some storm. Soon, however, in addition to the macaws, the passengers began to see other land birds. More importantly, they saw the trunks of enormous trees and other debris being carried out to sea by the current of an unseen river. Finally, at two o'clock on the last morning, Pedro Robledo saw something like white sand gleaming in the moonlight. It was, of course, Vera Cruz, the West Indies, the New World, and, perhaps, the land of his dreams.

PERIOD II
THE KINGDOM OF NEW SPAIN

Vera Cruz

*L*a Villa Rica de la Vera Cruz, or the Rich City of the True Cross, was Spain's first settlement on the coast of New Spain.[1] It was so-named because the site, which the Spaniards hoped would be one of rich lands, had been reached on Maundy Thursday with the soldiers disembarking on Good Friday.

Hernando Cortes had, against the orders of his commander, the governor of Cuba, founded the 'Rich City' in 1519. Now 58 years old, and looking its age, it merely sat there near a beach of dark sand[2] overlooking a fine but potentially treacherous harbor. Although in an advantageous position in terms of its landing, it had little else to recommend it. It was the home of approximately 300 *vecinos*, or Spanish citizens, and many Indians. These were relapsed idolaters, it was said, whom Bishop Diego de Landa had sentenced to hard labor in the disease-infested holds of ships sitting in the harbor. However, despite its sizable population, there was something about the village that gave it the appearance of imminent abandonment, for it appeared that no one, whether *vecino* or Indian, wanted to be there. It was, for most individuals, only a way-station for passage into the interior of the country, most notably the City of Mexico that lay 400 miles to the west, in the heart of the kingdom.

* * *

The day on which the ships of the merchant fleet approached the harbor at Vera Cruz was no prettier than many of the days that had preceded it. The August morning promised a coming storm. A stiff breeze came up offshore followed by a low, heavy fog. Even before the *Morning Star* began to roll in deep troughs, it was apparent that to sail into the harbor under these conditions would a very difficult and dangerous task. The stormy and treacherous sea was a counterpoint to the shouted commands of the captains as they attempted to maneuver their vessels in tricky currents. The fear of the passengers was that the condition of the sea would prevent a landing, for without the wind gauge, they could not avoid the reefs that surrounded the harbor.[3]

By the use of signals and other means of communication, which the captains had worked out prior to their departure, however, instructions were given to stand out to sea and to await more favorable conditions for landing. The captains knew that if the storm passed, surface temperatures over land would exceed 100 degrees by noon, burning off the fog and resulting in the uneven heating of the coastal plain and the ocean which fronted it. The air over the land would then expand and rise and cooler air would rush in to replace it. This would result in an onshore breeze under which each vessel could make a slow run with the wind into the harbor. Thus, as the squall passed, each ship in turn positioned itself with its mainsail at a right angle to the boat's direction thus creating the greatest wind resistance. The fleet dropped anchor and none were happier than the passengers of the *Morning Star*.

* * *

Some might say that the passengers of the fleet knew that this day would eventually come, but those weakened by privation and disease would have denied this. They were the ones who had contracted scurvy or who suffered from dysentery from spoiled food. Burning from fever and wracked with the pangs the illness can inflict upon an empty and retching stomach, many had viewed their hell as everlasting. Catalina, for example, had suffered a turned ankle during the first storm and shortly thereafter tore open a knee that refused to heal. She was in constant pain and did not want anyone to come near her. Bedeviled also by a sore mouth and bleeding gums, her teeth had begun to rattle in her head. Lucia had developed anemia, which was aggravated by hunger and thirst, and like many of the other passengers, had often seemed near death.

With their landing now secured, however, the helpless and emaciated voyagers of the fleet might be taken to the hospital on the slight rise above the harbor. More likely, though, they would be cared for by their family or friends in space they might secure in a private home or in an out-building in the small village. However, the resources of the community of Vera Cruz this August were being severely taxed by the circumstances in which it found itself. In fact, the fleet could not have chosen a less providential time to make its landing.

* * *

The people of New Spain were, in 1577, dealing with one of the most virulent scourges yet to be met by the people of the kingdom. The scourge, called the *matalzahuatl* (typhus), which had first occurred in 1544 and 1545, had, in 1576, again begun its insidious spread across the land. The Indians, who did not have a childhood immunity to the disease, were its direct victims and the only ones to experience its puzzling and horrible symptoms. These were a violent headache and a severe rash that appeared from the third to the seventh day of the illness's onset. The rash, which was accompanied by a tenacious fever, appeared as small reddish or purplish spots caused by minute hemorrhaging. The spots eventually began to run together and blend into one. One afflicted by the rash and fever could not bear to be covered and even the lightest touch caused intense pain. The only relief was to roll on the cool ground until death ended the suffering about the seventh day. The malady (which occurred for the last times in 1588 and 1596) was attributed by some to scanty rains and severe heat, both of which had been present in the interior of New Spain for some time. Many thousands had died from hunger, thirst, and the effects of the cruel disease, so that not only houses, but also whole villages, were left without inhabitants. It had become necessary to open great ditches as graves for those who had died, although many remained unburied. Because the survivors lacked the resources necessary to handle the scourge, many bodies had been left in their huts, in the fields or on the public roads. The passengers of the fleet were warned that it would be folly to enter the interior under these conditions. However, with few resources available to them in this village, some ignored this advice. They began to arrange for the organization of a mule train to begin their 400-mile trek to the City of Mexico.

*   *   *

The decision for the Robledos was complicated. Each member of the family was gaunt and debilitated, and four-year-old Lucia was suffering from anemia and a low-grade fever that ebbed and flowed in its attack. Perhaps with rest and proper nourishment she could be nursed back to health, but attempting to penetrate the interior of the country under the present conditions seemed impossible. There were, in addition, other factors that argued for staying in Vera Cruz at least for the present. Twenty-eight-year-old Catalina Lopez, who could no longer hide her bulging shape under a full skirt, was now visibly pregnant, weak and unable to maintain her balance. She would be unable to walk and would likely be unable to ride a mule either. Then, there was the matter of their cargo.

The unloading of ships at Vera Cruz was a dangerous undertaking generally accompanied by the loss of many lives. The time required for unloading the cargo was an incredible four months, then nine or ten months would elapse before the ships would be ready for their return trip to Seville. Those who now chose to enter the interior of the kingdom were carrying with them only those parcels that had been in their cabin. In contrast, the Robledos had deep in the bowels of their vessel the trunks and valises, boxes and barrels of cloth for their new venture. This material—from brocade to sackcloth—had been stored in Seville awaiting this transit, but earmarked for Pedro's first cousin, Miguel de Sandoval. Sandoval and his wife, Catalina Sanchez, whom Pedro had described as 'personas muy ricas' in his petition of 1574, and with whom Pedro and his family were to have lived, were tragically no longer in the picture. Senor Enriquez, agent for Catalina's father who had met the Robledos in Seville, had received the cloth. He had overseen its storage and placement aboard the Morning Star. This was weeks before the Robledos arrived from Toledo. This cargo was now sitting among the rats in the dark hold of the Robledos' ship, and it might take several months to retrieve it. A wait by the Robledos at Vera Cruz would not be wasted though. This would give them the time they needed to examine their surroundings and to determine what their next move would be.

* * *

Vera Cruz was located in a hot, humid coastland below the *Sierra Madre Oriental*, a range occupying the area's central and western portions of the kingdom. Immediately along the coast, the lowland was very flat and bordered by offshore barrier beaches and lagoons. The rivers, of which there were many, had as their source the *Sierra Madre Oriental* to the west.

From Vera Cruz south the plain was poorly drained and had numerous swamps and lakes dotting its surface. These contributed to the proliferation of insects that carried the tropical diseases prevalent in the area. The poor drainage of the south coastal region was exacerbated by the area's tropical wet climate of both the year-round and monsoonal types that resulted in intense summer rains. The rains in the past year had not been excessive, but in the three-week period just preceding the arrival of the fleet, this began to change with rain falling every day.

Somewhat inland and to the west, was an exceedingly dense rain forest on mountainous terrain with savannas and palm savannas on the wetter portions. The slippery slopes of this rain forest loomed as the passengers' first trial after leaving the plain. The rain forest presented a difficult but not insurmountable, barrier to their final destination which, for most of the passengers, was Mexico City.

The watery world of tropical rain forest, savannas, swamps, lakes, lagoons, and rivers constituted an unhealthy environment. It was under these soggy conditions that the Robledos sought shelter. They needed a place where they could regain their strength and equilibrium for their eventual move into the interior.

Fortunately, the offer of shelter was almost immediate, though not motivated by charity. A certain merchant from the City of Mexico, a *Senor* Mattos, was in Vera Cruz seeking to buy the cargo of the fleet. If sold to him, he said, they would not have to wait for their cargo to be unloaded. Thus unencumbered, they could go into the interior where the comforts and amenities of the City of Mexico awaited them. *Dona* Catalina should not have her baby here among these Indians and poor peasants, he said. Also, he added, if they remained in Vera Cruz, they would be subjected to the *mal aire* (the musty and bad smelling air of the swamps) and would catch some dreaded disease. "Think of yourselves. Think of your children!" he implored. With much sighing and wringing of hands, his attempts to persuade them continued unabated, but, when it was finally apparent that the Robledos did not intend to sell their cargo, the merchant relented.

Yes, he had a storehouse, he said. It was near the foundations of Cortes's disintegrating fortress with its earthen walls, bricks, and timbers. Yes, the adobe structure, mostly dry, and with a straw floor, was nearly empty. However, he might be successful in buying cargo from yet another prospective merchant and some portion of his warehouse would then be filled. Yes, he would become their landlord and perhaps their partner. Who knew how their relationship might develop!

It was while trying to make this space habitable and secure that Pedro Robledo bought his first firearm. The merchant, Mattos, a very persuasive fellow who sold munitions along with shirts and socks, insisted that Pedro Robledo arm himself. When Robledo was able to secure his cargo, *Senor* Mattos said, the barrels and crates would have to be broken down into parcels that could be carried by a mule. Then Pedro would need an armed escort to successfully transport his cargo to Mexico City. Moreover, Mattos insisted, Pedro himself would have to be armed.

Pedro Robledo did not require a great deal of convincing. He had learned from his experience in the forest that he and his family needed the protection a firearm would help give them. The only question was what to buy and from whom to buy it. *Senor* Mattos had the answer.

"You'll need a forked metal stick like this one," he said, holding a metal crutch in the air. "These damn locks are heavy, perhaps half an *arroba*, maybe more. You put the barrel of your gun on it like this while you aim and fire," he demonstrated by placing one arm in the crook of the other. "You'll need powder, a ramrod, wadding, lead, and a bullet mold. You'll need a powder flask and a pouch, and a *harquebus*, of course. This one's French," he added excitedly, removing a finely tooled implement from the crate in which it was stored, "but I have Italian and Flemish ones, too, if you'd prefer one of those. Actually, it doesn't matter which one you take. They're all pretty much the same in terms of the equipment you'll need. You'll need it all, lock, stock and barrel!"

So it was that 39-year-old Pedro Robledo got his first flintlock, a Flemish piece with a beautifully incised gunstock. He knew that Mattos had probably made a considerable profit from its sale, but it did not matter to Pedro for he was exceedingly satisfied with his purchase.

* * *

Under conditions of almost constant rain, which only increased or decreased in intensity, the Robledos attempted to reconstruct some semblance of family life. This was exceedingly difficult, for they lacked both cooking and baking facilities. Because of this, they were largely dependent on what they could buy from their better-established neighbors who lived in scattered homes throughout the village. They also obtained foodstuff from the village market where Indians from the interior and from the coast sold fruit, vegetables, fowl, *maize*-cakes, and baked fish.

Daily, in torrents of rain, Pedro Robledo worked to build a lean-to that he began to affix to the south side of the Mattos warehouse. The mud through which he trudged while foraging for building material was a fetid mess of soil, water, and rotting vegetation. Walking in it was a near impossibility. Every motion required great effort, and it was difficult to remain shod in steps that gurgled in his passage. Falling constantly, especially on the forested slopes, he kept re-injuring the shin that he had first severely bruised while climbing over a fallen tree.

Although he had at first denied the request by six-year-old Diego to help in building the lean-to, Pedro now found that he badly needed him. Pedro would cut the fronds from the bank of the nearby swamp and carry these to the road. From there, in torrential rain, Diego would drag them home. Diego loved working with his father, and they cemented their relationship forever while working together on this undertaking.

* * *

After several days of rest, and with a diet heavy with fruits and vegetables, both Lucia and Catalina began to improve. Catalina was now able to walk to the Indian *tianquez*, or market, to buy the food they needed. It was here that she encountered the Indian woman. She had noticed her on her first visit, an Indian woman of uncertain age holding the hand of a child approximately two years old. Among all the others whose dress and physical characteristics looked, to Catalina's European eyes, so very much alike, this person was different. In contrast to the other market-women, who kneeled or sat on *petates*, the mats on which they displayed their wares, this individual just stood there with her child and did not appear to be a vendor. Perhaps she was with her mother or sister, Catalina thought. The Indian woman, who drew her attention and whose eye she had caught, looked as though she was waiting for someone. Catalina thought little about her until she saw her again on a second, and then on a third day. She asked *Senor* Mattos if he knew who she was, this woman who appeared so detached from what went on around her. Mattos did not. However, he suggested that she might be the wife of one of the individuals who worked at the docks, perhaps one of those Indians sentenced there for idolatry by "that damned Landa." Mattos's supposition proved to be correct, and the woman, Maria de Totonac, and her child, Anac, were to be the first among a long line of Indians, men, women and children, whom Catalina was to befriend.

Maria accepted a position as the Robledos' cook, but she and Anac remained in the sodden forest living in whatever shelter they could obtain. Eventually, however, she reluctantly allowed Pedro to establish a very small corner of the lean-to as their sleeping quarters. With an outdoor oven and a stone bench on which the family did its cooking, the six of them settled down to some semblance of family life, though Maria and Anac were never truly to emotionally join them.

Although *Senor* Mattos had warned Catalina not to "go looking for five feet on this cat," she could not help herself. She attributed the psychological distance she felt between herself and Maria to her inability to communicate adequately with her. Therefore, she tried to learn Maria's words for simple things such as mud, rain, and fire, but she was not successful. When she spoke one of those words, Maria merely looked at her with a vacant stare and then, with flywhisk in hand, returned to her work. The children were slightly more successful with Anac. Although they could only speak to her when her mother was not present, for her mother jealously guarded her interactions, they managed to learn the words for eyes, hair, and different articles of clothing, but little else. The six of them occupied the same world but were not in it together.

Most significantly, Catalina discovered that Maria prepared meals, and even *panes* or loaves of bread for herself and for her child separate from what she cooked for the Robledos. Catalina discovered this when she attempted to serve the Indian family a portion taken from a larger loaf of bread she had just removed from the adobe oven. Not only did Maria refuse to eat it, she forcibly removed from Anac's mouth a piece that Anac had been eating. Then, with Anac in tow, she angrily left the lean-to and proceeded toward the rain forest.

Although the Robledos did not know what to make of this behavior, the bread was a clue, for by the thread one comes to the ball of yarn. Catalina was horrified to learn from *Senor* Mattos, that Maria, who was attempting to gain revenge for the incarceration of her husband, was among those who were willfully trying to contaminate the Spaniards with the *matalzahuatl*. They did this by either throwing dead bodies into the ditches of running water from which the Spaniards obtained their drink, or by mixing diseased blood with the bread they made for European families. Nonetheless, despite her feelings of revulsion and terror, and her need to protect her family, she did not want Maria punished, for Catalina could not bear ill will toward anyone. At any rate, it did not matter, for Maria had removed herself beyond punishment. Maria and Anac had disappeared into the woods from which they had come.

* * *

During the months of August and September in which the *matalzahuatl* was most virulent, a few small mule trains left Vera Cruz for the interior. Most individuals, though, were content to wait on the plain for a break in the weather and for a decline in the epidemic. However, in the interior, far removed from those who waited on the soggy beach, others were making their own attempts to deal with the disease.

In the City of Mexico, Viceroy Martin Enriquez de Almanza, Archbishop Pedro de Moya, the regular and secular clergy, civil authorities, and all the people, especially the rich, did what they could to assist those afflicted with the scourge. They established infirmaries to provide the Indians with the medicine, food, and clothing they so badly needed. The clergy visited the sick to comfort them and also to ensure that none died without the Last Rites. However, the clergy was not successful in these latter endeavors, for Indian deaths exceeded more than 2,000,000, with 100,000 in the state of Tlascala alone. The clergy could not, in this vast country, reach all those who needed them, and the scourge continued.

The day dedicated to St. Hippolytus, August 13th, came and went, and nothing happened to ease the suffering. Finally, in despair, the people of Valley of Mexico asked that *La Nuestra Senora de los Remedios* (Our Lady of Remedies) be removed from her shrine in the village of Tacuba and, by solemn procession, taken to the City of Mexico. It was hoped that during this passage, the Virgin would see the devastation the disease had caused and would request an intercession by her Son.

Our Lady of Remedies was the statue of the Virgin Mary allegedly discovered by Juan de Tobar (his Spanish name), a *cacique*, or village chieftain, who lived on the western side of the Valley of Mexico. In 1540, it was said, while hunting on top of a hill near his home, Juan found a very small wooden statue of the Virgin Mary. She was about a hand high and was holding her Child on her left arm and a scepter in her right hand. Like the image of the Virgin of Guadalupe reputedly carved by St. Luke, and found in 1325 near Trujillo (and like numerous other statues of the Virgin buried throughout Spain in the wake of Muslim invasion), the present statue lay almost completely hidden among some rocks beneath a *maguey* plant where it had supposedly lain for almost 20 years. It was dropped, it was said, by one of Cortes's soldiers as he fled the Aztecs on *la noche triste* (the sad night). Tobar took the statue home and made a little altar for it where it stood until 1555 when popular demand required he place it in the village church. Later, when the Virgin interceded in the curing of his blindness and his crippling condition, he had a chapel built to honor her on the spot where the statue had been found. This was the chapel, currently a splendid church (since 1574 under government patronage), from which the citizens now removed *La Gachupina* (the European Spaniard) the name by which the statue was also known.

Thus, on a dark and gloomy day in mid-September 1577, the Virgin was taken from Tacuba to the City of Mexico. She was accompanied by the viceroy, the *audiencia* (a council of magistrates), the *ayuntamieto* (or town council), and the most prominent citizens of the Valley. All held lighted tapers as the procession moved through the streets. Then, for nine consecutive days (a *novena*), Masses were said. Like the Virgin of Guadalupe, which had been paraded through Rome around AD 600 in an effort to end the plague, *La Gachupina* was carried through the streets of Mexico for the wonder and veneration of the community. Prayers were offered and promises made. The populace asked for mercy, not for themselves in this instance (although they, too, might fall), but for the Indians who were dying in great numbers. Soon the pestilence began to subside, and, finally, following a two-year period during which almost two-thirds of the Indian population of New Spain perished, the scourge disappeared.

After the epidemic, there was a scarcity of food and a fear of famine, the fields having long been abandoned. In his 'benevolence' toward the native population, the viceroy made two pronouncements in their favor. The Indians would be temporarily exempted from paying tribute and the public granaries, as well-stocked as possible under the present circumstances, would be made available to the poor. Here they might buy their corn and wheat at reasonable prices.

The Staging Area

The pleas for an intercession by *La Gachupina* were made during mid-September 1577. Also in mid-September, despite the negative reports still being received from the interior, the Robledos began to plan in earnest for their trip. Daily, trains laden with logwood and with dried insect bodies arrived in Vera Cruz from the lakes region. It was from these insects, the female *Dactylopius coccus*, 70,000 of which were required to obtain one pound of product, that the Spaniards obtained the natural dye cochineal. The insects, which were then shipped to Spain for processing, were used to dye wool the crimson, carmine, and scarlet of royalty so highly prized on the continent. Once the packs were unloaded, the Robledos could rent these mules and their muleteers for the return trip to Mexico City.

Following the disappearance of Maria and Anac, the Robledos destroyed the small shelter they had constructed for them within the lean-to. They used much of the cleared space along the back wall where the shelter had been to set up a packing table. When they were finally able to obtain their goods from within the hold of their ship, they moved them to the Mattos warehouse where they began the chore of unpacking and sorting. With oilskins bought from *Senor* Mattos, they began the lengthy task of re-packing their goods into bales, each approximately 50 pounds in weight, two of which would comprise the burden of a mule. They had been told that they could hire Indian porters if they wished, each of whom could carry 50 pounds of baggage for 15 miles of travel each day. This had struck them as impractical, so they had chosen the mules instead.

Senor Mattos was the one to tell them of Juan de Penol. "A *mestizo*, born of a Spanish father and an Indian mother. Cortes himself had a son like him. He's absolutely dependable," he said, emphasizing the "absolutely." "You can't do better. I've used him many times. Don't lose him," *Senor* Mattos continued emphatically. "Penol has no *mulas de retorno* who go back without a load. There will be many who'll want him, and he and his men will be ready to go back to the City of Mexico by Thursday."

Pedro Robledo was unsure they could be ready by that time. He blamed himself, although he knew that he had obtained his cargo as soon as it had become available to him. He also knew that he and his wife had begun the tasks of unpacking and sorting as soon as they were able, although, Pedro thought, perhaps it could have been done more efficiently. Perhaps they could have worked longer or harder and would now be finished. It was while he talked to himself in this manner (a trait which would become more pronounced as he grew older) that Juan de Penol, wearing two enormous leaves as a raincoat, appeared out of the rain.

"*Senor* Mattos told me that you need a guide," he said, his hand outstretched, not even bothering to introduce himself.

Juan de Penol, who was known to his men as *El Arriero*, The Muleteer, was a tall, broad-shouldered individual with a long, pockmarked face. Although coarse in dress, he carried himself with dignity.

"You could do no better, *Senor*," Penol said. "My village is on the shores of the lake, and I've made the trip many times—always without incident," he added as a means of bolstering his credentials. "You need a guide?" he asked rhetorically. "I'm your guide." He moved closer to the pot brewing on the stone hearth. "*Senor* Mattos tells me you're a very intelligent man, *Senor* Robledo, interested in everything. He said I could learn much from you. I think, maybe, that you can learn something from me too. We'll make a good team," he added with a toothsome grin. "We'll leave on Thursday!"

Pedro explained that he and his family could not be ready to leave on Thursday. Perhaps they could be ready by Saturday, but Sunday would be better. "You know," Juan said thoughtfully as he gauged the number of finished bales the packing would produce knowing he could not carry it all. "I could make a deal with another, *Senor*," he said as he pinched and patted the cloth Pedro was packing. "There are many who want me, but I want to go with you. We'll leave on Friday. What you've not finished packing, you can leave here. There'll be other trips, *Senor* Robledo. Many others. What you don't have ready on Friday, we'll take later."

And so it was. When Juan's mules came up the sand-packed path of the hill overlooking the harbor at Vera Cruz, Pedro, Catalina, Diego and Lucia were waiting for them. The work of placing saddlecloths (*jergas*), sheepskin pads, and saddles on the mules, and of attaching packs to these saddles occupied the better part of the morning. It was a process they would repeat in reverse order each evening so that each mule would receive the same packs and load the succeeding day. After eating the remains of their *maize* cakes, and drinking a bit of chocolate, the Robledo party left the area of the warehouse. They moved across the soggy field to the road—less muddy now that the season of the monsoon had abated—and left their first home in New Spain. Many others would follow.

In the Footsteps of Cortes

There was no want of advice or information concerning what the Robledos would meet with on their trek of nearly 400 miles. They had been told they would cross a series of mountains and three natural terraces as they

78

followed in the footsteps of Cortes. The first of these terraces, they had been told, would be the *tierra caliente*, or hot region, where Vera Cruz was located. The inhabitants of the coast thought of this as the area of *mal aire* arising from, they thought, the decomposition of rank vegetable matter in the hot and humid soil. The *tierra caliente* would continue inland for some 60 miles and extend upward to an altitude of approximately 4,000 feet. At that point, they would enter the second terrace, the area of *tierra templada*, or temperate zone, a land of perpetual humidity. The third terrace, the *tierra fria*, or cold region, would occur at between 7,000 and 8,000 feet above sea level. After that, they would be on the Central Plateau. This tableland would maintain an altitude of 6,000 feet across its great expanse until they came to the ramparts surrounding the Valley of Mexico. After climbing this final barrier at 7,000 feet above sea level, they would descend into the valley. The entire journey from Vera Cruz to the City of Mexico, they were assured, would constitute a trip of less than two months.

The Robledos left Vera Cruz in the middle of September eager to see what lay beyond the broad expanse of the coast with its sandy plains and marshy areas of deep, luxuriant growth. They found that this tract of aromatic shrubs, wild flowers, thickets and towering trees extended for a considerable distance inland. They spent the first two nights on the trail amid soggy surroundings. After a trek of perhaps 50 miles, they left the vanilla, indigo, and flowering cacao-groves behind and entered a broad savanna that demonstrated quite dramatically that they had crossed into a new zone. They spent the night of 19 September on the savanna out of the weather, their tents pitched near a stand of trees.

On their first three days of travel, the Robledos had noted that they had not seen anyone on the trail. They had also not come across any areas of habitation. Juan had told them there were Indians who lived in this region, but that the party was unlikely to see them. The elusive hunters of this area, individuals who lived on the eastern slope of the mountains fronting Vera Cruz, would be making the best of the weather by hunting deep in the forest. The tremendous rains of the last month had diminished and would soon become a distant memory. It was anticipated by all who knew the district that it would continue to become drier as the season moved into fall.

On the savanna the Robledo party found deer grazing on the meadows and considered spending a few extra days there as it was important to obtain deer, fowl or other food. They had brought cooking pots and a grinding stone in nets they had attached to their mules, but the only food they carried was *maize* meal. They had to obtain any additional food they needed by purchasing it, or bartering or hunting for it. Unfortunately, they left the savanna on 20 September, at dawn, without having been successful at killing any game. Pedro had had two opportunities to kill a deer—and had even fired his *harquebus*—but the distance was too great, and he was unable to hit his target.

After leaving the savanna, the Robledos passed along mossy pathways through a land scarred and fractured with volcanic canyons. The trail passed through vast tracts of lava frozen in innumerable fantastic formations. On the margins of the road were enormous chasms bursting with rich blooms and the most verdant vegetation the family had ever seen. They spent their fourth night at Jalapa, a village some 60 miles from the coast but already 4,681 feet above sea level. Nearby was *Cofre de Perote*, once blazing with volcanic fires and still resplendent with its mantle of snow. Here, with a cool breeze blowing off the 14,048-foot cone of the extinct volcano, they spent an extra day.

"Dawn broke in a luminous haze," reads Pedro's entry for 22 September. Still climbing, they found cultivated fields of corn and wheat that lay beside the road and extended for some distance beyond it. Wooden crosses with strips of red cloth attached guarded the fields. They were there to ward off eclipses and spirits that might cause these crops to fail. After a day of difficult travel, they approached the village of Socochima. This was once a fortified hamlet of exceptional beauty, its old stone fortress hovering on a precipice towering above a magnificent cataract. Here they found many vines of the *granadilla*, the fruit of the passion flower, and an abundance of good food, and so they spent an additional day.

At Socochima the children for the first time donned their *papahigos*, a half-mask covering the face, while Catalina began to wear Pedro's *gaban*, a greatcoat with a hood. Here the family also obtained cloaks and caps of a material unknown to them. The caps, similar to the *montera* of Central Spain, caused them untold misery with itchy scalps. However, Pedro felt that the caps, which he insisted his family wear on the trail, were essential to ward off the chill and to hide the crimson locks of their owners and make them less conspicuous targets.

As Pedro tucked an errant lock within Lucia's cap, it may have occurred to him how out of place these children were in this primitive environment. This was especially true of Lucia who, with her red hair, small, freckled face, and hazel eyes, appeared doll-like on top of her enormous mule. How odd it was that she would be transplanted here. What Lucia remembered about this moment, as her father swept back her hair, was how she had briefly seen herself reflected in her father's eyes and how she had never before noticed that his red hair was becoming gray. As she clutched the lead rope of her mule and moved out to catch the others, her father hoped he had made the right decisions regarding his family's future.

Beyond Socochima the party crossed a pass over some high mountains and moved through another village called Texutla. Here, the forest of large oak trees and an extensive stand of pine, reached toward the summit of the *Cordillera* of the Andes, the colossal range that loomed before them. After leaving Texutla, they completed their ascent of the mountains.

The party awoke the next morning to find their heads ringed with a coating of frost. However, when the sun broke through the trees at 8,000 feet above sea level, it warmed them somewhat and helped to make them feel better. They left the area early and entered another pass where they found a very small group of houses amid the ruins of what had been a stone temple. Again, they found it very difficult to find food and the cold in the shadowed depths of this mountain pass was severe.

Beyond the pass they came to the territory of Zautla or Xocotlan. Here they found an Indian village that had been renamed Castilblanco (White Castle) by some of the Portuguese soldiers with Cortes. These men said that Castilblanco's flat-roofed homes and white-painted idol-houses reminded them of a town of that name in Portugal. The train was able to obtain food here, though it was sparse and barely enough to feed the party.

After leaving Castilblanco, they entered the province of the once-proud Tlascala. These were the Indians about whom Diego and Lucia had heard their grandfather speak. A number of these Indians, Aztec and Tlascalan chiefs among them, had been presented to Emperor Charles at Toledo in 1528, a spectacle which their maternal grandfather had witnessed. These were also the Indians who had been so devastated by the scourge of the *matlalzahuatl*. The party became aware they had crossed into the territory of the Tlascala when they found a stone wall, half again higher than a man, which Tlascala's neighbors, like Hadrian, had built to protect them from raids by an unwanted people. Here, as Cortes had done before them, they followed the Apulco River through a steep canyon and continued on.

In the province of the Tlascala, the home of perhaps 50 *vecinos* and an Indian population that had once exceeded 200,000, the Robledos found the Andes spread before them like a vast tableland. The plateau they encountered maintained an elevation of more than 6,000 feet for a distance of nearly 600 miles. The *vecinos* had been warned in 1552 that they could not form estates here to the detriment of the Indians, but now with the Indian population much depleted, small groups of Spaniards had begun to move into the area. The party found it very difficult to obtain food and so went to sleep without any. The Robledo party had been on the trail for eight days and everyone was cold, tired and hungry.

Across the *Cordillera* of the Andes, a ragged procession of mountains stretched in a westerly direction as far as the eye could see. Of tremendous height, some of these peaks formed the highest land areas on earth. Here the Robledo party found a massive stone jaguar, like one of the mighty stone bulls of *Guisando*, carved in volcanic rock and pointing toward the glacier-clad *Pico de Orizaba* (or *Citlaltepetl* as the Aztecs called it—'the mountain of the stars'). This extinct volcanic cone, which rose 18,855 feet above sea level, was the highest peak in New Spain and the third highest peak in North America. Its crown, and many of the other peaks that spread to the west, was in an area of perpetual snow. The air was exceedingly dry and the soil, although naturally good, was not clothed with the luxuriant vegetation of the lower regions. The land had a parched appearance owing partly to the greater evaporation that took place on these lofty plains. The Robledos followed a path upward across a dry, forlorn stretch of rock and thorn forest, but the tableland, when they reached it, was thickly covered with larch, oak, cypress, and other trees, some of extraordinary dimensions.

Days later, in Tlascala, on 15 October, the Robledos came to the little town of Xalacingo. About six miles from there, they came to the ruins of what had been a very strong fortress. This fortress had been built of stone and cement, so hard that Cortes had found it very difficult to demolish it, even with iron pickaxes. It had been built to defend the towns of the Tlascala from their mortal enemies, the Indians of Mexico. Although this fortress was now in ruins, and was not defended as it once had been by Indians with swords, shields, and lances, the site itself still concerned the Robledos. They were certain that if a party of Indians lay concealed and waiting in ambush, it would be at a site such as this. However, the Indian population had been decimated, the dead lying unburied in their huts, fields and roads for months. No Indians appeared and the Robledo party continued its slow march through what they considered potentially hostile territory.

As evening approached, the heavens were an infinite ceiling of light, the trees seemingly blazing with the sun's last rays. Bats and birds swirled in the evening sky, and the members of the mule train slept with the low moan of wind rushing through the mountaintops. Because the wind masked most sounds, they slept with sentries posted and tried to keep their ears tuned to anything that might foretell disaster. The wind moaned ominously through the night but ceased at dawn, and with the light of day became calm and placid.

Still in the province of the Tlascala, the Robledo party finally began to see signs of human life. They saw people in their huts and in their fields of *maize* and *maguey*, the plant from which the Indians made their *pulque* (a fermented drink). The country was beautiful with a soft breeze blowing through the branches of the trees and here and there a little brook from which they could obtain drinking water. The party went through a small village and on 25 October slept by a stream with a double stand of sentries posted. They remained certain that the Tlascaltec would steal their cargo and kill them if they were able. It was on the bank of this stream, at the edge of this possibly hostile Indian village that the Robledos ate dog for the first time.

Unable to find food, except for green plums that they ate with a relish, the party for the third day had little to eat beyond the *maize* they carried. If they were to maintain their strength for their daily march of

15 miles, they had to have food. The two small dogs that wandered into their camp that evening seemed to present themselves as potential nourishment. Although the Robledos initially refused to eat the dogs that Juan's men roasted on a spit, hunger eventually triumphed over cultural barriers. The small dogs proved to be a fine meal.

As they sat around their campfire that evening, Juan de Penol described to his men and to the Robledos, the practice the Tlascaltec had once engaged in of eating the people they captured. "This," he said, "you may find hard to believe, but only 50 years ago, these people kept men and boys in cages to fatten them for the slaughter. Boys like you, Diego," he said, pointing to the six-year-old who moved closer to his father for comfort. "Most of those who were sacrificed were captives, but sometimes they sacrificed their own people, hundreds of them on some occasions, depending on what they were asking from the gods. Their *cues*," he continued, "their idol-houses were smeared with the blood of those they killed and their priests were filthy with clotted blood on their clothes and under their long fingernails and matted in their hair so that it could not be parted. The stench of rotting flesh," he continued as though he himself had experienced it, "the stench of rotting flesh was horrible. You could not get it out of your nose, and it stayed with you and you would wake up years later, my father said, with this horrible odor in your nose and on your skin. So, eat dog!" he bellowed. "This is nothing. These people planned to eat my father with tomatoes and peppers and perhaps a bit of salt. No, eating dog is nothing," he said, finally spent. "Today, we eat dog, and tomorrow, perhaps a mule," he laughed. "We'll be happy to eat what we can get. You'll see." And with this, Juan sat back on his pack, and, with the juice of the meat running down his hairy arms, began to devour the piece in his hands.

* * *

In the province of the Tlascala the ground, although flat and wooded, was quite broken and difficult to traverse. In this difficult terrain, a number of Indians still lived in underground houses like caves, which was the custom of this particular group. Near the village of Tzompantepec, the Robledos came to an enormous plain. This was the site where Cortes's 400 soldiers had met a Tlascaltec force of several thousands. Juan de

Penol recounted how the Spaniards, who were required to use their wounded soldiers as combatants, had been victorious. They accomplished this, Juan said, by having superior weapons, steel armor, a better command of strategy, and the very significant advantage bestowed by having horses. However, Juan also pointed out, if it had not been for Cortes's Indian allies, some of whom were his mother's people, Cortes would have been defeated. With these expressions of pride by Juan for himself and for his muleteers, the members of the mule train set up camp. They spent the night of 28 October on the unprotected plain, in a cold wind that blew off the 14,636-foot cone of *Malintzin* (*La Malinche*) that lay immediately to their south.

Food was now more plentiful and the Indians, though more numerous, were quite friendly. Nonetheless, the members of the mule train remained on guard. They knew that they must not trust the Indians' apparent peacefulness. It was a good custom, Juan said, to be prepared, and to conduct oneself as though an attack was imminent. The Indians, however, remained friendly, and the Robledos were able to purchase a considerable variety of foods from them wherever they went. These included fowl and even prickly pears or figs, an edible fruit of the flat-stemmed cactus family that was in season and plentiful in these parts.

* * *

From Tlascala, two routes were possible. They could go through the town of Huexotzinco ('a place surrounded by willows'), or through Cholula, the route taken by Cortes. Each was in the same general area south of Tlascala, but as the former was 7,516 feet above sea level, and the latter somewhat lower, it was decided to go by way of Cholula. Either route would take them by the 17,887 foot Popocatepetl ('Smoking Mountain'), an active volcano with smoke coming from its cone. It had last erupted in 1539 and seemed to present no great danger. What the Robledos hoped to minimize were additional frigid nights within the mountains.

* * *

Cholula was a large town on a vast plain with lofty towers and almost 400 great *cues*, or temples, now in ruin. The party found that it was a land rich in *maize*, peppers, and in the *maguey* from which the Cholulans brewed their alcoholic drinks. The people made excellent pottery of red and black clay painted in various designs. They supplied Mexico and all the neighboring provinces with pottery in the same way that Talavera and Placencia did in Castile. Pedro Robledo remarked that Cholula looked from a distance like their royal city of Valladolid in Castile. With many neighboring towns in its vicinity, it seemed a good choice both for travel and for obtaining the food they required, but the distance across the undulating plain from Tlascala to Cholula was greater than they had anticipated. With Catalina eight months pregnant and in great distress, it was decided to camp on the banks of a river. This was near a stone bridge within site of the town approximately three miles in the distance. At this encampment there were some abandoned huts, each consisting of one room with a hard-packed dirt floor. The party took shelter in them. From Indians dressed in cotton smocks they obtained poultry and *maize*-cakes. They posted sentries and remained in camp for three days until Catalina was again able to travel.

* * *

From the time they had left Vera Cruz, the entire party had been concerned about Catalina. The child she carried was pushing her organs aside in it movement toward birth. She was eating and breathing for two, and there were times when she was in severe pain and could neither walk nor ride. Although her pregnancy would have been ignored under most circumstances, as was the custom of the times, her painful condition could not be. Pedro feared she would miscarry and the loss would kill her. He was resolute that his beloved Catalina would not lose the baby! Pedro's determination to travel only when she was able to do so required that they spend more days in camp than would have been normal. Therefore, they doubled and even tripled the length of their stays on several occasions. This had appeared to suffice, but it was now apparent that even greater periods of rest would be required and he decided to provide them.

When the party was finally able to leave their encampment, Juan's mules were hobbled and blindfolded so as to get them to perform their task of crossing the stream. The party was lucky that the stone bridge was in place, since without it, they would not have been able to cross the river. For several days it had been a raging brown torrent. The flood carried logs, trees, brush and boulders that resounded in the dark of their camp like cannonades as they rolled and smashed their way down the streambed. The river was still in flood when they left their encampment on 3 November and moved into the town.

In the town of Cholula itself, where the god Quetzalcoatl had stopped on his way to the sea, the Robledos took up residence, moving into one of the large courtyards. Here Cortes's soldiers had successfully defeated the townsmen who had conspired with the Indians of Mexico to annihilate them. The courtyards, which comprised a portion of the temple complex dedicated to the worship of Quetzalcoatl, stood undemolished as a memorial to this history. The members of the mule train remained here for an additional two days, hoping for better weather, but really praying that Catalina, now bleeding rather than spotting, would again be able to travel.

While in Cholula, during one of their daily excursions for food, Pedro and Diego, led by Juan de Penol and three of his men, rode to the so-called Temple of Cholula. Here, Diego and his father were astonished to see a pyramidal mound, built with, or rather encased in, unburned brick. It rose to the height of nearly 180 feet, the largest pyramid by volume in the world. The traditional belief of the Indians, Juan related, was that a family of giants who had escaped the great flood had built it. They had designed it to be raised to the clouds. However, the gods, offended with their presumption, bombarded the pyramid with fires from heaven and compelled them to abandon the attempt. What remained was a remarkable structure greater than anything either of the Robledos had seen in their native Castile. Pedro probed Juan and his men for additional information regarding this pyramid but could learn no more. The Indians of their train, most of whom came from the Valley of Mexico, knew nothing of the mound beyond what they had heard from the Indians of Cholula. What they did know a great deal about was how to obtain bounty from the land.

The Indians of the Valley of Mexico provided abundant information about the richest and most diversified flora to be found in any country on earth. The medicinal plants they enumerated could provide a remedy for everything from flatulence to gout. They told about vanilla, bananas, and sugar, the latter which they obtained from the stalks of corn, and spoke at length of beans and plantains: "Not as sweet as the banana," they said, "but from it we make flour." They extolled the virtues of cacao from which they obtained chocolate, and they expounded on the virtues and uses of *maize*, sisal, and especially *maguey*. It was from this latter plant, an agave, that they obtained paper, *pulque*, as well as a sweet and nutritious food when roasted in a pit oven. When not on the trail, all of the muleteers tended small fields or kitchen gardens they had beside their homes. The men chiefly did the tasks of cultivating the soil with the women scattering the seed, husking the corn, and taking part only in the lighter labors of the field. In this, the Indians presented a remarkable contrast to the people of Spain who so abhorred agriculture. These men with whom Pedro worked were excellent teachers and Pedro an apt and avid pupil. He had nothing to teach them, but as Juan had told him (and as he was happy to discover), he had a lot to learn from them.

The weather on 5 November was a repeat of the previous four days, the rain continuing unabated. In spite of this, after three days in the area of Cholula, the party was again on the move. They traveled to the village of Iscalpan where they stopped momentarily at a Franciscan monastery. The good fathers asked them to stay. With winter fast approaching, however, the Robledos thanked them for their hospitality and were again on the move. Although the members of the train knew that Popocatepetl was immediately to their south, they were unable to see it due to an extremely heavy fog. All remarked at how incredibly still and quiet it was as they left the courtyard of the mission with not a bird or creature within sight or sound. The area abounded with thickets and ravines and the caravan was ever at the ready for an attack.

At Iscalpan (Calpan), perched at 8,233 feet on the slope of an extinct volcano, the train began to climb the towering rampart which nature had provided the Valley of Mexico (ineffectually, it turned out) to protect it from invasion. Upon reaching what they had mistakenly believed was the summit, they found two wide trails, one of which had been laid out by Sebastian de Aparicio who had begun transporting freight between Vera Cruz and Mexico City in 1536. Juan told them that the right-handed path led to Chalco by way of Tlalmanalco. The left, Aparicio's, which was more direct, led through pine forests to Amecameca. The latter track was the one they were to take, and again, this track began to climb.

At the 'Pass of Cortes,' more than 12,000 feet above sea level, Juan pointed out the remains of stout tree trunks placed there by Moctezuma's allies to block Cortes's progress. Cortes's men had painstakingly removed them from the road. Remarkably, some of these trunks, which lay in adjacent ravines, were still intact, although, they were perhaps, only remnants of their former selves. It was cold now; the air crackled in a slight breeze, and, when they reached the top of the pass, it began to snow.

The snow began to accumulate as they trudged through the mud in the dimming light of the late afternoon. In this period before darkness, the sky to the west was magnificent, a bright salmon in color, that spread across the entire horizon. As the sun slipped behind the skyline, however, it grew very cold and the party knew it was imperative they find shelter before nightfall. They slept the night of 7 November in some huts that had been used as a sort of inn or lodging for Indian traders. The inn, or *mesone*, had originally been located here to provide shelter for itinerant Aztecan merchants. They made their journeys to the most remote borders of the land and to the countries beyond, carrying merchandise of rich stuffs. Now the owners of the inn, who appeared to live off the distressed condition of the traveler, provided lodging and firewood at a very high price. As night came, the members of the pack train ate well, but experienced intense cold, despite the small fires they lit within their lodgings.

Leaving early the next morning in sharp, clear air, they soon came to Amecameca which Juan said was only two days from the City of Mexico. Despite being very close to their final destination, they again decided to find lodging and to stay for a day. Food was plentiful now, and they had no difficulty finding abandoned huts within which to stay. That evening there was an additional stunning sunset. The flaming rays of the setting sun slipped beneath a bank of clouds to the west, coloring them so brilliantly they irradiated the mists below. As the sun went down, though, the sky turned a dull red in color and the temperature plunged again.

Two days later, on 10 November, the party set out for what they determined would be their final two days on the trail. The valley, for the most part, was level now and travel was easy. Covering about 15 miles on this day, they could see a magnificent lake, sky blue in color, extending before them as far as the eye could see. It glimmered in the sun and a forest of pinewoods grew down to its shores. Finally, over lava flows, they arrived at a village named Ayotzingo on the banks of Lake Texcoco where half of the houses were in the water and half on dry land. On the slopes of a low mountain that came down near the water's edge, they found an inn where they spent the night. This would be their last night on the trail. Tomorrow, after 57 days in transit, 40 of which they had spent on the trail, they would be in the environs of the City of Mexico.

Texcoco

The day was far along when the mule train neared Texcoco. A cold rain began to fall, the rain soaking clothing, and dripping from the chins of those in the file as they plodded through the late afternoon. It was nearly dark. The sun, a reddish ball which the riders could see through the mist, taunted them with its hidden warmth as they rode into a small corral.

"We're nearly there, Catcha," Pedro said to Catalina. "A few minutes more and we'll have you in a warm bed."

Catalina, who had, on this last day, been carried between two mules on a litter made of poles and hide, did not respond. Unstable and uncomfortable, her litter, which had been constructed from saplings, and from rawhide, just barely met its urgent need. The injured mule, which had provided its lattice-like bed, had been shot and skinned, its hide sliced into strips and woven onto a rectangular frame.

The rain came down in a fine mist, a murky cloud of chilled droplets hugging the earth and concealing all about them. Juan and Pedro steadied the litter as it was being released from its bounds, taking it from helpful hands, and carrying it toward a house now revealing itself at the edge of the corral. The children followed.

Lacking a hearth, and unused in the winter, the house was poor, and cold, and damp. With only a bed in each of its two rooms, and no other furniture, it barely met its offer of shelter. Juan said that the house, one of two which he had on the shores of the lake, was the one in which he was born. If Pedro was going to stubbornly refuse to stay at Juan's more comfortable home—with a hearth in every room—then this poor home was at Pedro's disposal. The children, Diego and Lucia, were put in one bed, while their mother was placed in the second. After covering the beds with layer upon layer of blankets, which he had taken from among his cargo, Pedro, removed his own wet clothing and got into bed beside Catalina. He lay there quietly for a long time, listening to her coughing, to the falling rain, and to the sounds of his children who were sleeping in the next room. He stretched out at full length beneath the blankets, feeling cold and miserable. And still the rain fell.

The air was keen, the night biting. The room was spare and unbelievably cold, and Catalina's condition worried Pedro greatly. He was in anguish at the unfeasibility of warming the room, and decided that in the morning, he would have to do something to improve their situation.

Catalina had a raw throat and was shivering almost uncontrollably. She had caught a cold and was chilled to the bone. During the night, she was feverish and her cold became severe, her condition seeming to have deteriorated into a serious malady. She now had a soaring fever, a convulsive cough, and an unbearable cramp in her side.

The next morning, Pedro stood at the door of Penol's old home, looking at the early morning sky. The clouds were gray and dreary. Patches of pallid fog, delicate and as fine as corned gunpowder, had settled on the lake. A shorebird, unseen but still present on the waters, beat its wings noisily.

Pedro's children stirred, but the house remained quiet, the Penol family nowhere to be seen. Mules stood in the small corral looking sad and forlorn, shaking water from their backs. Pedro looked beyond them, over the wall of the stone corral, and could see Juan, trailed by a small woman and three ragged children, leading a pack-laden mule up a footpath.

"*Y la senora*," Juan asked as he unlatched the gate to the corral, "how is she?"

"Sleeping," Pedro responded, leaving the doorway and moving into the muddy yard. "I'm worried," Pedro said, addressing himself first to Juan and then to Maria, who stood behind her husband. "I've heard nothing from her."

"And her fever?" Juan asked. "Is it still with her?"

"It was even worse last night," Pedro responded, "but I think it's gone down now."

"She may not wish to eat when she awakens," Juan said, "but we'll have food and a fire ready anyway. Maria," he said to the woman who stood with him in the stone corral, "perhaps there's something you can make . . . *chaquegue* or *atole* maybe.[1] The children will want some of that when they awaken," he said, again addressing himself to Pedro. "My papa used to make me *atole* when I was sick. It's wonderful! These little urchins here," he said, pointing to his own children who were hiding behind their mother's skirts, "they pretend illness just to get some. We've got meal and everything else you might need on the mule."

"I'll pay you," Pedro said.

"Your money's no good here," Juan responded. "You're my guest, and while you're here you'll pay nothing."

In the lean-to-kitchen, built of poles and cornstalks that stood against an outside wall of the *placita*, Juan worked to start a small fire and the group enjoyed its warmth.

The Robledo children were roused from bed by the smell of food, and by the pungent scent of a brushwood fire. They appeared in the doorway, cold, stiff, matted, and looking waif-like. They continued to stand in the doorway, appearing shy and unsure of these people whose home they had taken, and holding themselves apart from Maria and from the Penol children who also seemed shy. A litter of puppies occupying a den beneath the house provided a catalyst for play, and the children soon began to warm to one another.

Juan's wife, Maria de Anahuac, who was there to receive the Robledos, was decidedly the mistress of the household. An individual of perhaps 30 years of age, she had a remarkable presence. Her small face, prominent nose, high cheekbones, and wide forehead were of a reddish-brown hue approaching cinnamon in color. She had straight black and exceedingly glossy hair. Her most arresting feature was her eyes, each of which seemed to be directed towards the bridge of her nose. The Robledo children were afraid of her for she looked like no one they had ever seen.

"Do you think we should wake her?" Pedro asked of Maria who had gone into the house to look after Catalina. "I'm not sure what to do and I'm sick with worry."

"She'll wake when she's ready," Maria said. "She still coughing, but I think she's better now. Her body will tell her to waken when it requires water. You'll see. She'll be all right."

Towards mid-day, Catalina awoke from sleep, spoke a little, drank some water, and then sank again into a deep slumber. Her bed was moved to the other room, a trifle smaller, but nearer to the small fire in the kitchen outside her door. Then, at two or three in the morning, in her peculiarly soft and sweet voice, which so marked her, she asked Pedro to take her outside where she might use a latrine. He offered her a bowl to use as a bedpan, but she refused, waving it off and struggling to rise from her bed. Weak, and only able to walk with Pedro's assistance, he led her through the corral to a narrow trench being dug for a new stone wall. Then, tearfully admonishing Pedro not to look at her, she hiked the hem of her nightdress above her thighs, and squatted over the slit trench, remaining there a long time.

The stars were shining now; it had stopped raining; and, with his wife again demanding her privacy, Pedro felt that his beloved Catalina was going to be all right.

* * *

There remained some concern regarding the baby she carried, but she insisted that she could feel her hungry dancer kicking every afternoon around sundown. She had even given him a name, Alonso, to honor her father. Within some days, Maria confirmed both viability and gender. It was a very active boy, she said, but Catalina would have to remain in bed for some time if she was to carry him to term.

As time went on and the children saw their mother improve, they began to experience life as lived by a family that had the lake's bounty at its doorstep. Here, in these peaceful surroundings, with the waves of the lake gently laving the shore, the Robledo children learned to maneuver a dugout canoe and to use a butterfly net to catch fish that inhabited the lake's shallows. They learned to milk a goat and took great pleasure at squirting its milk at one another. They picked greens and learned which were edible and which were not. As the Robledo and Penol children watched their fathers ready themselves for their next trips, however, the Robledo children wondered what their next move would be.

La Carrera
Direct Commerce with the New World

Direct commerce with the Castilian West Indies required that one have a base of operations either in the City of Mexico itself or in one of the outlying communities. Alonso Lopez had suggested Valladolid in the Valley of Guayangares in Michoacan, west and slightly north of Mexico City. As the capital of Michoacan, Valladolid had been established somewhat away from the Indian communities of Tzintzuntzan and Patzcuaro, traditional native complexes which had first served the Spaniards as administrative centers. He and Pedro had also spoken of Zamora near Lake Chapala as a possible site for their business operations, but they were quite unsure of the desirability of this location. The reports coming to Spain from the West Indies were that silver, gold, copper, tin, and zinc were being discovered everywhere. It was said that one had only to pick the right spot to make a fortune, either in the mines themselves or by *La Carrera*, direct commerce with the New World. Pedro and his father-in-law were not so naive as to believe that this would be as easy as it was made to sound. Nevertheless, they were confident that their nest egg—left among the brambles to fool the bird of fate into continued laying—would result in a productive flock.

At daybreak, Pedro Robledo left Texcoco, riding southwest along the margins of the lake. It was a daylong trek into the city which lay like a sleeping hulk on the lake's far shore. The huge lake, like the great *Meotide*, shone a dazzling white as the sun became more prominent in the eastern sky. In this glittering light, amid the calls of millions of shore birds that fed in the shallows of the lake, Pedro came to a small rivulet flowing dark of peat within a vast thicket of weald. Here and there along the banks of this small stream were women who knelt on the rocks, scrubbing and wringing their poor clothes of autumn to which they would soon have to add additional layers. They took no note of him as they chatted to the rhythm of wet clothes being slapped against the stones upon which they knelt.

Riding along the banks of this creek, he rode by small farmhouses with their pungent odor of pig. He exchanged greetings with Indians and *mestizos* as they carried their large water pots to the stream or led their livestock away from the lake and toward pasture. Dogs yapped gently and wagged their tails to show they were friendly.

Pedro repeatedly asked directions as he approached the city for he was picking his way amid a maze of huts, paths, corrals and high fences that crossed and crisscrossed the perimeter of the lake. The address that Pedro was seeking was just off the *Zocalo*, or main plaza, that now covered the site of the old Aztec capital's main square. This was where the emperor's palace and the Great Temple had once stood. As he approached his destination, the cacophony of the trade grew increasingly louder until the square and the market within it became visible to him.

The market at Mexico was the largest Pedro had ever seen. The edges of the plaza were given to heaps of cabbage, an Old World food, that, by legend, had sprang as tears from the eyes of Lycurgus. The cabbage, which had found its way here in all its varieties, was white and red, hard, and crinkly and curly. Mountains of lettuce, onions, radishes and tomatoes were placed here and there, while purple, rose and silver garlic spread out before him almost as far as the eye could see. There were baskets of eggs and boxes of fowl, chickens, mostly, but also small hens of a type unknown to him. There were shirts, and saddles, and shoes, hawk bells, and fruits of every variety without number. Pedro took note of all this, and of the bronzed and wrinkled Indians who knelt before their wares as he rode through the square. Intent on reaching his destination, however, he continued on without stopping.

The address Pedro was looking for—off the *Zocalo* and near the cathedral—did not exist. He was at a complete dead-end until he chanced to speak to an old gentleman who rode into the square with lumpish crock-pots slung across the withers of his burro.

The old man said he knew the merchant, Machado, or at least he knew of him. They talked as his jars were filling, with the old man giving a running account of Machado and how he was not to be trusted. *"Muy malo hombre,"* the old man said, *"bajo y vil"* (a very bad man, low and vile). He broke off this conversation the moment his crocks were full, climbed aboard his cumbrously burdened beast and clattered out of the square. He had suggested that if Pedro was not going to take his advice and return to Texcoco without seeing Machado, he should ask a priest for information since they knew everything!

Pedro could not leave without seeing Machado, though, for Machado was his primary contact for his plan for commerce in New Spain. Pedro's father-in-law, Alonso Lopez, had also said that Machado was not greatly loved and that he demonstrated an incredible genius for rubbing people the wrong way. Nevertheless, Machado knew the business and could provide letters of introduction and of credit if Pedro required these. He would know the rates of exchange, where the business lay (although he might not be willing to share this information), and what the means of transportation were.

"Don't do business with him, Pedro," Alonso Lopez had warned him. "Merely let him know you're there and are to be seen as a friend. Besides, he owes me a favor," he had added. "He could not have gotten his start without my assistance, and will be bound to help us."

What prompted Pedro to enter the cathedral, a majestic but unembellished building of enormous proportions, he could not say, for he could have found a priest on any corner. He found the dark chasms of these religious structures most depressing, although the history they held, sometimes lured him inside. He had speculated that he would, at some point *andar estaciones*,[1] and would, while carrying a scallop shell, visit the shrine at Tepeyac Hill where the Virgin was said to have appeared to an Indian almost 50 years ago. However, it was not the shrine itself that drew him, but rather the picture of the Virgin that was reported to have been miraculously imprinted upon the Indian's cloak. Yes, he would like to see that. If it was real, which he much doubted in his unvoiced skepticism about religious affairs, that would be a treasure! At any rate, he found himself standing in the interior of the enormous church looking for a priest.

Except for two large candles flanking an enormous cross that was on the main altar, the cavernous church was in near darkness. These tapers, and a myriad of small votive candles that were placed here and there throughout the cathedral, provided the enormous building with its

96

only light. The candles on the main altar lit up its ornate *retablo*, or altar piece, of gold leaf, which soared above the tabernacle. In front of the altar rail, built in front of the main altar to protect it from profanation, there was a man, a priest, it appeared, who was sweeping the steps. As he swayed silently back and forth, the cleric threw great flickering shadows on the walls with an odd and ghostly effect. This individual, it turned out, was not a priest but a lay brother.

Brother Joaquin Rodriguez, who wore his fine hair cropped short, but without tonsure, was a poor cleric. Dressed shabbily in a ragged habit and tattered sandals, he was performing a penance for having questioned the Churches' right to burn Indian idols, requiring him to sweep and scrub the steps leading to the altar. Jolly and irreverent, he was to become Pedro's good friend. With his smiling eyes, sunken cheeks, and stumpy chin, he was the *dueno* of the church and a repository of information.

"Do you wish to see the bones?" he asked, moving toward a reliquary of an odd shape that contained a bone set in precious metals and richly decorated. "It's St. John's finger," he said. "Perhaps one of 23 or so throughout the world," he added with a chuckle that expressed his disdain for the importance of bones throughout Christendom.

"No," Pedro told him, "it's not bones I'm seeking, but rather a businessman named Teo Machado, known to some as *El Pescador*".

Yes, he knew Machado, Rodriguez said, a lout who pretended honesty, but upon whom you could place no trust. "But I can't speak badly of him because of my holy vows," he said while continuing with his criticisms. "It's said that he was once one of us, singing the *Angelus* and his *Te Deums*. But they say he found there was more to be gained by fleecing the flock rather than leading it. In truth, *Senor* Robledo," the brother added with a twinkle in his eye, "he didn't know half the Mass and he's even thought to have a devil in the hollow of his walking stick. No, unfortunately, I can't speak badly of him, for to keep silence well is called holy. But if I were able, you would only have to watch my eyes," he said, as he sequentially squinted and then rolled his eyes in apparent disgust. "They would tell you more than my words!" Pedro could not help laughing as he watched these contortions. With the screak of burdened hinges, they left the cathedral by a side door in a vain attempt to preserve the dignity of the religious institution.

After leaving the cathedral, Brother Rodriguez led Pedro a short distance down the Santa Teresa, one of the streets that radiated from the *Zocalo*. There, at a building fronted by a crew of gaunt and grubby dogs who were digging in a mound of garbage, he told Robledo where he could find Machado. "Up those stairs," he motioned with a wave of his hand, adding, "God help you, and don't buy anything from him! He's been known to put quicksilver in the ear of a mule he wished to sell to hurry its pace. Remember Robledo," he said, "that many who go for wool come back shorn."

Pedro responded, "Yes, but you remember that the pitcher that goes to the well too often leaves either its handle or its spout behind. I'll bring mine back with me."

"Ah ha!" retorted Rodriguez to these pronouncements. "But between the hammer and the anvil, he does not put his hand who has a head." They laughed at this latter one as they traded proverbs signifying nothing. "Well, go if you must, my son," said Rodriguez with a sigh, "but don't come crying to me when he steals your mule."

It was with a smile that Pedro entered the foul-smelling building, an abandoned Franciscan convent, which was now filled with bundles of goods. There were sacks of insects, bundles of what appeared to be blankets, and most prominently, hides and skins of every variety. In the stench of this hide-house, sat a very large, slack-jowled, bearded individual with enormous hands. He was *El Pescador*, and he was waiting to reel in his next victim.

"There are many possibilities north of Zacatecas," Machado said with enthusiasm. "On the eastern side of the *Sierra Madre Occidental* there are several Spanish settlements and many mines." He then reeled off a number of these: San Francisco del Nombre de Dios, a Spanish settlement; San Lucas a mining camp; San Juan del Rio, where there was a Franciscan convent; Valle de Palmitos, where there were three *estancias de labor* on the Rio Nazas; Santa Barbara, where there were mines, 30 settlers, and four *estancias* in the mountains; and *La Villa de Vitoria*, on the Rio Florido, now abandoned, but still presenting possibilities.

Robledo and Machado also spoke of Acambaro, Queretaro, Cimapan, Coliman and Guanaquato, the latter where rich mines had been found in 1548. There were Spaniards in some of these mining towns, 250 in Zacutua alone, Pedro was told, but most of the towns were sparsely populated. Machado told Robledo that to the West, he would probably find his best pickings.

"There are many wild Chichimeca Indians there, to be sure," said Machado. "They've never been permanently subjugated and show no fitness for civilization. They'll eventually have to be enslaved or killed. But there are also mines there, and miners who need everything you have on your mules. I would happily buy your goods. If you're intent on using your cloth as a bargaining chip, though, perhaps your destination should be Guanajuato."

When Pedro emerged from Machado's warehouse in the late afternoon, the square was empty. Here and there, an elderly Indian with a broom of straw, swept up the day's refuse. Pedro thought about the possibilities presented him and of his decision to accompany Machado on his next trip to Guanajuato. He hoped this would be the opportunity for which he was searching.

* * *

Late in November of 1577, Pedro accompanied *Senor* Machado to Guanajuato and to Zacatecas. The weather was cold during their time on the trail with daytime temperatures in the mid 40s, and nighttime temperatures perhaps 10 degrees cooler. Their pack train went directly north from the City of Mexico to Pachuca and then to Cimapan on the Rio Moctezuma and their trip arduous. At Cimapan they turned West to Queretaro where they began to snake up the eastern side of the *Sierra Madre Occidental*, New Spain's wildest and most rugged mountain range, to Zacatecas. This was the mining center founded in 1548 by the 'Big Four,' Juan de Tolosa, Diego de Ibarra, Baltasar Temino de Banuelos, and Cristobal de Onate. It may have been on this trip through Zacatecas, nearly 30 years after its founding, that Pedro Robledo first heard the Onate name. Cristobal de Onate, the father of Juan de Onate who was to become New Mexico's colonizer, had died a decade earlier, on 6 October 1567, but it was his Zacatecan silver that was to finance the New Mexican venture. Therefore, although Pedro could not have known it at that moment, these mines at *La Bufa* would be his ultimate capital.

Although Brother Rodriguez had warned Pedro that "what you have to give to the mouse, you might as well give to the cat and spare yourself the trouble," Pedro had given nothing away and had learned much on this initial journey. In addition to the major sites detailed by Machado, there were mines at Avino where there was a small party of 10 to 12 Spaniards; mines at Soneto where there was a larger group of perhaps 50 Spaniards; and mines at Inde which he had been told were exceedingly rich and had been worked for nine years before being abandoned because of the Indians. It was on this trip, while Catalina was approaching her confinement, that Pedro made his decision to locate at Cimapan. There, in addition to the mines, was a Franciscan convent. The Franciscan's station, Pedro hoped, would provide Catalina with a degree of civilization while they awaited their new baby. He had much to learn.

* * *

Both north and south of the City of Mexico significant changes were occurring as the 16th century entered its fourth quarter. New political structures had come into being, and in some areas, urban life was starting to assert itself. It was amid this turmoil and dogged expansion that a mule train accompanied by Brother Joaquin Rodriguez snaked its way northward through the Valley of Mexico. The mule train, guided by Juan de Penol, left Texcoco and during the short days of December 1577 journeyed to Cimapan, the Robledos' new home.

Cimapan

Cimapan/Temazcaltepeque in the *tierra de guerra*, or war zone, was located immediately to the south of the area where the Suaquis and Tehuecos lived. These were two Indian groups hostile to the invaders who had held out successfully against the Spaniards and were in place when the Robledos moved to the region. Also in place were the Chichimecas whom the Spaniards had decided they could neither live with in *conviviencia*, (peaceful coexistence), nor convert. They had, therefore, decided to kill all male Chichimecas over 15 years of age and to send into exile those younger than 15. In spite of their attempts to annihilate the Chichimecas, however, many of these hostile people still remained and were hidden among the rocks and crevices of the *Gran Chichimeca* of the northern mountains from which vantage point, they menaced isolated villages.

The mines at Guanajuato, Guadalajara, Zacatecas, Sombrerete, and San Martin were taxed to pay for needed defenses against Indian depredations. Strong houses were erected at convenient distances along the trail from Pachuca to the northernmost outposts where travelers, along with their stock and goods, could rest securely. In addition, each mule train was furnished with a military escort, and each party was provided a fortified wagon. The latter was a small moveable blockhouse to which the women and children could retreat in case of attack. It was within this retinue that the Robledo party and a small group of religious made their way up the trail to their new home.

* * *

On 13 December 1577, Alonso was born to Pedro and Catalina Robledo at Cimapan. Ironically, this was the same day that Francis Drake, with a fleet of five vessels and a force of 164 men, sailed from Falmouth, England. Drake's plan was to explore the Pacific for England and to circumnavigate the globe and return to England by the long-sought northern passage. While Francis Drake was expanding our understanding of the world, Catalina was bringing Alonso 'to the light.' Although she would later tease him that he had been born in a manger, in truth, he had not. The Robledos' new home, although far from sumptuous, could never have been compared to a stable.

Trade for the Robledos was immediately successful, but also immediately problematic. Selling their goods presented no problem since the people of these mines needed everything. Most prized was cloth from which the settlers could make all sorts of apparel including *ropas*, or long robes, and *sayos*, or tunics. The medium of exchange was silver of which the miners had plenty. The problem was how to turn the profits into a long-term venture. Pedro's plan was to have the trains returning to Cimapan from the region of the mines, carry commodities sought in

Spain. These goods, however, were severely limited in terms of what New Spain had to offer: leather and skins, cochineal, cocoa and sugar.

It was to be a circular venture: bring cloth from Spain; sell it to the settlers for a considerable profit; purchase, leather, sugar and cocoa; ship these to Spain where they would be sold for an even greater profit. It started out well, but the cycle was almost immediately broken.

* * *

In December of 1578, almost a year from the day on which Alonso was born, Alonso, Diego, and Lucia gained another redheaded brother. He was Pedro, named after his father who was, at the moment of his birth, on his way back to their home at Temazcaltepeque with a new load of cloth.

Catalina had not been greatly concerned about her husband, for the party in which Pedro was traveling consisted of 60 wagons and a military escort. It was considered of sufficient size to be impervious to attack. Near the village of San Martin, the mule train carrying 30,000 dollars' worth of cloth, much of which was Pedro's, was attacked and the escort defeated. Pedro was not injured, but seven of the party were killed and everything on the train lost.

Pedro was devastated. Not only had he lost the profits of a year's work, but he had also lost that with which he was to make his living. He would not have an opportunity to replenish his supplies for another year, and then to make his purchases, he would either have to borrow the money from his father-in-law or from another. Perhaps most devastating to Pedro was the blow to his pride. In 1579, 41-year-old Pedro Robledo was the father of four children, eight-year-old Diego, six-year-old Lucia, two-year-old Alonso, and Pedro, an infant in his mother's arms. Catalina, now 30 years old, was beginning to feel older than her age, the past two years having taken their toll. However, there would be no 'going for soup' (that is, going to the monasteries where soup was given to the poor), for Pedro's pride would never allow this. Pedro needed a new venture. The obvious answer was the mines.

Temazcaltepeque

Although Pedro Robledo viewed working the mines at Temazcaltepeque as temporary employment, he experienced working in them as suffering a two-year stretch in the *gurapas*, Spain's dreaded galleys. The mines at Temazcaltepeque were some of the richest in New Spain. There was silver there in all its combinations: with sulfur, with arsenic and sulfur, with antimony and sulfur, with chlorine, with tellurium, with lead, and alloyed with gold, mercury and copper. There were mines close to the surface and deep in the earth, and all were exceedingly rich.

In the mining of silver, the common ingredient is sulfur, either by itself or in combination with arsenic and antimony. The pale yellow powder has almost no taste, but when rubbed, it gives off the stench of rotten eggs. In addition, while working in the pits, one is surrounded by gray brittle flakes of arsenic. Moreover, when the silver is smelted, white arsenic, a poisonous powder, is one of its byproducts. It was a dangerous, filthy, unattractive occupation, fraught with accidents and disease. Dragging oneself from one level to another was the means of extracting the ore. Whether working in a shaft, a raise, or a stope, Pedro Robledo preferred removing the ore that fell through the raises than operating in the stench that resulted from opening a new vein. Working in the mines contrasted meanly with working in the sun, wind, and rain of his native *meseta*. He must have hated it but suffered in silence while waiting for his next shipment of cloth.

During this period, Pedro Robledo made a further effort to expand his West Indies trade. With Teo Machado, he crafted a plan to purchase cattle in the kingdom's most remote eastern settlements and to sell these to settlers in the western regions. The cattle—500 head were planned—would come from three of the largest ranches in New Spain, the Geronimo Lopez, the Salvago, and the Rodrigo del Rio de Losa.

Waiting for Machado to meet him in Temazcaltepeque must have seemed like an eternity to Pedro, given the circumstances of his present employment. They were then to go to the *fincas*, or ranches, together. Unfortunately, avarice always bursts the bag, and Machado, upon hearing that the cattle available to them were fewer than they had anticipated, bypassed Temazcaltepeque and went directly to the *fincas*. Here, he made his purchase, abolishing unilaterally the contract and agreement he had with Robledo. There was in this sorry incident the memory of Pedro's father-in-law who had warned him, "Don't do business with him, Pedro. Merely let him know that you're there." Pedro had failed to heed this warning regarding Machado, and, although greatly disturbed by Machado's perfidy, he had luckily not put any capital into the venture and had, therefore, lost nothing but his pride.

Although men are not prone to advertise their own humiliations, Pedro did confide these unfortunate events to his journal. This diary and many others Pedro would eventually leave with Brother Rodriguez at the convent of Cuencame are extremely revealing regarding the Robledos' early years in New Spain. After that there is a gap of almost 10 years during which Pedro recorded almost nothing of the Robledos' lives.

The Beyond

Perhaps it was Brother Rodriguez who suggested it. He was being moved from Cimapan to Valladolid and may have hinted that it would be good if the Robledo family relocate with him. Valladolid was the capital of Michoacan and one of the commercial centers which Robledo had first considered in establishing a base of operations in New Spain. It was in the Valley of Guayangares, west and just slightly north of Mexico City. It was also a city with convents and markets and was a step further removed from the hostile Chichimecas. There were many mines in the area, Rodriguez must have assured Robledo, and he would do well there.

In any event, when Brother Rodriguez and his two fellow clerics left Cimapan for Valladolid in 1580, the Robledo family accompanied them. Their party was small, led by an armed escort, and they experienced no difficulties along the trail. Thus, when Francisco Robledo was born in 1580, the Robledo family was residing in Valladolid.

Valladolid, which was to be the Robledos's home for the next 16 years, provided a measure of stability they had not experienced for some period. Francisca, the last of the freckled-faced, redheaded children to be born into this family, would arrive on an auspicious day during the first week of October 1582.

How do you explain to a child who was born on October 4ᵗʰ that she was, on the next day, already 11 days old? Years later, Pedro would try—and he would try again on each succeeding birthday—but Francisca refused to be mollified. What had happened was that Pope Gregory XIII, in a bull largely written by Pedro Chacon of Spain, had made an enormous change in the calendar, a change that took effect on what normally would have been October 5, 1582. Chacon, who had been a member of the pope's 'Calendar Commission,' had presented his final report to the pope during 1581. The report was the culmination of years of work that had really begun in 1267 when Roger Bacon encouraged Pope Clement IV to make needed changes in the manner in which time was kept. The report presented a recommendation for correcting the Julian calendar (established in 46 BC) which was drifting ahead of the solar year, and thus distorting the time on which equinoxes, solstices and particular holy days fell. The Commission's recommendation dropped 10 days from October making October 5ᵗʰ of that year, October 15ᵗʰ. Francisca would have none of it, although everyone alive at that time had also lost 10 days of his or her life.

Although this change created some practical problems for Pedro regarding the calculation of interest payments and receipts for a month with only 21 days, the change was a major problem for Francisca. Somehow, in her mind, this had been done to her personally, and the only way to remedy the situation in subsequent years was for her to have a number of birthday celebrations throughout a ten-day period! Pedro and Catalina could only laugh. Their home had started to be a 'home of birthdays,' in 1582, and the family was still celebrating them in Valladolid a year later.

In 1583, Catalina received a letter from her father, Alonso Lopez. In it, he told of what he had heard at court, that Philip II had issued a decree seeking a colonizer for land north of New Spain.[1] The land under consideration was that which had been visited by the Franciscan *Fray* Marcos de Niza in 1539 and more thoroughly explored by Francisco Vasquez de Coronado between 1540 and 1542. When the missive from Alonso Lopez arrived, no one took much notice of the decree. A venture of this kind was, at this point, merely speculative and, if undertaken, would require an individual with a considerable fortune. Since neither the aging Lopez, nor the budding entrepreneur, Pedro Robledo, met this criterion, the venture was quickly forgotten. Others, however, were not so easily put off.

First to request permission to initiate missionary work in the new land during 1580 was a Franciscan lay brother named Agustin Rodriguez. The viceroy of New Spain gave permission but required the missionary group be a small one. In addition to Rodriguez, it contained two Franciscan priests, *Fray* Juan de Santa Maria and *Fray* Francisco Lopez, 19 Indian servants, and seven or eight soldiers under the command of Francisco Sanchez Chamuscado. After a year of preparatory discussion, this expedition, with both exploratory and missionary objectives, set out during June of 1581.

The group made a circuitous trek up the Rio Grande River and then east to the bison plains. Against the advice of the party, *Fray* Santa Maria left the group at this point to return to New Spain to report the discoveries. He paid the ultimate price for not heeding the warnings as the Maguas Indians killed him along the trail. The remainder of the group went west and then back to New Spain, leaving at the pueblo of Puaray in New Mexico, *Fray* Rodriguez, the other Franciscan, *Fray* Francisco Lopez, and several Mexican Indian servants. On the way home, Sanchez Chamuscado became ill and died. He was buried near Santa Barbara.

Almost immediately after Sanchez Chamuscado's men arrived in Santa Barbara, rumors of the possible murder of Rodriguez and Lopez by the Indians with whom they had been left, prompted the formation of a rescue party. The command of this little force was entrusted to Antonio de Espejo who mounted an expedition at his own expense since payment for expeditions of this kind from the royal treasury was forbidden. On 10 November 1582, with 14 or 15 soldiers, 115 horses and mules, and *Fray* Bernaldino Beltran, Espejo, who mirrored Spanish dreams and aspirations, left San Bartolome, a place nine leagues east of Santa Barbara.

Upon their arrival in the North Country, the rescue party learned that the rumors were true, that the missionaries had been killed because the Indians with whom they had been left wanted the horses, goats, merchandise, and ornaments which the friars possessed. The rescue party survived several skirmishes with the Indians but did not attempt to avenge the deaths of the missionaries. Their second agenda being exploration, they traveled into what is now Arizona. Later, they split into two very small groups, one returning to New Spain by following the Rio Grande, the second by following the Pecos River. Both groups returned safely with accounts of rich mineral deposits in the North Country and great hopes for the exploitation of both this mineral wealth and the souls that they had found there.

* * *

By 1583, plans were being made to colonize the northern territories. Before this could occur, however, Pedro de Montoya obtained permission from Fernando de Trejo, governor of *Nueva Vizcaya*, to resettle an area in Sinaloa, New Spain. This was a site in San Juan on the Rio Suaqui which the Spaniards had been forced to abandon in 1567. The Suaquis were again successful in routing the Spaniards, killing Montoya and 12 of his men. This massacre reemphasized the fact that making a New Mexico *entrada* through hostile Indian territory was not going to be easy.

Before officials could determine how best to proceed, two unauthorized and illegal incursions occurred. Gaspar Castano de Sosa, lieutenant governor of the state of *Nuevo Leon*, mounted the first of these in 1590. He recruited for colonization the entire population of the mining town of Almaden, today Monclava. He was eventually arrested and exiled and his colony dispersed.

A few years later, in 1593, two Spanish soldiers conducted a second illegal incursion. These soldiers were Francisco Leyva de Bonilla and Antonio Gutierrez de Humana. They had been sent out with a small party including Indians from New Spain to punish some rebellious Indians in *Nueva Vizcaya*. Accomplishing this, they continued north. This small group marched up the Rio Grande and settled among the Indians. Leyva and Gutierrez hunted for mines and stayed among the Indians for about a year before moving east onto the plains.

It is believed that these rogue soldiers ventured as far as the Platte River in Nebraska. Here, in a fight over command, Gutierrez killed Leyva. Later, some of the Indians from New Spain deserted. On the way south, the group was attacked by Indians who set fire to the surrounding prairie killing all except for one soldier and a mulatto girl who was with the party.[2]

Meanwhile, in 1590, while Juan Morlete was arresting Gaspar Castano de Sosa in New Mexico, the Robledos were having their own party in New Spain. Lucia Lopez Robledo, the four-year-old child who had accompanied her parents from Spain in 1577, was now 17 and about to be wrapped in a cloak with her new groom. Her intended was Bartolome Romero, a 27-year-old gentleman from the Spanish city of Corral de Almaguer, a village near Lucia's former home of Carmena.

The city of Valladolid in New Spain, where Lucia and Bartolome were to marry, had taken its name from Spain's noble city of Valladolid where Prince Ferdinand, disguised as a servant, met Princess Isabel to contract marriage. The prince, in 1469, disguised as a humble muleteer in ragged clothes, had presented Isabel with her *arras* or gifts. These were contained in two leather pouches that he carried on his mule.

By astonishing chance, the document recording the *arras* bestowed upon Lucia at her marriage has survived in the archives of the church of Valladolid. Bartolome Romero presented Lucia with a small silver box, beautifully tooled, with her name in raised letters. Within the box, Lucia's mother had asked Bartolome to place a broach of small pearls and gold filigree. This was the broach that by family tradition had been given to Catalina, her mother and her grandmother at their own marriages.

From her father, Lucia received sleeves[3] and, most symbolically, seven acorns (signifying the family's surname) which her father hoped would provide them with an abundance of delicious fruit. He also gave Lucia a ram's horn and a white stone, both of which had come from their home in Carmena. And to Bartolome (and, apparently echoing the legendary bequest to the Franciscans by the Count of Orgaz), Pedro gave "two sheep, 16 hens, two wine skins full of wine and two loads of firewood." He also gave Bartolome a pair of oxen and a black bull, representative of peace and prosperity, but as dotal property, it was Lucia who would retain these.

Lucia's gift to Bartolome was equally symbolic. She had sewn into the face of a bolster a picture of a lone cannon (*ballestero*) upon a field (*llano*) of grain. The *ballestero* and *llano* represented the 'B' in Bartolome, and the 'L' in Lucia who would forever be united in marriage.

At the time of Lucia's marriage in 1590, Diego was a 19-year-old working with his father on the trail or in the mines when the circumstances of their life demanded it. Occasionally, his brothers, Alonso, Pedro the younger, and Francisco, at ages 13, 12, and 10 accompanied them, but for the most part, it was he who worked with his father. As the boys became more mature, the younger three went to work in the mines, but Diego wanted nothing to do with mining. He, like his father, preferred life on the trail. He would work in the mines if required, but he and his younger brother Pedro II wanted to be soldiers.

Although life on the trail did not provide Diego with much of an opportunity for romance, it did not entirely escape him. His love was Micaela de Vera, the daughter of a Portuguese mine owner at Guanajuato. He loved Micaela from a distance, though, and never made his feelings known to anyone except his father. His father offered to prepare a letter of proposal to be read in the presence of the intended bride's parents as was the custom, but Diego would have none of it. His father then encouraged him to take up residence in Guanajuato where he might have an opportunity to meet Micaela and to make his intentions known. Diego would not do this either. He was unwilling to risk being dealt the *calabazas*,[4] or to have his proposal rejected. Instead, when their work brought them to Guanajuato, Diego would wait outside the church just to be able to follow Micaela with his eyes. Or he would perch upon the hill above the Vera home hoping to catch a glimpse of her as she helped her mother or one of her sisters in some household chore. He watched and waited, neither daring to go near her home, nor speak to her. And in the end, she was gone, married to another, he was told, and returned to Portugal.

Diego did not easily forget this lost love, and perhaps the saddest fact was that Micaela never knew he existed. He berated himself for his inability to speak his mind and to make his feelings known. He swore to do better and to be more assertive the next time. In truth, however, he knew, that if his love object did not herself approach him, he was probably doomed to be a bachelor.

The year 1590 came and went and the Robledos' life on the frontier continued. In 1594, at the age of 33, the Jesuit, *Fray* Gonzalez de Tapia, became the first martyr of his order in Sinaloa. Nacabeba, a native who claimed to be a sorcerer, was flogged at the cleric's request for his habitual sins of missing Mass, and being drunk among other offenses. After trying unsuccessfully to incite his people to revolt, Nacabeba murdered Father Gonzalez when he came to Nacabeba's village to renew his complaints about the alleged sorcerer. After the murder, Nacabeba fled to the hostile Suaquis and Tehuecos in the north bearing with him the head and arm of *Fray* Gonzalez. In orgies of victory he used the victim's skull for a drinking-cup and tried to roast the arm. However, fire had no effect upon the sacred relic and the priests' proselytizing, magic, and martyrdoms[5] continued.

Misfortunes and Infamy

Troubles never come singly. Pedro was not well, and Diego had broken his leg in an accident in which his mule had fallen on him. That Diego was not more severely injured was a miracle. Immobilizing his leg in a cast of *istiercol* (a wrap made of cow droppings and muslin) and getting him back to Valladolid had been an arduous experience. Now, both Pedro and Diego were back in Valladolid and recuperating, but neither was immediately able to go to Vera Cruz to secure their latest shipment. It was critical they obtain it as soon as possible, as they had lost their consignment of the previous year on the shoals at San Juan de Ulua.

Pedro was in a quandary. Except for *Senor* Mattos, he knew of no one in Vera Cruz whom he could trust. Therefore, through Juan de Penol, he asked Mattos to secure the cargo for him, and to place it within his warehouse. During their interminable wait for the cargo, Pedro and Diego tried to speed their recovery. Pedro sucked on pebbles which he had obtained from an ant hill (a treatment for heart disease which had been suggested to him by one of his Indian *arrieros*), while Diego ate tomatoes and bell peppers in an attempt to grow new bone. As soon as Pedro or Diego was able to travel, he would bring their new load of cloth to Valladolid.

Although both Diego and his father had made the trip many times, neither relished it. Somehow their work along the eastern side of the 900-mile *Sierra Madre Occidental* seemed more attractive, perhaps because it was home. In any event, the round trip of almost four months from the City of Mexico to Vera Cruz and back again was tedious. Except for Cholula, which lay mid-way in their journey, it offered few markets. Also, they were simply anxious to return to their usual stomping grounds.

Nevertheless, when the time came to go to Vera Cruz both were able to make the journey. Upon emerging from the rain forest above Vera Cruz on this occasion, they noted that there was something about the village below them which appeared odd. Almost immediately the reason struck them. There were no boats in the harbor that was usually teeming with masts. Startled as they were by this reality, they were stunned by what loomed before them as they approached more closely. It was the burned-out hulk of the Mattos warehouse, along with severely charred wharves and docks. With their hearts in their throats, the Robledos first searched the area of the warehouse and then rode into the village.

Their frantic inquiries led them to a dock steward and then to *Senor* Mattos who tried to assure them that, although they had lost the portion of their cargo which he had just begun moving to his warehouse, most of it had be saved. The boats, he assured Pedro, had been moved to other ports to save them from the fire (purposely set, it was believed) which had engulfed the docks. His own vessel had been taken to San Juan de Ulua, while that of Machado and Robledo, "yet fit to pass the banks of Flanders," he said, had been taken to Campeche. Finding their ship proved to be like looking for pears on an elm tree. Their vessel was not at Campeche, nor was Machado, who, they learned, had moved his operations to Guatemala.

With Machado laying claim to all of the surviving cargo, the Robledos sought to have the shipment divided between Machado and themselves in the same proportion to the ownership of the original shipment but were unsuccessful. Although the Robledos were later to bring charges against Machado for his larceny, they never received reparation for the theft. It was as though both Pedro and Diego had received a *buzcorona*, or cuffing over the head when they least expected it. This was a story as old as the itch. He who had clipped them had also kept the scissors, and they were again to return home empty-handed.

New Horizons

The two decades following the Robledos' arrival in New Spain had offered the greatest of promises, and also the greatest of disappointments. The opportunities were there, and certainly a few had turned these opportunities into economic success and even titles of nobility, but in reality, only a few had amassed great wealth. It was the members of Spain's third estate, its ordinary people, who experienced most of the failures and some were profound. Although Pedro Robledo had realized his dream of seeing new lands, the hardships and disappointments he had experienced on the frontier had nearly broken his spirit. He openly wondered whether it had all been worth it, and had begun talking to himself. He likened himself to the tailor of *El Campillo* who threaded his needle and stitched for nothing, repeatedly asking questions of himself in a futile search for answers. For what purpose had he brought his family to New Spain? What had they accomplished? His wife and especially his children tried to assure him they had not suffered, and, in fact, had benefited from the emigration. (Had not Lucia found her husband there?) And, they insisted, it was not over yet. There were other opportunities that awaited them, and who knew on what mule and in what guise these opportunities might arrive.

"I'm unable to void all that I need to," he said sadly but with laughing eyes. "And falling asleep has become impossible. I lie in bed until three in the morning awaiting a new tomorrow. But what can you do, Pedro?" he sighed in resignation.

"What are you trying to do?" Pedro asked.

"I don't know," Brother Rodriguez replied sadly. "I only trouble you with these matters because if such ills continue, I must sooner or

112

later have to vacate my position here." He looked at Pedro as though seeking a note of sympathy. "When? Well, who can say? But it might be in the near future. Until then, I will of course, give all necessary attention to my duties. In short, I might find myself obliged to resign because of poor health, but I remain at my superior's disposal," he said with assurance, "and am his most true subject and faithful servant."

Pedro looked at his friend, Brother Rodriguez, for a long time before responding, really wanting to ask him to stick out his tongue or otherwise do something by which Pedro could gauge his health. "What are you telling me," Pedro asked? "I've never known you to be sick, and except for your voice, and your manner of speaking, I don't see it now."

"You don't believe me then?" Brother Rodriguez asked with a look that said that he did not believe either.

"No," Pedro responded. "I don't believe you. How much, if any of this, is true?"

"A little," Rodriguez responded with a sly smile. "I have to get up off my mat several times a night to pass water, but otherwise I'm well."

"Then what are you up to?" Robledo asked, smiling at his good friend Rodriguez. "Are they trying to get you to sweep the steps or to perform some other penance?"

"No, not really," Brother Rodriguez responded. "I'm really trying to get reassigned, and was hoping that if I feigned illness, my superior might be disposed to let me go. Father Marquez told me that one of the Onates, Juan de Onate by name, is going to sign a formal contract as the colonizer for 'the Beyond,' the name given to the land unsettled north of New Spain. And you, Robledo," he said emphatically, "you've got to go with me."

Pedro said nothing and Brother Rodriguez continued in a tone which announced his sincerity.

"I understand that a great *auto* was held at Lima during December where 10 *conversos* came before the Inquisition. Four of them were 'relaxed,' Pedro. That is, they were handed over to the secular arm of government because, as an ecclesiastical body, the Inquisition cannot itself be a party to inflicting the death penalty. I understand that one of the Peruvian backsliders, a Francisco Rodriguez, was burned alive.

"They've been here for a long time, too, Pedro," Rodriguez continued, speaking of the Inquisition. "They've been in New Spain for almost 25 years, but it wasn't until 1574 that we had our first *auto* here. Only one New Christian was called before it at that time, and he for a minor offence only. And it wasn't until 1577—the year you came—that the first *converso* suffered. But now, with the Inquisition actively at work to our south, our New Christians, both Spanish *conversos* and Portuguese *convertidos*, had better begin looking for new places to hide," he said to Pedro with a knowing glance. "There will be many who've reverted to their ancestral faith who will seek to be among the Onate colonists."

"And you want to go with them?" Robledo asked rhetorically.

"Yes," Rodriguez responded, "but not as a preacher. Maybe to protect the Indians, *don* Pedro? I don't know," he said as though having a hard time explaining his interests, even to himself.

"And you think that by pretending to be an invalid they'll take you out of the *convento* and send you into the wilderness?"

"It's not going to work, is it?" Rodriquez asked.

"I don't think so," Pedro responded with a smile. "You're just going to have to display a fitness for something . . . but I can't imagine what."

"A teller of falsehoods, perhaps?" Rodriguez offered.

"Maybe. Or a sweeper of steps."

"They don't have steps.

"Who doesn't have steps?"

"The Indians, the natives of the Beyond. They have no steps."

"Well . . . maybe we can think of something."

"We'd better," Rodriguez said emphatically. "And you'd better think about coming with me *don* Pedro. I'll bring *Fray* Marquez by," Rodriguez said. "He'll tell you what's planned."

* * *

Brother Rodriquez was speaking of a curious priest, *Fray* Diego Marquez, who had, in 1587, been captured at sea by the English, and taken as a prisoner to London. There, Queen Elizabeth herself interviewed *Fray* Marquez. He told her everything about the Spanish colonies, ostensibly because he was required to do so, but really to frighten King Philip into accelerating Spain's push into the northern borderlands where the opportunities for missionary work abounded. His collaboration resulted in a swift release, and he was permitted to proceed to Spain where he reported to King Philip. He told Philip what had transpired between himself and the queen, emphasizing that the English had shown an extraordinary interest in New Mexico. On his return to the colonies, he had encouraged Juan de Onate to submit a contract as colonizer of New Mexico, and now, he and Onate had together begun looking for a few good men to make up their colony.

* * *

Two days after Rodriguez's initial discussion with Pedro Robledo regarding the New Mexican venture, Brother Rodriguez was back. He was followed, shortly after, by *Fray* Marquez who arrived on a great mule caparisoned with a garland of wild flowers.

Fray Marquez was one of those uncommon individuals who was at home wherever he found himself, whether living as a prisoner at Queen Elizabeth's court, or eating with workmen in the fields. Although described by *Fray* Rodriquez as jovial and light-hearted, *Fray* Marquez exhibited neither of these qualities as he sipped his claret, and spoke to the small congregation who sat or lounged on cushions scattered about the Robledos' salon.

"She might be described as having good skin," he said, continuing a discussion they were having regarding Queen Elizabeth, and directing himself to Catalina, Lucia and Francisca who sat on cushions at his feet, "although I'd describe it as somewhat sallow in tint, . . . what's that they say . . . *olivera?* Although the French poet, Pierre Ronsard, has suggested that her beauty rivaled that of the queen of Scots, I much doubt that. Her hair," he continued, "perhaps blonde when she was a child, is now a bright golden red. And although pulled back from her face and crowned with a golden tiara, it hung down in little red wisps that gathered about her ears, hiding the glittering earrings she wore. And her waist," he continued, now speaking to the men as well as to the women who sat about the room, "she had none . . . but would I could say the same regarding her character. She appeared headstrong, stubborn, extravagant, and, one might even say, vain and deceitful. Members of her court told me that she had learned in childhood to hide her feelings—'those

115

dangerous traitors within her breast,' she is reputed to have said. Yet, at one point in our discussion, she turned on me like an angry snake, suggesting that we should draw apart in case I further angered her by my speech. She didn't wish to be witnessed giving a display of '*choler*' and '*stomache*' as she has been known to show to others. I was so terrified that my hair stood on end," he said laughingly.

Pedro motioned for Francisco to again fill the good father's glass, while *Fray* Marquez rearranged his seating, pulling his frock this way and that, brushing crumbs from his clothing. "Oh, these *biscochitos*!" he exclaimed, remarking about the cookies he was eating. "Like my mother's—I kiss her hands. The anis, brandy, and cinnamon are just right, *Senora* Robledo. I'll have to get your recipe."

Catalina, who was no longer dressed in mourning, and who had risen to get *Fray* Marquez his own tray of the fragile delicacies, responded with a curtsey, a "thank you," and a question. "Would you like to have some to take home, Father?"

"Oh, please!" he begged. "I'll hide them in my cell."

Francisca placed an additional tray beside Marquez's cushion, while Francisco and Pedro the younger again filled glasses with wine. *Fray* Marquez sipped some, ate another cookie, and brushing crumbs from his beard, continued.

"I could well see her beheading her cousin," he said, speaking of the Protestant queen, Elizabeth, and her Catholic cousin, the queen of Scots. "One has to wonder how Mary's trial could have even been legal," he said. "Mary Staurt was the queen of a foreign country. How could she be tried for treason? She wasn't, in any sense, one of Elizabeth's subjects! She could, perhaps, have been expelled from England," he said, again speaking of Mary and placing his hands before his face in the gesture of rendering a prayer. "But executed? Never! Elizabeth wanted her killed, and if the court hadn't made a determination to murder her, Elizabeth would probably have done it herself. Perhaps I should have been even more frightened than I was," he said in a slightly more somber tone. "In any event, it wasn't my fear which resulted in my cooperation, but my holy vows. She made me take an oath to speak truthfully regarding Spain and New Mexico, so I had no choice."

He then sat there quietly, looking out of the window into Pedro's beautiful courtyard, with thoughts of Mary and Elizabeth and England floating through his mind. "England itself is beautiful," he continued, "but the pretensions of Elizabeth's court are beyond belief. It's a by-word for frivolity! Nothing is treated earnestly. He who invents the most ways of wasting time is regarded as one worthy of honor.

"Stupidity! Oh, my God!" he said, blowing through pursed lips and shaking his head. "Vainglorious stupidity beyond belief. Gold leaf. Gold plate. Gold everything! The queen's use of ceremony, and her vast display of wealth, has been put to good use in subjugating the imagination of her subjects. Even her carriage is of gold," *Fray* Marquez told them. "Wouldn't our good father, *Fray* Fernando, love to have that?" he asked Brother Rodriguez regarding their superior. "I don't know what he needs a carriage for anyway," the good father said to Bartolome directly, continuing a conversation in which they had been previously engaged. "What can he want one for in a village with fewer than 100 *vecinos*? We've no roads here, and the people must travel on muleback wherever they go. No wonder our people and the natives think badly of us. Greedy and avaricious, they say. We've got to leave this place," he said to those in the room, "and the Pueblos of New Mexico will provide us with our escape!

"But it's not for our need alone that we go to New Mexico," *Fray* Marquez continued, looking at the family sitting about the room. "Fortunately, the needs of the king, the church, the natives, and our citizenry, overlap sufficiently to make the venture good for all of us." He began a dissertation regarding the many opportunities the New Mexico expedition offered. "Look at what Onate will give you," he said enthusiastically. "You'll have titles as *hidalgos*; Indian vassals in the form of *encomiendas*; building lots, pastures, farming lands, and ranches. It's all there, *Senor* Robledo," he said directing himself to Pedro, initially, but finally to all of the men in the room. "These are the items of an all-embracing title with fields, vineyards, woods, pastures and streams. You will, at the end of five years of residency, be *hidalgos* of an established lineage, hold *encomiendas* for three generations, and your lands will be inheritable by your children and descendants. When good luck comes along, one must open the door and let it in," *Fray* Marquez exclaimed to the entire group. "You must come with us, *Senor* Robledo!" Marquez then

117

added, addressing himself to the patriarch of the family. "This is your chance to fulfill all your dreams."

*   *   *

The chatter following this presentation was extreme, with each member of the family expressing an opinion regarding the potential venture. Bartolome was the most vocal in regard to the opportunities offered, but the Robledo children were no less enthusiastic. This was especially true of Diego and Pedro the younger, who were bursting with dreams of exploration and military glory, and of Francisco, who hoped to find mines. Lucia, of course, echoed the sentiments of her husband, Bartolome. Alonso alone held back. Only he expressed reservations regarding the colonization. He waited to learn what his mother wanted, the two having formed a special attachment from the time of Alonso's birth.

When *Fray* Marquez left the Robledos' home that evening, Brother Rodriguez stayed behind, hoping to have a private conversation with Pedro. The courtyard's heavy gate, which had been opened to allow *Fray* Marquez and his mule to exit, was now closed, the small door recessed within one section of the double gate, open and inviting. With *Fray* Rodriguez standing on the inside of the courtyard, and Pedro on the outside, they watched as *Fray* Marquez rode away.

Placing his hand on Pedro's wrist, and tugging at him gently, Brother Rodriguez brought Pedro back into the courtyard after which he closed and latched the small door. "Although I haven't received permission to accompany *Fray* Marquez," Rodriguez counseled, "I'm still urging you to go. And I must tell you something of great importance. Although *Fray* Marquez is going to New Mexico in his role as a Franciscan missionary," he said, "he's also going as an agent of the Inquisition." He waited to see Pedro's response to this before continuing. "I'm not supposed to know this, *don* Pedro, for the matter is being kept secret from everyone, especially the viceroy who should have the right to make decisions in this matter. Marquez has received an appointment from the Holy Office to be its representative in New Mexico."

"Why are you telling me this?" Pedro asked.

"Because, unlike others of my faith, *don* Pedro, I don't claim exclusive possession of religious truth. I don't want to go to New Mexico to proselytize, but rather to protect the rights of the natives. We've seen it here, *don* Pedro, . . . over and over again . . . the natives paying lip service to Christianity, but in the privacy of their huts, faithful to the traditions of their own religion. So it is with all *Anusim*—the 'Forced Ones,' " Rodriguez said, "individuals who've been required to accept a religion that's not their own. The natives' disbelief in our dogmas—the so-called religious truths established by Divine Revelation—may be objectionable to some Christians, but their disbelief is also totally understandable. Their adherence to their traditional beliefs and ceremonies is also understandable, and isn't offensive to me, nor should they be to the Church as a whole.

"As it is with the natives, *don* Pedro, so it is with you," Rodriguez said, "and I mean to protect you. This Onate, I think, may be sympathetic to the plight of New Christians. *Fray* Marquez, who's said to be Onate's intimate friend, told me that Onate's fourth great-uncle, Pablo de Santa Maria, was in fact Solomon ha-Levi who had, at one time, been a rabbi. Ha-Levi's conversion may have been sincere . . . I don't know. In any event, ha Levi subsequently rose to the dignity of Bishop of his native Burgos, and became a member of the Council of Regency of Castile. But that's not enough for those who continue to find fault with New Christians. It's never enough!

"Some have said that Onate keeps his credentials at church, and that his pedigree is dubious in terms of the 'true faith,' " Rodriguez said. "But I find no reason to look for his *abito*.[1] It may have been worn by one of his ancestors and be hanging from the rafters in a church. But these attempts to preserve the purity of blood,[2] and to forever identify the descendants of *conversos* as somehow unworthy, are ill conceived and must end! In their continuing demands for proof of pedigree," he said, "the Church and our Spanish authorities have been successful. Obviously, time has not obscured or extinguished the memory of your ancestors as practicing Jews. Onate may not have been truly born and bred, according to the Church's' thinking in these matters, but he's a loyal and true Spaniard, and I think you'll find a friend there."

Pedro stood beside Brother Rodriguez in the courtyard of the Robledo home, neither confirming nor denying the statements made, but pondering the sincerity and passion of his friend's words. Theirs had

119

been a friendship of nearly 20 years, yet never had they spoken regarding these matters.

"You place yourself at risk by telling me this," Pedro said. "Why do you do so?"

"There's little explanation needed, *don* Pedro," Rodriguez said. "Friendship sometimes requires risk. And without some risk," he said, "life would be as insipid as a dish without salt." Rodriguez lifted the latch of the small door, opened it, and said. "Think of what I've told you, *don* Pedro. Share my thoughts with *dona* Catalina but no one else. She'll help you make the right decision."

*   *   *

It had been long dark when Pedro finally entered his bedroom. The moonlight, filtering through diaphanous curtains covering the windows, cast a veiled light on the walls and floor, so that he could have seen the objects in the room even had there been no other light. The flames in the corner fireplace burned low, requiring that he place a few upright sticks there, bringing the fire to a blaze again. Before the room's hearth, one could make out the simple things that identified him: his leather jacket, his boots, his saddle and its blanket, his leather-bound journal, open and seemingly awaiting his words. He took off the clothes he had been wearing, put on a nightshirt, and placed his clothing on the chest at the foot of his bed.

The scent of ambergris and rosewater was held in the sheets and blankets of their bed as he moved in beside her. He brushed her shoulder. She shifted in bed, turned towards him, and only then did he discover that she wore no clothes. She was asleep. Yet she pulled herself to him, her face tucked neatly beneath his chin. She awoke slowly, and they remained like this for a long time.

"Catcha," he whispered, using her pet name. "What should we do?"

There was no need to determine what Pedro was speaking about, for he was obviously asking about Rodriguez, Marquez and Onate. Although her father had asserted his right to determine when and whom she would marry, she had learned to love this man, and knew that this question would be uppermost in his mind. *Such a good man*, she thought

120

to herself. *So much like my father. Hardworking and responsible, and full of dreams.* "I don't know, Pero," she responded, now fully awake. "We've done well here. Do we need a new home?"

"There's so much to consider," Pedro responded, placing his curled hand on the roundness of her below her waist, his thumb on the point of her hip, "land and honor and a title of nobility. Not for us, Catcha, but for them," he said, speaking of the children.

"You have my support in anything you want to do, Pero," she said. "Who knows? Perhaps it'll be your land of birds."

He ran his hand up to her shoulder, and then to the nape of her neck, kissing her softly on swollen lips. He lowered his head, putting it beneath the covers, kissing one of her breasts, and then the other. She drew the sheet up to her chin, and then, commanding quietly, said, "*Ropa afuera, mi senor*" ("clothes off").[3] He moved lower to the soft of her stomach and kissed her there, his nightshirt now lying on the floor. She put a hand on the back of his neck, ruffled his hair, and then with both hands, held the sheet while she too slipped beneath the covers.

"*Con silencio, mio senor,*" she whispered, while trying to staunch her laughter. "*Con silencio,* Pero!" she giggled. "*Los hijos!*"

It was only as a family that they would make the decision to join the New Mexican venture, and it was not a decision easily made. Pedro weighed the arguments for going and for staying, and, in the end, his decision was to follow the desires of his children. It was they who were most important.

In this determination, Catalina reluctantly agreed, appreciating that they could continue to live in New Spain and expand their enterprise. For despite the disappointments they had experienced, they had achieved a measure of success in Valladolid and could reasonably expect to spend the rest of their lives there. She also considered that the New Mexico promises seemed real, and they would go. But she did wonder who this Onate was who held out these inducements, and what he would require in return.

Drumming

The process of selecting a leader of the New Mexico expedition had begun with all applicants submitting their credentials. In addition to Onate, the king and viceroy had looked at everyone: Hernando Gallegos (who had been the diarist with Sanchez Chamuscado), Antonio de Espejo (who had led the rescue expedition), Juan Lomas y Colmenares (who claimed to be the wealthiest man in western New Spain), Francisco de Urdinola (lieutenant governor of *Nueva Vizcaya*) and many others. Each was rejected for various reasons: Gallegos, because he exaggerated his responsibility for the Sanchez Chamuscado expedition, and because he did not have the wealth needed to carry out the project; Espejo, because he made his petition to the wrong man and did not have the standing necessary to carry out the colonization; Lomas y Colmenares, because he asked for the moon; and the bulbous and misshapen Urdinola, because he was accused—albeit falsely—of killing his wife. Therefore, in 1595, with a number of the others eliminated as rivals, it looked as though Juan de Onate might get the nod. Nothing regarding the New Mexico expedition, however, would be simple.

Onate sustained high hopes, for he who has friends in high places goes to court with assurance. So it was that Onate's personal friend, Viceroy Luis de Velasco the younger, finally awarded him the post. Onate's standard, which was provided him by Velasco himself, was a Castilian-figured white silk, stamped on one side with pictures of the Virgin Mary and Onate's patron saint, St. John the Baptist. Both images were surrounded by a rosary and had a picture of the Onate coat of arms below them. On the reverse side was a picture of *Sant' Iago*, St. James the greater, patron saint of Spain. He was, as he had been at Clavijo and in Flanders, Italy and India, armed with a sword of dazzling splendor and mounted on a white horse. Below this originally peaceful fisherman, St. James, was Viceroy Velasco's coat of arms. This was the banner that Onate would take with him into New Mexico.

* * *

From its inception, the colonial venture was a family affair. First, Juan de Onate asked his four brothers to represent him at the viceregal court.

122

He then requested that his nephew, Cristobal de Zaldivar, form and provision the expedition. These five were to remain in New Spain where they were to act as his agents. For the leadership of the expedition itself, Onate chose Cristobal's brothers, Juan and Vicente de Zaldivar. He named Juan *maese de campo* (field marshal) and asked Juan's younger brother, Vicente, to serve him as his *sargento mayor* (lieutenant marshal). There were, in addition, other family members he wished to take with him among whom was his nephew, *Fray* Cristobal de Salazar, a Franciscan priest, who would provide spiritual guidance. These were members of his extended family and men he could trust. Upon completing the appointment of this cadre, Onate began his recruitment efforts.

In Mexico City, Puebla, the villages and towns of *Nueva Galica*, and especially Zacatecas, the Onates had begun drumming up recruits for the new campaign. Proclamation and bugle summoned the *vecinos* of the various villages to their plaza. Here, they would hear one or more members of the Onate family tell about the prospects for colonization. They spoke of the probability of finding gold and silver. They spoke of the promise of grants of *encomienda* in which the Indians would render the colonists valuable tribute. They spoke of the privilege of *hidalguia*, the lowest rank of nobility, which would be given to every head of household. With nobility would come the designation of *caballero*, or knight, the privilege of using the title '*don*' (which may stem from the Hebrew term '*Adonai*,' the Divine Name), exemption from taxation, and freedom from arrest for debt. Religion was not left out of the equation either. If gold and silver were to be found in this 'new' Mexico, the friars among them contended, it was because God had placed it there to lure the Spanish expedition into the wilderness where many souls awaited them. The recruitment appeared to be going well, the ranks of Onate's potential colonists swelling. Then fate intervened.

Three days before Onate was to meet with his friend Viceroy Luis de Velasco to sign his contract, a new viceroy landed at Vera Cruz. He was Gaspar de Zuniga y Acevedo, Count of Monterrey, and he was not connected to Onate. The outgoing viceroy extolled Onate's virtues, and the incoming viceroy gave provisional approval for him to proceed, though he was already hearing negative whispers regarding Velasco's choice.

It took a considerable period for Viceroy Zuniga y Acevedo to begin examining the Onate contract, and when he did, he began to pick it apart. Significantly, he refused to allow Onate to skirt his authority and report directly to the Council of the Indies. Most damaging to Onate, however, was the time it was taking the viceroy to reach a decision, for while he wrangled with the Onate family over the contract, their prospective colonists were waiting in the mud.

Time was Onate's enemy. Daily, potential colonists rode into Zacatecas eager to hit the trail. At first, the prospective colonists were a rough group, miners mostly, and idlers looking for a quick strike. The blackguards and vagabonds among them were also quick to desert, though, and as time went on and nothing happened, many of these less desirable individuals drifted away to new adventures. However, there were others, more valuable individuals, who continued to wait in the mud. Day after day, while some men rode off, new carts rolled into camp. New Mexico's potential colonists looked to the south for permission to get going.

Second Thoughts

In late August 1596, a vanguard of soldiers left Zacatecas for Santa Barbara. The Robledos waited with the main body, however, mindful that Diego and his brothers who had gone to Vera Cruz to obtain their final New Spanish shipment had yet to arrive. Bartolome offered to work his way down the trail to meet them, but this suggestion was quickly abandoned for Diego's route was not known, and Bartolome might miss him on the trail. In any event, there was little Bartolome could do to hurry Diego and his brothers along. Therefore, the family waited in anxious anticipation for they did not want to leave without them.

Two weeks later, though, with Diego, Alonso, Pedro the younger, and Francisco still absent, the Robledos and the rest of the main party, also left Zacatecas. The group was led by Juan de Onate and was accompanied by the inspector of the expedition, Lope de Ulloa, his aide, Francisco de Esquivel, and a collection of additional personnel. Apprehensive now because of the unknown whereabouts of Diego and his brothers, the Robledos considered abandoning the venture but were quietly assured by Captain Gaspar Perez de Villagra that Diego and his train would catch up to them at the Rio de las Nazas. If, for some reason they did not, Perez de Villagra assured them, they could, at that point, leave the expedition and return home. There was in this, the denial that the soldier-colonists were subject to military discipline. They were in fact, in a private army, and their captain could impose severe penalties. He could, if required, even impose capital punishment for the most grievous offenses. Leaving the expedition at any point, for example, might be seen as mutiny.

Then, on 9 September 1596, disaster struck. Onate's long-awaited messenger rode into camp and gave Inspector Ulloa the packet of dispatches that Onate had so eagerly sought. Unfortunately, it was not Onate's marching orders that he received, but his suspension. The viceroy had, with little ceremony, ordered Onate to halt since he had decided to review the offer of yet another candidate for the position of colonizer of New Mexico. The viceroy had, also, in a dispatch addressed to Inspector Ulloa, instructed Ulloa to announce the particulars of the postponement to the colonists. Ulloa was to warn them that failure to act in accordance with the arrest of the expedition would be considered a betrayal, which carried with it the punishment of death and the loss of all possessions. The colonists were also to be told not to obey the commands of Onate.

The Robledos, who were in the married people's quarters, did not hear these commands and threats, nor did the other members of the expedition, for while Onate was crushed by the instructions he received, he begged Ulloa to delay in announcing them. Instead, Onate behaved as though he had been given permission to continue while waiting for these orders to be reversed. Even had the Robledos had any sense of Onate's duplicity, their own elation would likely have blocked it out, for Diego, Alonso, Pedro the younger, and Francisco, with a long string of heavily laden mules, had just ridden into camp.

* * *

How *don* Pedro Ponce de Leon, Count of Bailen, fits in to all this no one quite knows. He may have personally appeared at court in Spain, asking to replace Juan de Onate as New Mexico's colonizer. The king's counselors were pleased with his petition, and the Council of the Indies extolled his many virtues, especially his wealth, which they insisted, was far greater than that of Onate, who, they said, was destitute. Perhaps of equal importance was the question of Onate's leadership abilities. Who would want to follow this ineffectual and impecunious leader, they asked, except rejects, misfits and vagrants? They suggested to the king that he choose Ponce de Leon.

In the end, though, Ponce did not have it. He was in ill health and had been obliged to mortgage his estate to finance the expedition. He had even attempted to borrow money from the crown. In a reversal of decision (for the king had already accepted Ponce's proposal), Philip II instructed Viceroy Monterrey to determine whether or not Onate was still there—waiting in the wings so to speak—and, if he was, to give him permission to get going. But it was not over yet for Onate; there were many slights, insults, and injuries yet to come.

* * *

That Onate and his colonists were able to weather these storms speaks to their individual drive and stubborn will. Many of the members of his colony, especially the officer corps, were members of his family, while others had served with him in the Chichimecan wars. Others, however, the Robledos included, had no tie to Onate. Yet they waited, and it was upon these latter settlers, that the colony would be anchored.

Caxco

With orders of continuance put on hold, the fate of the Onate expedition was placed in Limbo. The question was how to give the illusion of movement while remaining mired in the mud? The expedition was stalled, and, although Onate worked to shield this reality from his troops, everyone knew it.

Onate, who was passionately anxious to take things into his own hands, asked for permission for Lope de Ulloa to continue his inspection and for authorization to move the expedition forward some 70 miles to

Santa Barbara where he had a detached unit. At Santa Barbara, he said, there was greater pasturage for his herds and flocks. This was pasturage he could not secure among the sterile hillocks and tablelands on the Rio de las Nazas. In the long wait before this could occur, many, including several of the priests that had been assigned to him, deserted his camp, taking with them badly needed supplies. Discipline began to crumble, and some of his men became marauders, accused of stealing oxen and mules and even the kidnapping of several people including Indian servants from a neighboring hacienda.

Although Ulloa could not give Onate permission to move to Santa Barbara, he did allow him to move forward a brief distance to the excavations at Caxco. These were reached on 1 November.

* * *

While others were stealing away in the night, Pedro and his family were trying to complete inventories of their goods and equipment as required by Ulloa. "*Quantos?*" he asked of Francisco who was counting the swords, lances, and saddles laid out before him.

"There are five Papa, and a cutlass, and a *dalle*."*

"Five swords, one cutlass and a *media luna*," Pedro repeated slowly as he transcribed his notes onto a clean sheet of paper. "Don't get ahead of me, Francisco," he asked. "I have to write this down. And saddles?" he asked.

"We have six *jineta*** and Bartolome has another."

"No, Francisco! Please," his father begged of his 17-year-old, "don't tell me anything about Bartolome. We have to do his separately," he said

---

* This *media luna*, or half-moon blade, was called a *dalle*, an Old French word used to designate a curved, cutting instrument like a sickle. In the 16th century this *dalle*, or *hoz*, was occasionally used to hamstring the bull in a bullfight or as an offensive weapon. It was, nevertheless, used primarily for cutting grass for horses.

** The *jineta* was a saddle adopted from the Moors which had a pommel, a cantle, short stirrups and little armor. The term derives from the word *jennet* (Arabic *Zenata*) which refers to a small Moorish or Spanish horse, but which originally referred to a horseman of the Berber tribe a group noted for its cavalry. From the word *jineta* comes the style of riding known as '*a la jineta*' in which the stirrups are high and the horseman required to bend his legs. The saddlebows were high, especially the one in front, so that when the rider stood in his stirrups, his body would not clear over the saddlebow, and he could not easily be thrown from his seat. This type of saddle was preferred for jousts, for tournaments and for fighting.

127

with a note of exasperation in his voice. "We've no *estradiota*?[#] How can that be?" he asked, continuing his questions regarding their inventory. "We had some. Where are they?"

"Alonso has one, Papa, but I think he means to sell it. Maybe you should make a separate list for him too."

"Oh, you boys make it so hard!" Pedro exclaimed, speaking to Francisco, and then addressing himself to his 19-year-old son, Pedro, who had just entered their tent. "What of the horses, Pedro? Do we have a count?"

Pedro knelt beside his father's cushion, taking note of what his father was writing before responding. "Diego and Bartolome had to count them several times, Papa, because they kept coming up with different numbers. But I think they've got it right now," he said. "We've got 66, and Bartolome 20 more!" he said triumphantly. "That is unless we count Babieca among the dragons," he continued, grinning at his father. "We could, you know, Papa. I don't know about that Babieca!" he laughed, teasing his father regarding his father's horse. "I think we should list him among the fire-breathing monsters! I mean, have you seen his wings?"

"He'll be counted among the horses where he belongs, "his father laughed, ruffling his son's hair, "he's the best banana in the bunch!"

In the end, Pedro prepared and readied three statements regarding the goods and equipment he, his sons, and Bartolome were to take to New Mexico. The first, which he wrote for himself and for his four sons, was as follows:[1]

I was informed of a decree published in this camp by order of your grace, and in compliance with it, I present this statement for myself and four sons who are going on this expedition. My sons are Diego Robledo, Alonso Robledo, Pedro Robledo, and Francisco Robledo. For our personal equipment, we are taking the following: five swords, five harquebuses,[##]

[#] The *estradiota* or Croatian saddle was used by mercenary light cavalry, and was, in contrast to the *jineta* saddle, a rather heavily armored war saddle. It had high saddlebows fore and aft, and its stirrups were long so that the rider rode with his legs stretched out at full length.

[##] The *harquebus* was a smooth-bored instrument with a match or flintlock. It had been invented in Spain in the mid-16th century (c 1567) and became popular throughout Europe. Although it was the first weapon fired from the shoulder, it was often fired from a support against which the recoil was transferred from a hook on the gun. Its names (*arquebus, haskbut, hackbut* or *hackenbusche*) seem to derive from German words with this meaning. It had an effective range of less than 650 feet.

*three lances** and a javelin; one hooked blade, one cutlass, and a dagger; five coats of mail*** with cuisses (thigh guards); five bevors;# two chamois jackets and one of buckskin;## four sets of horse armor;**** 40 horses; six colts; five mules; 20 mares; one cart with 12 oxen; six tame cows; six jineta saddles and two for bridle; 10 bridles, spurs, and other things necessary for the expedition.*

Pedro's note for Bartolome was equally detailed: *one cart with oxen and one plowshare; three coats of mail; two pairs of cuisses and two pairs of bevors; two swords and a javelin; one jineta lance and one hooked blade; one harquebus with powder flasks; one pistol; some horse armor; 20 horses and six mules; one buckskin jacket and another of chamois; one jineta saddle and another for bridle; two dozen pairs of horseshoes with nails; bridles and spurs; two boxes of his clothes and two others for his wife.*

And, finally, for the items Alonso said he wished to sell, Pedro listed the following: *one harquebus; one coat of mail; one bevor and cuisse; three horses; one saddle mule; two saddles, one jineta, the other estradiota; four pairs of shoes and some calfskin boots.*

The appropriate inventories were signed by Pedro, Alonso, and by Bartolome in the Valley of San Bartolome, Santa Barbara, on 6 December 1597.

* * *

---

* Although a number of soldiers were to carry the spear or long lance into New Mexico, they were never to bring it successfully into battle. It could be thrown as a projectile, held over one's arm to deliver a jab, or tucked firmly under one's armpit so that the horse, rider, and lance became a single penetrating instrument, but as we are to see, the Pueblos were to counter these potentialities by engaging the Spaniards in battle where horses could not be brought into the field.

** The coat of mail was apparently a *lorica*, a long-sleeved garment slashed below the waist both in front and in back for greater ease of movement. It was made of thousands of steel rings interwoven, linked, and riveted together to form a kind of defensive metal cloth. This material was highly resistant to slashing but less effective against piercing and crushing wounds. This formidable-looking but less than perfect garment was worn over a buff leather doublet made from bison skins.

\# The *babera*, or bevor, was a high collar of mail or plate covering the lower half of the face. It, too, was formidable-looking but vulnerable to crushing wounds.

\#\# These highly prized protective leather coats were *haketons* or *cueros* (literally skins). They were made from as many as six layers of heavy buckskin with the purpose of arresting or deflecting an arrow from its true course.

*** This was made from the hides of bulls, cows, or calves.

On 9 December, after repeated urging, the accommodating Ulloa agreed to initiate his review of the troops and of Onate's supplies. He then left camp and returned to the City of Mexico, having heard of his appointment as general of the Philippine fleet for 1597. The completion of the review was left to his assistant Francisco de Esquivel.

At the completion of Esquivel's review of the troops and of his inspection of supplies, it was determined that Onate had 205 men, five more than required, and that he had exceeded the requirements of his contract in nearly each grouping of supply to which he was dedicated.

* * *

Through the winter of 1597, Onate's colonial army, dressed in motley, hungry, and undisciplined, shivered in its wintry encampment, eating its provisions, losing its strength, deteriorating in its readiness. Winter moved into spring, and still the potential colonists waited. King Philip II had issued the royal *cedula* or decree that lifted Onate's suspension on 2 April 1597, but it did not reach the viceroy in Mexico City until that summer. When Viceroy Monterrey received this, he asked Onate if he was still willing and able to carry out the colonial enterprise. Upon receiving Onate's answer in the affirmative, Monterrey dispatched a third person to conduct yet another review. Onate was disgusted. Another indignity. Another delay. Onate told his colonists that the inspector would arrive within two months. However, when he failed to do so, some of the colonists accused him of lying and further desertions followed. Some of these potential colonists had been waiting for two years!

But better the person you know than the devil you don't know, for the inspector who finally came up the trail was a disaster. He was Juan de Frias Salazar, a native of the mountains of Burgos, resident and mine operator at Pachuca. Frias, a pompous and arrogant individual who had fought in Flanders and made a fortune in the mines of New Spain, arrived to add further insult and injury.

Honor and Pride

No me saques sin razon;
No me envaines sin honor.

Draw me not without reason;
Nor sheathe me without honor.

A welcoming salvo of *harquebus* shots announced the inspector's arrival as he and his entourage—a multitudinous retinue of aides and armed men—rode into camp. Although he had not been formally announced, smartly formed ranks of colonial soldiers were there to greet him, a cranium shaved buffoon sporting a felt hat over a perfumed wig. The hat with a large brim and multicolored plumes barely covered the tight skin of his bald head which Onate's page was later to describe as being "as smooth as a babies ass." Grinning a slyly satisfied smile, the inspector, Juan de Frias Salazar, appeared, not in belligerent armor, as one might have expected, but in peaceful hose and chamoised doublet, and with a heady odor of time, and horse, and trail.

In contrast to his leather-clad pikemen, archers, and *harquebusiers* who were dressed in bull-hide jackets thick enough to turn an arrow, he wore clothing similar to those of Onate's: a closely fitting doublet supported by a frame of whalebone designed to give him a more imposing bearing. Covering his doublet was an open tunic embellished with false sleeves that flared out from the shoulders. His breeches, fastened at the knee with false calf-muscles (*pantorillas*), added a small measure of shapeliness to his legs wizened from too many years of sedentary duties. As Frias dismounted from his beautifully caparisoned horse, its forelocks and mane freshly braided with ribbons, his huge cape snagged on the cantle of his saddle nearly causing him to fall. His entire appearance suggested that he had changed into this attire while on the trail for the purpose of making a grand entrance, as he and four crossbowmen galloped into the encampment. The meaning and intention of these elaborate arrangements were not lost on Onate who, with his *maese de campo*, and several other officers strode briskly to where Frias was standing.

131

"Remember to address him as 'My Lord,'" Onate said to his nephew, Juan de Zaldivar, while waiting for Frias to become disentangled from his mount. Frias stood with his left hand grasping the pommel of his saddle as through questioning whether to remount or to remain standing recumbent against his horse. A head shorter than Onate, in enormous boots which curled at the toes, he asked "Juan de Onate?" as if anyone else of any note would be there to greet him.

Onate studied him for a brief moment. The gangly-legged man was hot and filthy from the trail. His right hand slapping his wide-brimmed hat against his thigh was gloved and well protected. His eyes were narrowed with a taint of scorn, square on Onate. His lips were dry, and he wiped at them with the back of his non-gloved hand, now freed from his saddle. Onate looked down at the old man's boots and then back at Frias. He had expected a taller man. He said, "Your Grace. Your arrival has been long anticipated and with great expectation. I welcome you to my camp."

"Yes . . . yes," Frias responded. "And we too are glad to be here." He and Onate briefly embraced in the Spanish style, kissing the air of both cheeks, only slightly touching. "Juan de Onate!" Frias exclaimed. "I knew your father of course. Cristobal de Onate. Not well. Not well," he repeated in his tinny voice. "I was to have served on his staff . . . but . . . that never happened. The nature of Spanish service, you know. 'Many are called and few are chosen,' as they say. Like father, like son I suppose?"

"If it should please God," Onate responded.

Frias leaned forward a little and peered at the array of carts and white canopied tents surrounding the listing field. "And your tent?" he asked.

"There," Onate responded motioning with a tilt of his chin to a large tent of frieze, made of sixty yards of sackcloth festooned with silken banners. "We go there now for a welcome respite."

"You only," Frias said.

"But my men . . . my officers . . . ," Onate began to explain.

Frias' eyes slid over Onate, pinched, and flared all at once. His hand held the brim of his hat. He lifted it and thumped it down hard against the skirt of his saddle. He then looked back at Onate and repeated. "You only!" he said sternly. "What I have to say is for your ears only. You may then do as you wish with the information." Frias smiled at him then. He twisted the remaining glove off his hand and placed it with its mate in the waist of his breeches. Onate did not smile back; there was a slight tremble in him despite himself. Frias lost his smile and ran his eyes up and down Onate, the way one would when taking the measure of a man. Alone and leaving his officers to tend to the men of Frias' retinue, Onate strode to his tent where he awaited the inspector who lagged behind in anticipation of the receipt of his diplomatic pouch, surveying the men and the field of the encampment. Onate then raised the flap of his tent and stepped aside to hold it open. He said. "I bow to your authority Your Grace," awaited Frias' entrance and then stepped inside.

While standing before his tent Onate had had an opportunity to sniff out Frias and to take his measure. Surrounded by an *olor de santidad*, the so-called odor of sanctity, often attributed to monks who eat and sleep in an unwashed garment throughout their monastic lives, Frias appeared to be one of those men who considered physical dirt as a badge of honor. The color of his doublet, which is often called 'Isabel' in complement to the royal Princess, daughter of Philip II, who had vowed never to change her clothes until the Flemish port of Ostend was taken,[1] was of a brownish-yellow color covered with the grime of numerous engagements. Though hesitant to be entombed with Frias inside his buttoned tent, Onate sealed the entrance while steeling himself to hear further unwelcome news. He said, "would you like to freshen up before dinner?"

"I've no need for that," Frias said, his hand searching for whatever was causing an itch beneath his wig. "I go whenever nature calls and who has need for anything more? We may as well begin."

"You didn't pass the equinoctial line in your travels and so perhaps the buggers are still alive,"[2] a jocular Onate said. "Perhaps I can offer you a bath. A total bath is often successful in drowning the creatures one may have picked up on the trail. And a meal, too, would be good for everyone."

Frias' face colored red with blood, his mouth becoming a shard of disapproval. "I look at bathing as did the Visigoths," he retorted, "as invariably encouraging softness and effeminacy. Bathing is an occupation for babies and women," he said. "And although the food of these camps often makes me feel as though I've eaten a mule that has died from having been ridden too hard and lain too long in the sun, I'll accept your offer of a meal and my men of course must be fed."

Onate, who knew exactly how many men were in Frias' guard and what arms they carried said, "We've seen to that already, Your Grace. Perhaps a glass of wine?" he offered, attempting to put their meeting on a less formal basis.

Frias face blackened and his scratching continued, his right hand now working in the recesses of his breeches. "There is, perhaps, something we should set from the beginning, *Senor* Onate," Frias said completely ignoring the convention of high flattery and overpraise. "Do not expect any niceties from me and I'll expect none from you," he said, his eyes drifting to the pages and servants who were attempting to set their meal. "Do not offer me trifles, *Senor* . . . statues or medals or coins—especially coins, *Senor* Onate, for I'd have to consider them a bribe and would have to act accordingly. We'll do what I came to do, inventory your men and equipment. And, if all is as it should be, you may then be on your way."

Onate winced, but caught himself up short, biting his tongue while Frias' face glowed with pleasure. He admonished himself for having styled himself too soon. A subordinate. A lackey, awaiting the approval of an idiot. He said nothing, bidding Frias to sit on one of the cushions strewn across one side of the tent.

In contrast to his field tent which was essentially bare and absent of adornment, Onate's council tent or pavilion was the largest and most beautiful in the camp. Raised on posts and usually somewhat open, its walls of a thick woolen cloth with a shaggy nap on one side were hung with tapestries, its floor lined with rugs. Saddles covered in chamois skin— some of the pale yellow of its natural state, others dyed in scores of brilliant colors—were placed strategically where one might lean against them while dining. Low tables were graced with pretty lamps, silver dishes and ornaments. Servants set a dish of *manjar blanco*, an appetizing meal made of the breast of fowl, with rice flour, milk, and sugar. Onate sat across from Frias and said, "You knew my father?"

"Yes," Frias responded. "First as Lieutenant Governor and then as Governor of *Nueva Galica*. And then later as a mine operator at *La Bufa*." He sat for a time before continuing. "I always wondered what it was about your father," he said his lips working but silent. "Made acting

134

governor of *Nueva Galicia* only, and then replaced by Vasquez. It's odd, is it not?" he asked. "Ironic that Vasquez de Coronado would be sent to explore the lands you now seek to colonize? It should have been your father that led that expedition. But Mendoza had other ideas . . . both about the governorship and the exploration. Perhaps he saw a deficiency . . . A flaw, perhaps. Who can say?"

Onate looked at him but said nothing. It was as near an insult as he was able to withstand, but he would let it pass.

Frias reached into his pouch and pulled out a leather-clad journal within which he had made notations regarding Onate's contract. Continuing as though trying to provoke a response he began a searching inquiry. "And your great-grandfather was . . . ?"

"Cristobal Perez de Narriahondo, resident of Onate in Guipuzcoa," Onate responded as Frias made notations in his journal.

"And your grandfather?"

"My grandfather was Juan Perez de Onate, resident of Vitoria in the province of Alava," Onate responded.

"Your father I know. Resident of Spain as I remember?"

"Yes my father, Cristobal Perez de Onate, came here in 1524 as an assistant to the accountant of the royal treasury, Rodrigo de Albornoz, former secretary of the king."

"And you were born at Panuco, is that correct?" Frias asked, mentioning the village where the Onates had their home rather than the *villa* of Zacatecas of which the hamlet of Panuco was but a suburb.

"Yes, of the same issue with my brother, Cristobal," Onate laughed. "My mother told each of us that we came first, so I don't know which of us is the older."

"One of seven children, I understand. And your mother, too, I believe, came from Spain."

"Yes, my mother, *dona* Catalina de Salazar—I kiss her hand—was the daughter of Gonzalo de Salazar, business manager of the royal treasury.

Frias waited a long moment, making lengthy notations in his journal before continuing, and without looking up asked, "And you have another sister, do you not? It seems that I've heard something about another marriage for your mother." He then raised his head and smiled, his open mouth revealing large gaps and spaces between yellowed teeth. Looking proud of himself for the manner in which he had broached the subject—for not specifically mentioning the bigamous marriage in which Onate's mother was rumored to have engaged—he smiled and waited. Scratched his scalp with a long, black fingernail, and waited.

Onate said nothing.

"Does your sister, Magdalena, ask about her father?" Frias asked. "Magdalena de Mendoza . . . y Salazar, do I have that right?"

"You have noted that correctly," Onate responded. "Her father is dead."

"Dead?" Frias asked as though unsure of the response.

"Yes, dead," Onate said stiffly.

"Well," Frias said. "Perhaps I've been misinformed. Who can tell anything regarding the whispered secrets of maids and those who gather at the palace to hear the latest gossip?"

"I miss your point," *Senor*. What do you imply?" *don* Juan asked, his hand moving to the hilt of his sword which lay at his feet.

"Nothing. Nothing really," Frias responded, backing off from the subject, feeling that the bolt he had loosed had already done its damage. "Nothing," he said again, his hand waving in the air. "May we continue?"

"Do you bring up a matter of honor," Onate asked. "Something about my mother or one of my sisters?"

"No!" Frias said, as though Onate had misunderstood him. "No, no, no! Nothing like that."

"For to dishonor my mother or one of my sisters, Your Grace, would be to dishonor me and my father," Onate continued. "And as you know—in the words of the code of Partidas—there are two things which balance each other, killing a man and sullying one's reputation. For a man who has lost his good name, even through no fault of his own, is deprived of all worth and honor. Better for him to be dead than alive."

"I don't mean to sully your mother's reputation or that of your father," Frias countered. "I only wished to apprise you of some of the gossip I've heard. Gossip of which you need to be aware."

"There is much gossip," Onate acknowledged. "Much of it initiated by my rivals for this position. Gossip intended to damage my reputation and that of my family. My father—may God in his mercy bless and keep

136

him—held the rank of captain over a troop of cavalry, one of Guzman's most trusted subordinates. He was one of the founders of Culiacan, and one of the first to explore the state of Durango. He was key in establishing the city of Guadalajara, and, with other worthies, one of the founders of Zacatecas. And my mother could well have been buried with a palm."

"Well, those who gossip in the 'flagstones of the palace,' " Frias said in reference to the so called '*mentideros*,' or 'lie parlors,' "see it differently. You know how they are," he said. "Gonzalo de Salazar, they say, was a master of duplicity, whom, they say, and with good reason, usurped power from Cortes causing major mischief. And Guzman, they say, with whom your father allied himself, was, as president of our first *audiencia*, sent here to share power and to protect the king's interests. It was him, they say, with your father in tow, who tied Indians to cannons to show them a lesson. He was eventually arrested and imprisoned, you know," Frias bellowed. He waited a long moment before continuing. Glancing up at Onate and fingering his glass with deliberation he said. "But what do they of the *mentideros* know? Providing advanced news of events that have yet to happen. Who knows of the validity of their pronouncements! It's all gossip."

Onate looked at him with dismay. Looked about the tent and then back at the inspector. Frias' comments regarding Beltran Nuno de Guzman, with whom his father had allied himself, were true. And the comments he had made regarding his maternal grandfather, Gonzalo de Salazar, known to some as '*El Gordo*' were correct as far as they had gone. But his father held none of their beliefs. Exhibited none of Guzman's or Salazar's behaviors. His father, he knew, had exhibited the values of prudence, and courage, and even nobility, and was an *encomendero* who had returned the tributes he had received from his numerous *encomiendas* back to the Indians for their health and maintenance. He said nothing and was glad that his *maese de campo* was not there to hear these words. For his nephew, he knew, less prudent than himself, would have demanded retribution for these insults. At another time or place he, too, might have thrown down his gauntlet and demanded an apology . . . demanded satisfaction for Frias' many insinuations. But there was much at stake here and he knew that he must act carefully. Frias' comments had been rendered for the purpose of provoking his retaliation. He must not give him the pleasure.

Frias waited for a response to his comments regarding the Onates and the Salazars—of ill repute, not so grand, and even, perhaps, with a skeleton among their many possessions—and when he received none he said, "Well. If there's nothing further to be said regarding these matters we may as well continue.

"And of your household staff?" he asked. "Who are they? I might as well make note of them now."

"*Alferez* Diego de Benavides is my chief waiter," Onate answered. "And Antonio Conte de Herrera, my lord of the bedchamber and master of ceremonies."

"Master of Ceremonies? Frias said with pursed lips. "Interesting. I'm going to have to get one of those," he mocked while making a notation in his journal. "Go on."

"Alonso Nunez Maldonado is also a lord of the bedchamber, while Francisco Vido here is one of my pages."

"And you have others, I suppose?"

"Pages? Yes. I have three others: Cristobal Guillen de Quesada and Francisco de Villalba who assisted you in dismounting from your horse are two of them. My most important page, I assume, is Jorge de Zumaya, native of Zacatecas, one of four sons of Miguel de Olaque who are with the expedition. And this young man here," he said while grasping his sleeve, "is my servant, Domingo Lopez, while Juan Pimero and Baltasar de Obregon over there are attendants in my household."

"No cutters or tasters" Frias asked while examining his notes.

"No," Onate said. "I have no need for those. And each of the men I've named, as well as any in the camp, are at you disposal. You've only to ask."

Frias waited a long moment before continuing, finally saying, "And the men of your camp. How many are there?"

"There was a time when the number approached 1,000," Onate said. "But with time, and as the result of the many delays I've suffered, that number is now greatly diminished. I'll have enough to fulfill my contract, of this you may be sure. Twenty-six of them married and bringing their families. You'll meet them tomorrow."

138

"Well not tomorrow," Frias responded. "We must await my chair. It's being brought on a cart and should follow shortly. And not here," he said. "The timing of an inspection must be perfect."

What followed was a dismal meal with many complaints from Frias including one regarding the absence of 'Italian forks' among the cutlery, while, from time to time, a servant threw handfuls of medicinal herbs in the fire to purify the air.

While they ate, Frias apprised Onate of the rules under which they would be operating. "Of the rules," he said, "there are only two. The first is that there are no rules except for those I make. And the second is that you're to do nothing to get in my way! You're to obey my commands and are not question them for I'm here to assure the welfare of the soldiers and colonists and to avoid vexing the natives. For it's likely," he continued, "that the natives will suffer losses if your group does not bring sufficient provisions and stores to last a long time. I'm here," he told Onate, "to inspect the people, arms, horses, munitions, supplies, and any other stores to be used in the pacification, colonization, and subjugation of the provinces of New Mexico where you're going in order to bring them to the knowledge of the Lord our God. You're to throw no obstacles in my path," he repeated as though disciplining a subordinate. "I'm a terrible man when I'm aroused!" he warned. First, you're to immediately start north."

* * *

Somewhere up the trail, the moody and ill-tempered Frias told Onate, they would stop—whenever the spirit moved him—and he would begin his inspection. This strategy was being employed to make sure that Onate did not conduct a 'false muster' ('*plaza muerta*') which was common to all armies of the era. This ploy allowed the captain to pass off borrowed men, goods and supplies as his own, and Frias was there to prevent this.

"I know that you, Onate, would not be of this type," he said with the haughty gesture of his hand. "But others would, and we can't take that chance, now can we? No!" he bellowed. "Up the trail with these *peones*! Can any of them even ride a horse? I'm here to see that the people taken are orderly and disciplined and cause no harm, and that they are corrected and punished if they cause any trouble."

139

Onate was livid but said nothing, for what further was to be gained by saying *tus tus* to the old dog. He also bit his tongue when Frias demanded that one of his men be flogged for not having appropriately demonstrated his subservience, for he was afraid that Frias was merely looking for an excuse to damn the entire project.

Onate had been ordered to start north immediately. However, 'immediately' was to take forever, since Onate had his men here, his supplies there, and his livestock in far distant pastures. It would take almost a month to collect all of them and to get going. During this time, he was continuously admonished for the laxness of his preparations. "You've had two years to get this together!" Frias bellowed. "Why are you not ready?" And when the caravan finally lumbered into motion, Frias, with a deeply furrowed brow, rode beside it. He noted that some of the men were decidedly 'out at elbows,' and were without the requisite number of horses, that is, at least three for each man. He didn't like the looks of things, and Onate was to pay.

Santa Barbara

Two days out of Santa Barbara, the caravan creaked to a halt with Frias and a group of his heavily armored soldiers riding up to the head of the march. They were followed closely by a two-wheeled cart carrying tools of measurement, rods, cords, and scales, Frias' field tent, and the emblems of his office including his chair which was now being lowered to the ground. Here, on 22 December 1597, Frias administered an oath to Juan de Onate and began his meticulous inspection. Everything was counted: flour, corn, wheat, jerked beef, horseshoeing material, horseshoe nails, footgear, medicines, iron goods, unfinished iron, paper, frieze, sackcloth, articles of trade.

Onate was obliged to furnish a large quantity of livestock: 1000 cattle, 3000 sheep, 1000 rams, 100 black cattle, 150 colts, 150 mares and 1000 goats. However, when the inventory was completed on this occasion, he was short in both men and supplies, the cost of waiting. In supplies, he was deficient by 2,300 pesos, and he only had 129 men of fighting age. This was 71 fewer than his contract demanded.

The viceroy had instructed Frias that should Onate be deficient in supplies, he would accept bond for them. Therefore, Juan de Onate sent Gaspar Perez de Villagra south to the *finca* of yet another nephew, Juan Guerra de Resa, who was married to *dona* Ana de Zaldivar y Mendoza, one of the Zaldivar sisters. The war-weary Guerra, who had previously committed the total yearly proceeds of his holdings to assist in financing the expedition, was now being asked to post bond. He, of course, complied, as members of the extended family were wont to do. Onate was to name him *teniente*[1] *adelantado de la Nueva Mexijo*, or lieutenant governor of the kingdom, and to place him as second in command of the soldiers. Guerra, however, was never to join him in New Mexico.

Once Frias had Onate's bond in hand, he continued with the contract negotiations. He made Onate certify he would recruit and supply 80 soldiers who would, when secured, be sent north to join Onate. Although the number demanded was nine more than his contract required, Onate agreed. He was willing to do anything to get himself out of the clutches of this vulture who was just waiting to pluck at him to his last feather. In the end, Frias gave permission for Onate to go, but with the stern warning that should Onate be unsuccessful in meeting any of his warrantees, he would forfeit all of his lands, property and other benefices.

On 26 January 1598, under threatening skies, the caravan again headed north. Frias and his retinue remained with Onate, for the plan was for Frias to conduct a parting ceremony at the Conchos River, or so Onate was led to believe.

When the caravan reached the Conchos River four days later, they found it a muddy barrier swollen by downpours. It appeared they would have to wait there for the floodwaters to recede before making a crossing, but Onate was not about to delay. Although the soundings suggested that a safe crossing could not be accomplished due to the present depth, Onate drove his horse across and returned, demonstrating quite dramatically that it could be done. His people followed, moving over stones that rolled with the racing current. They drove their oxen and cattle into the raging stream and entered after them with their carts. To get the sheep across, they built a bridge of the material available to them. First, they removed the wheels from their carts. They anchored these to rafts and strung the whole in a line across the river. Then, working upon this slithering foundation, the colonists placed a deposit of brushwood and bark and covered this with a macadam of earth they dug from the steep banks of the river. Then, the sheep, which would have been incapable of swimming due to the heaviness of their water-soaked wool, crossed the Conchos, and they were on their way to New Mexico.

* * *

January 31, 1598 was the day for which the entire caravan had been waiting. On this day, the hated Inspector Juan de Frias Salazar was to provide the credentials of official recognition which would give the expedition its final approval. It was anticipated that there would be a lavish ceremony similar to those that had been held for previous *conquistadors*. After Mass on this, perhaps the most important day of their lives, Onate, surrounded by the 500 of his expedition, stood to receive the patent and approval which they had long awaited. However, Frias, as unmoved and indifferent as his name implied, merely gave them permission to proceed. Then he and his men swung aboard their horses and headed south.

Juan de Onate was appalled and wounded to the quick. So important was the Francisco Vasquez de Coronado expedition of 1540, that even the viceroy had proceeded to Compostela to give his encouragement and to superintend its final preparations. In the ceremony at Compostela, which had been attended by the royal *factor*, *veedor*, and Juan de Onate's own father, Cristobal de Onate, the Vasquez de Coronado army had marched out of Compostela, drums beating, banners flying. Every man in his army had taken an oath, required by the viceroy, to obey the orders of their general and never to abandon him. Onate got nothing, no ceremony, no speech, no 'to God' (*'Adios'*).

In disbelief, Onate, with 30 of his men on swift horses, rode to overtake Frias whose party was receding in a cloud of dust on the far distant horizon. The pretext for this move was to offer Frias a mounted escort, but really it was to receive the document that would seal Onate's authorization. However, the escort was denied, and Onate returned with dust caking the cold sweat of his brow. With wounded pride, he tried but could not make sense of this for his equally diminished colonists. His only recourse was to achieve greater success than Vasquez de Coronado who, injured in mind and body, and in gloomy disappointment, had returned to Culiacan empty-handed. His own expedition, Onate declared, must be successful. He would show them.

The Initiation

The members of the expedition had a lot to learn and the Chihuahuan desert was about to provide them with their primer. On 3 March 1598, above the Conchos River, the group of Franciscans sent to replace those who had deserted caught up with the expedition. They were escorted there by Captain Marcos Farfan de los Godos, native of the city of Seville, who, with his servant and a small body of soldiers, had been sent back to accompany them through the area of the Tepehuan Indians who were presenting difficulties. Led by *Comisario Fray* Alonso Martinez, the group now consisted of eight priests and two lay brothers, falling two short of the apostolic 12. Among the new religious were *Fray* Diego Marquez; Pedro's good friend, Brother Joaquin Rodriguez; and Onate's confessor, the ancient (almost 70 years old) *Fray* Francisco de San Miguel, (described as a saintly, old, barefooted and naked-poor friar).

* * *

Shading his eyes, and gazing intently down the trail, Pedro could just make out a white-topped cart laboring up the valley. The cart, fully loaded and being pulled by a team of eight oxen, had, arrayed around it, a bedraggled set of individuals covered with mud. Onate sent two captains together with a small squadron of soldiers to give them welcome. He followed with an even larger troop composed of himself, his cousin, *Fray* Cristobal de Salazar, and many in the camp. When he could make out the faces of his great friends, Fathers Marquez and San Miguel, he sent forth from his vanguard six ranks of men with a second courteous greetings. Two friars, Marquez and San Miguel, came ahead to greet him, and when joined by the Father Commissary, *Fray* Alonso Martinez, *harquebusiers*, their muskets spitting live flames into the still air, rendered

143

a grand salute. The friars and soldiers dismounted in a bower where tables had been set for a grand welcome. And there, the captains and officers, together with the friars and the other members of their entourage, sat down on cushions and rugs for a sumptuous banquet.

Later, with the supper board cleared from the table, Pedro caught the elbow of his friend Brother Rodriguez who during the meal had been seated apart from him among the friars with whom he had traveled. "I was afraid you weren't coming," Pedro said.

"It was an incredible trip, *don* Pedro," Rodriguez responded. "Walking some and riding some, and the last two days have been hell!"

"The Indians?" Pedro asked.

"Them and *Fray* Marquez," Rodriguez responded, placing his arm about Pedro shoulder, and giving him an *abrazo*. "For days he's had his chin on his shoulder. And then two days ago his worst fears were realized. A courier sent up the trail by our superior told him that he has to go back . . . and he's livid! You should have heard the words coming out of his mouth!"

"Go back? Pedro questioned. "What do you mean? You were supposed to go to Cuencame . . . but you're here, and now Marquez has been recalled? What's going on?"

Rodriguez did not immediately respond to Pedro's question, asking instead, "Where's your camp?"

"Up there," Pedro said, pointing up the valley to a greened hollow of clover fields containing a number of carts. "Can you camp with us?" he asked.

"Tonight, yes," Rodriguez responded, "then I'll have to join my brothers. But we'll see," he laughed, while giving Pedro another hug. "We'll see how things go."

A small creek, looking cold and black and smelling of peat, ran lank and long in the shallow basin. Bordered by acacias, and the saber-leafed variety of cottonwood called water willows, there were tents and white-topped carts scattered on both banks of the stream. Smoke rising from campfires identified individual campsites. As Pedro and Brother Rodriguez walked among the settlers who were busy at their chores, Rodriguez told Pedro what had transpired regarding *Fray* Marquez, and why Marquez was being commanded to return.

"It was as I told you, *don* Pedro," Rodriguez said. "The viceroy learned that Marquez had been given authority by the Inquisition to act as its agent in New Mexico and he was unwilling to grant his approval. He asked the Holy Office to rescind Marquez's commission, and when it refused, the viceroy asked our superior to have Marquez recalled. Marquez is only here to replenish his supplies and to meet with Onate for a final time."

Robledo and Rodriguez continued in their ramble, walking down a slight incline to the creek's bank, and then up a meander along feather-like mimosas to the Robledo campsite. "I wouldn't have been able to come myself if there had been 12 priests to fill our allotment," Rodriguez continued, "especially with my superior, *Fray* Fernando, likening me to another Las Casas.[1] But frankly, Pedro," Rodriguez asserted, "things in Mexico are an ecclesiastical mess. No one knows who's in charge. Maybe the mother province of the Holy Gospel in Mexico City," he offered, referring to Mexico's original Franciscan province. "Who can tell?" he asked with a shrug. "Zacatecas, my own province of Michoacan, and even the bishop of Guadalajara, are asserting their authority to select friars of their order as missionaries for New Mexico. Incredibly, with all of them demanding their rights, and privileges, and clamoring to make the selections, we were still short in the count, and that's why I'm here." He joined Pedro and Catalina at the Robledo campsite where they continued, discussing the Inquisition, Marquez, and their expectations for the expedition.

"Where are the children?" Rodriguez asked of the Robledos.

"They're where you'll always find them," Pedro responded, motioning up the valley to one of the other carts. "They're with the Perez de Bustillo family."

"And who are they?" Rodriguez asked.

"That tent over there," Catalina answered. The big one with the red top. Those are the Bustillos. They have a number of youngsters including a bunch of girls who seem to attract the young men of the camp like flies to honey."

"Well the Bustillos have some boys, too," Pedro added. "That's why Francisca's there. But it's the girls who are the biggest draw, and the rules of courtship have been suspended. No *duenas* (chaperones), just *diablos*! The Varelas, the Olaques, the Hinojos, and the Robledos, too, brothers all, behaving like *pollinos*, ass-colts, sniffing around, and surveying the possibilities."[2]

"Pedro!" Catalina said, in an attempt to hush him. "We have the brother here! You'll have to forgive him," she said to Brother Rodriguez in her soft, sweet voice. "The undisciplined behavior of some of the young people is beginning to get on his nerves."

"You don't need to apologize for *don* Pedro," Rodriguez said. "We go back too many years for either of us to apologize for the behavior of the other, and each of us knows that the other is not a saint. What is it now, Pedro?" he asked of his friend. "Twenty years? Twenty years! Who among us would have ever predicted two decades ago that we'd find ourselves here?"

"No one."

"No one. Certainly not me. I was performing a penance, and you were looking to have your mule stolen." They laughed, and Catalina looked from one to the other as though asking for further explanation.

"What are you two laughing about?" she asked.

"We were just remembering how we found each other, and how ridiculous were our circumstances," Pedro said.

"Well, it's been an interesting life, that's for sure" Rodriguez said, "although it might have been better for each of us to have been born a nobleman and to have had land and sheep. As it was," he said, "my parents were . . . how did my papa describe them . . . 'well-to-do peasants,' he would say, 'with too many mouths to feed.' And the two of you," he asked as he sipped at a cup of chocolate, chasing it down with a cup of water (for it was very thick), "do you come from large families?"

"I had one brother, only," Pedro said, "but both he and my mother died soon after he was born. And Catalina, also, had only a brother."

"Only one brother each." Rodriguez repeated, "you might as well have been only children. Of the 11 children in my family, only four survived into adulthood. My brother became a priest, and one sister, a nun. My second sister, Margarita, married . . . most unhappily, I'd say.

"Brothers!" Rodriguez said emphatically. "How important a concept. I wouldn't be sitting with you on this beautiful hillside if it wasn't for my brother." He sipped at his cup before continuing. "I was, like him, to have become a priest," he said. "In fact, when I came to Mexico from Spain, I had most of my training behind me. But I never completed my novitiate, or professed my vows."

Pedro thought it improper of him to ask his friend why he had not completed his training, but Rodriguez needed no prompting to continue his explanation.

"My brother and I were among a group of 23 friars who came here in 1573 to establish the custody[3] of San Francisco de Zacatecas in the country of the Chichimeca," he said, "and it was among the Chichimeca that I became interested in things other than the priesthood. My brother, who had been sent to Yucatan, told me that a Mayan book dealing with astronomy and mathematics had been found there. He said the Mayan astronomy was superior to European astronomy and the mathematics as good as ours own. The Mayans had an advanced form of writing," Rodriguez said, "done on bark-cloth paper, and bound in leaves placed flat on each other, rather than being rolled together like our scroll. Few of these books survive, for our priests are bent on destroying them without giving any thought to the intellectual treasures they may contain. In Mexico alone, in seven years, my order claims to have destroyed 500 temples and 20,000 images, idols and books! My God! What have we lost?" he said to the Robledos with a shrug. "The tragedy is that we'll never know! Anyhow," Rodriguez said, "my brother and I are bent on saving as much of the native material as we can—even if we have to help the natives hide it. I wish I could have gone to university like you, *don* Pedro, and had developed some skills to facilitate my interests."

"In only one thing are you wrong," Pedro replied. "I didn't go to university, although it was not for lack of trying."

The three continued talking, listening to the sounds of those around them, and watching the activities of a campsite replete with its campers now at their leisure.

Pedro related how he and his father had made a trip to Salamanca to visit the university there, and how that trip had shaped his life. He could not afford to attend the university, but his father had acceded to their local priest's plan to obtain the necessary funds. The church, the pastor had assured Pedro's father, could provide them with some of the money, and he himself would provide Pedro with a license allowing him to beg for alms as a *capigorrista*[4] at Salamanca and in an area six leagues around the university. Although his father was grievously offended by the suggestion, his father had agreed to consider the possibility. The trip, unfortunately, had been a disaster.

Pedro recalled how he and his father had explored the place where Pedro would live, and the dark rooms with calcined walls and high-beamed ceilings where his classes would be held. They had also met with some of 'masters of the pillar' who would guide his studies. But mostly his father had focused on the cost of it all, especially the cost of graduation should Pedro get that far. There would be honorariums to be paid to the professors, beadles, and examiners; tips to the master of ceremonies, workmen, kettle-drummers, trumpeters and bell-ringers; money for a banquet for all members of the faculty; and even the expense of the *corrida* (bullfight) he would be expected to stage. His father had thought that all of this was ridiculous, but most of all, he could not abide the stupidity of the students they saw at the opening of classes. And it was what they had observed in one of the courtyards that had put an end to Pedro's quest for a college education.

There, in a tree-lined courtyard, a freshman, a *novato* (identifiable to everyone because of the prim and proper way in which he wore his square cap and new gown) was being harassed by a group of upperclassmen. The tormenting started with verbal taunts as to his manhood, but quickly moved to the tearing and crumpling of his garb. This was followed by a final stage of humiliation in which they spat upon him until his gown was white with spittle.

Pedro's recollections regarding this event were a mixture of amusement and sadness. He remembered how his father had talked to himself half the way home, muttering below his breath and even slapping his forehead in continuing astonishment. His father could not accept the behavior of these entitled ruffians, and of the incredible practice of *sacar nevado* (making a *novato's* gown as white as snow) which they had observed. He refused to subject his son to this idiocy, whether at

Salamanca, Alcala or Siguenza and would hear nothing more about the furthering of Pedro's education.

"So, we're even more alike than we knew," Pedro said to Brother Rodriguez, "incomplete in our education and training."

"Without vows, and free to continue our vocations," Rodriguez added. "So what are we doing on this hillside?" he asked. "We've got worlds to conquer."

* * *

Rodriguez camped with them on that night and for many nights to come, for the entire group, soldiers, settlers, and religious were to wait at this campsite for nearly a month while an advanced party scouted ahead. Two days after Rodriguez's arrival, however, *Fray* Marquez, fingering his rosary, and carrying a religious statue which Onate had given him, left the campsite and returned to Mexico.

The Trail

Earlier forays into the North Country had demonstrated there were many large settlements of heathen Indians who, according to the Franciscans, lived in ignorance of God and of the Catholic faith. The friars' purpose was to bring Christianity to the natives so they might have an orderly and decent Christian life. And one of Onate's responsibilities was to assist them in this endeavor.

Previous expeditions had traveled down the Conchos River to the Rio Grande at present-day Presidio, Texas. From there, expeditionary forces then snaked up the Rio Grande Valley into the North Country. Onate, however, felt this trail was too long and planned to head due north. While he waited at his encampment on the San Pedro for the Franciscans to catch up, he sent Vicente (the younger of the Zaldivar brothers) with 17 men to find a trail, one of which he hoped would offer water and grass for his herds.

The scouting expedition which 25-year-old Vicente undertook was exceedingly difficult. Following a desert plain with mountains upon its margins that were indistinguishable from the blue sky, the small party rode northward. Lacking water and sufficient food, they soon became lost and wandered in circles. They were saved by finding a small group of Indians who led them to the Rio Grande. With the Indians showing the way, the party continued northward. Here, Zaldivar divided his group and sent half of his men back to Onate. They were to tell him, but no one else, of the difficulties they had encountered. Then, Vicente and his men moved on, finally arriving at the river on 28 February.

In the meantime, Onate, who was concerned about the failure of his nephew to return, sent Captain Perez de Villagra with some troops to find him. After a dramatic rescue and some further exploration, both groups returned on 10 March with the determination made that if Onate's expedition was to succeed in using the trail Villagra and Zaldivar had blazed, it would have to hug the mountains where pastures and springs might be found. With this information to guide them, the expedition left immediately.

* * *

Although the exact route of Onate's travel is unknown, a look at a present-day map shows that, even now, the area of more than 100 million acres is a vast desert plain with dry washes and stark mesquite grasslands still displaying a dismal brown. Although the desert contains vital wintering sites for Great Plains birds such as the long-billed curlew, mountain plover, and Baird's sparrow, the absence of water was, and is, a major obstacle to the birds, as well as to the colonists. The tanks of *Sant' Greco*, the *Nombre de Dios River* and the *Agua de San Joseph* among others[1] provided the expedition with some relief; otherwise, there was nothing but wasteland between them and the Rio Grande. Scouting parties were constantly being sent ahead to find water, but many marches were waterless.

After a march of nearly two weeks the expedition reached the Rio Sacramento, so-named because they encountered it on Holy Thursday. Here, they stopped, built an outdoor chapel, and spent the night in spiritual communion. Beyond the Sacramento, they were blessed with a downpour. They watered their stock in pools that formed on the desert floor and thanked God for His bounty.

A week after the party received their rain from heaven, they reached the edge of *Los Medanos.* This was an area of sand dunes that extended for many miles toward the Rio Grande. To negotiate the sand dunes, which Onate was no longer able to skirt, he was required to divide the train into two sections. Taking the oxen from one section, he used them to pull his carts for a day's travel through the sand, all the way to the river. When this was accomplished, and after a day's rest, all of the oxen were taken back to repeat the process with the second section. Several days later, the entire train was united at the river some 25 miles below present-day El Paso. After an arduous journey of nearly three months, the expedition then rested.

The Taking

After a march of three months through the Chihuahuan desert, the area at the river must have seemed like a paradise. There was a riverine forest of cottonwood, willows, large and small mesquite, and thick brambles that grew to the water's edge. These provided cover for herons, and flocks of white-faced ibis, ducks and geese winging low to rippled landings.

From the mucky limits of vernal pools which dotted the south bank of the river, sprang leopard frogs, their cranky croaking, and the babble and clack of insects providing a continual backdrop of clatter for those sitting in the grass. As the colonists rested in the rushes, with the frogs advertising for mates, they watched as a cloud of dragonflies fought for space with territories being gained and lost, rivals run off and mates wooed. They watched as some of these magnificent creatures, males of the species *Anax junius,* seized and ate mosquitoes in mid-flight. Some males bullied each other, making dizzying loops and spreading their wings as if trying to make themselves appear larger than they really were. Each fought for a few square feet of water, and defended it against relentless male competition as the best way to get a mate. A child among a group who had waded into a shallow pool, squealed in delight as one of these beautiful creatures flew into his grasping hand. As he extricated his catch,

151

its huge wings like brittle gossamer held between his thumb and forefinger, adults and children swarmed around him to see what he had caught. The dragonfly was shaped like a knitting needle with a five-inch wingspan, its length and breadth the size of the child's hand. It was a beautiful creature, blue and green in color, with huge wraparound eyes that met in a seam at the back of its head. The colonists examined it closely, and then let it go. For it was only with freedom—and life—that this exquisite predatory insect could serve God's purpose.

*   *   *

After a week at this landing, where the river's sandbars and marshes were a lure for teeming throngs of waterfowl, and its banks home to other wildlife, the caravan began moving upriver. In their march northward, the colonists would take, from these boggy groves, deer and turkey and fish[1] as they sought to replenish their food supply. The caravan continued in this manner, hunting and fishing, as it moved northward along the southern bank of the river.

What Onate sought was a ford by which to move his expedition to the north bank of the river. He found this by following a deeply worn Indian trail to a spot where the wild North River flowed swiftly through a narrow defile among sugar-loaf stone bluffs. Here, just below the pass of the river and the ford (which they christened 'Las Puertas' or the portal, but which would later become known at El Paso), Onate called a halt. They were about to enter New Mexico, and the day called for a special ceremony.

One can only imagination the elation of the members of the caravan, and especially Onate who had waited a lifetime, for this day. The day began with a Mass on this Feast of the Ascension, celebrated in a bower formed by the overhanging boughs of trees. The entire contingent then adjourned to a grassy area under giant cottonwoods, where Onate was at last able to make the formal pronouncements regarding the 'act of possession,' or entrada. The army, perhaps for the first time having donned their ancient armor, placed themselves in formation, with Ensign Pedro Robledo the elder, Royal Standard Bearer, holding Onate's banner aloft as Onate began to speak.

152

I take and seize tenancy and possession, real and actual, civil and natural, one, two, and three times, one, two, and three times, one, two, and three times, and all the times by right I can and should, at this said Rio del Norte, without excepting anything and without limitations, including the mountains, rivers, valleys, meadows, pastures, and waters. In his name I also take possession of all the other lands, pueblos, cities, towns, castles, fortified and unfortified houses which are now established in the kingdom and provinces of New Mexico, those neighboring and adjacent thereto, and those which may be established in the future, together with their mountains, rivers, fisheries, waters, pastures, valleys, meadows, springs, and ores of gold, silver, copper, mercury, tin, iron, precious stones, salt, morales, alum, and all the lodes of whatever sort, quality or condition they may be, together with the native Indians in each and every one of the provinces, with civil and criminal jurisdiction, power of life and death, over high and low, from the leaves of the trees in the forests to the stones and sands of the river, and from the stones and sands of the river to the leaves in the forests.[2]

With this, at midday on 30 April 1598, the Kingdom of New Mexico became a reality.

PERIOD III
THE KINGDOM OF NEW MEXICO

PART I

The Year of Two Seasons

Cualacu

Although the colonists now found themselves in the desert, it is its mountains that most define New Mexico. In all, more than 70 ranges and 300 peaks stretch from north to south. Seven of these peaks rise more than 13,000 feet above sea level, and an additional 80 are at least two miles high. By draw, ravine, and canyon, the snow packs of these mountains drain into the valleys below, and the greatest of these valleys is that of the Rio Grande.

The Rio Grande, which is the nation's third-longest river, begins life as a meander of streams in the San Juan Mountains of present-day southern Colorado. Its flow is controlled and directed by the Rio Grande Rift, one of the few such fissures on earth. The rift results from a pulling apart of the earth's crust that began 30 million years ago. It is a major break in the earth's surface that extends from Colorado through the Mexican state of Chihuahua, and consists of a series of step-like trenches (called echelon grabens) that transect New Mexico from north to south. The tension of the earth's crust millions of years ago, resulted in a huge, long, v-shaped piece sinking thousands of feet between two fault zones.

Vast quantities of gravel, sand, and clay sized sediments filled the valley providing a usable, but tortuous, course for the river, and resulting in a complex meandering system in the parent stream.

Over time, a braided twist of oxbows, and oxbow lakes formed as the river cut a meander neck to shorten its course. This caused old channels to be blocked off, and migrate away from the lake. Where one loop was cut off, the lake formed was crescent shaped. Where more than one loop was cut off, the resulting lake appeared as serpentine or winding. Some of these oxbow lakes became silted up, forming marshes at various places for the entire length of the river.

In the south, the faults that edge the west side of the rift are staggered in such a way that sloping terraces lead down into the valley. It was along these terraces, oxbow lakes, and marshes—and through four life zones—that the colonists began working their way up the river.

Immediately upon crossing the river, Onate called for one his junior officers, Juan de Vitoria Carvajal. Thirty-seven-year-old Carvajal, the son of Juan de Carvajal, and a native of the town of Ayotepel in the Marquisette of the Valley of Mexico, had been here before. Serving as *alferez* (ensign or second lieutenant) for Onate, Carvajal, a strong-featured individual of medium stature, chestnut beard, and a mark on the right side of his face, sat there on his horse looking northward. Onate observed him with keen interest as Carvajal surveyed the terrain for clues to his previous exit from these lands.

On Friday, 27 July 1590, eight years before the Onate expedition, Gaspar Castano de Sosa had led a previous expedition into these lands. He was lieutenant governor of *Nuevo Leon*, a practically boundless region north of the Rio Panuco and east of *Nueva Vizcaya* in New Spain's northern borderlands. Portuguese by birth, Castano had joined a fellow countryman, Luis de Carvajal, in colonizing *Nuevo Leon*. Shortly, however, Carvajal who had been named governor and captain general of *Nuevo Leon*, became embroiled in a major controversy, a controversy that had European beginnings.

The beginnings of the persecution of Jews in Portugal in 1497 drove large numbers of *marranes* or *convertidos* to the New World. Many of them emigrated to New Spain where they entered every area of industry and commerce and became experts at conducting the colonial trade. All importations, from embroidery to sacking, came through their warehouses. They were accused by their Castilian counterparts, of purchasing on credit the merchandise of entire *armadas*, which they then apportioned among themselves, thus making money unnecessary. So quickly did their power increase that in 1571, King Philip II set up an Inquisition in New Spain for the purpose of ridding the continent of Jews, especially those from Portugal.

Caught up in this hate-filled web of political, economic, and religious intrigue, was a gentleman by the name of Francisco Rodriguez Mattos, who was described by the Inquisition as a "dogmatist and rabbi of the Jewish sect." Mattos died before the Inquisition could punish him, and his son escaped punishment by flight. However, his four daughters, one "of whom, the youngest, a girl of 17, was reported to know all of the Psalms of David by heart and to repeat the Prayer of Ester and other hymns backwards," were forced to repent and were punished. Their uncle, Luis de Carvajal, refused to denounce his nieces, and for this failure, was prosecuted by the Inquisition, deprived of his office, and imprisoned. What was his lieutenant governor, Castano de Sosa, Portuguese by birth (and perhaps himself a *convertido*), to do? He set off for New Mexico.

Although specifically forbidden to attempt to colonize New Mexico, Castano, with the entire settlement of Almaden took off. Juan Morlete, sent by Viceroy Luis de Velasco, later captured them. Before he did, however, the wheels of Castano's carts (which had entered the country by way of the Pecos River) scored the surface of New Mexico's seemingly untouched earth, from the Pecos to the pass of the Rio Grande in the south. Castano was later tried for invading lands inhabited by peaceful Indians and was sentenced to service in the Philippines. His colonists, one of whom was Juan de Vitoria Carvajal, were dispersed.

Juan de Vitoria Carvajal appears to have been a scion of the Luis de Carvajal family. Deprived of his first opportunity to establish a homeland in New Mexico, he was now here with Onate for his second try. He looked up the valley in the distance and spied the unmistakable ruts of Castano's 10 carts. Looking at Onate with a broad grin, he said nothing, but with a whoop and a holler, he spurred his horse, and galloped northward. He knew which way to go.

With a bald eagle hovering above them on rising columns of warm air, the caravan resumed its journey northward. There were 83 wagons and ox carts (24 of which were Onate's) and almost 7000 head of livestock, the whole train stretching out along the trail for several miles.

The men, including a number of hired drivers and packers, kept the train and its livestock on the move. They attempted to maintain the cattle separate from the horse stock, although this was never totally successful. It took as many men on the point to keep the herds from mixing as it did in the drag to keep them moving forward. Mounted men circled the herds of the wild and wiry long-horned beasts (descendants of their ancestors, the wild aurochs), while additional drivers and their dogs, purchased and trained for this purpose, corralled the flocks. Here and there, a shepherd shook a noisy gourd as a means of keeping the flocks on the move. Mounted, spurring men shouted "*Arre!*" at the milling cattle, whipping the laggards over the back with a rope or prodding them with a goad. While the men were responsible for the larger animals, the older children and the few women who accompanied them herded goats and sheep. Thus, the entire caravan moved forward at a snail's pace beneath a blanket of dust.

Both the wagons and carts, the *carros* and *carretas*, were two-wheeled vehicles drawn by oxen or mules. The most common type of conveyance at that time in central and southern Spain, these vehicles had a framework of braces and upright poles upon which an awning could be stretched. Most often, the wheels of the *carros* had iron rims (although, on occasion, so did the *carretas*), and they were constructed to carry a heavier load than the carts. Both vehicles were springless, with the cart's bed mounted directly on top of a cottonwood axle. To the axle were affixed two solid or segmented wooden wheels. The solid wheels were usually cross-sections of a cottonwood tree, bored through the middle and cottered to their axle by a wooden peg.[1] Those wheels, without metal rims, were susceptible to damage from rocks that were spread on the banks of the river. Ordinarily, no one occupied the ox carts, but, here and there, an elderly woman would be seated on top holding a small infant to her chest, while the immensely weighted cart swayed from side to side beneath them.

The heavy carts, some carrying lead and fine-corned gunpowder, moaned and wailed as their languorous draft animals moved ahead. They traveled alongside groves in places four leagues wide of cottonwood and white poplars in what is presently the nation's largest continuous cottonwood forest. As they went, the settlers picked the leaves of the prickly pear for the purpose of stuffing these into the wheel hubs to lubricate the shaft. For brief moments, the groaning was quieted, only to resume as soon as the wheel and its shaft had ejected the pulp. Meanwhile, as they drove the sheep and goats, the women and children picked dead vegetable matter and even the dried dung of animals unknown to them with which to kindle the night's fire. They put what they gathered into sacks tied to the side of each cart. And so, in this manner, the caravan plodded northward.

* * *

Diego, a member of the outriders who scouted to the east of the caravan, was one of those who saw a lake on the distant horizon and asked to explore it more closely. Approaching from the south with a smaller group of four individuals, Diego observed the sun seeming to shimmer off a vast expanse of water captured in a shallow depression. As the outriders rode nearer, however, the illusion evaporated. The crusty lake bottom was dry except for a few shallow pools that were fed by runoff from the mountains to the east. Gullies leading to the 'lake' suggested that it once might have held some life-giving water, but now there was nothing there. Surrounded by mesquite, creosote, poppies, and tumbleweeds, the outriders hastened back to join their group.

* * *

The caravan, assisted by a group of friendly Indians, had crossed to the east bank of the Rio Grande during the first days of May 1598. After finally reaching New Mexico, Pedro Robledo felt that it was time for him to meet with his sons and to speak with them regarding their futures. Sitting with them under an enormous cottonwood beside the river, its banks lined with luxuriant grass, he began with a biblical maxim, as was the custom. "First of all, my sons," he said speaking solemnly, "you're to fear God, for therein lies wisdom." Pedro then poured out the thoughts about home, and family, and country that seemed to have been bottled up inside him for decades. "If I had spoken to you yesterday regarding these matters," he said, his light blue eyes alive with excitement, "I would have told you that there were three things that helped man to prosper: learning, the sea and the royal household. Now, however, I can speak of learning and nobility and omit the sea." He said this with a wry grin, and his sons laughed at the remark, recalling their father's stories about the ocean passage.

"Remember" he continued, his gray hair silvered by the shadowed light, "that knowing is worth more than having, for the wise man may be rich, but the rich man cannot purchase wisdom. We've taken it upon ourselves to establish the first settlements in this new Mexico and will, therefore, be granted titles of nobility and become *hidalgos*. That in itself is an honor. But it's more honorable to pursue knowledge and to use that knowledge for the good, for every man is the son of his work.

"In the beginning," he continued, "men held the earth in common, with every man sowing and feeding where he pleased. Natural right to the soil is superseded, though, when an individual raises crops and improves it. We've entered a vast land, a land that was once held in common by all men, but the people who inhabit it have improved some of it. They are to retain, and we are to respect their right to, whatever land they have historically occupied or used, whether contiguous to their pueblos or located elsewhere. In addition," he said, "we're to assure that these people retain the grounds and boundaries of their pueblos, as well as any land they may need for settlement, farming or pasture.[2] However," he continued, looking around at the attentive young men who sat as his feet, "that which is not occupied or improved may, by natural law, come to another. You're to be granted a title of nobility, and, with this, you're to receive a homestead with lots for house and garden, fields for vegetables, others for vineyards and olive groves, additional land for irrigation, the necessary water, and common pasture for our herds and stock. Although this land is being given to us as some of its first settlers, it's for you to secure. In securing it," he said, "we won't swear to perform noble deeds, for we're not yet noble, or to live in perfect harmony with our neighbors, for we're not perfect. We can only pledge to do our best and to make our garden grow. That portion of the land that you take as your own must be improved and held by you for five years. Five years, my sons!" he said emphatically. "Mark it with red ocher like the lists on the professor's chair. In five years it will be yours!"

* * *

On 12 May, Pablo de Aguilar, with a scouting party that included Pedro and Diego Robledo, was, for a second time, sent ahead on a reconnaissance mission.[3] He was, on this occasion, to conduct an exploratory survey of the Pueblo country in order to seek out information regarding the location and provision of their villages. This reconnaissance, Onate had commanded, was to be conducted in strict secrecy. He said he would impose the death penalty for violation of this order since it was imperative the Pueblos remain ignorant of their presence lest they abandon their villages and take their food stores with them. These were foodstuffs, grain especially, which Onate badly needed, for, despite the supplement provided by the river, he was running short of supplies.

Diego remembered looking at his father as they mounted their horses on this occasion, and wondering whether his father should be going with them. He had always thought of his father as sturdy and robust, much younger than his stated age. However, during the past two or three years, since they had lost their cargoes at Vera Cruz in 1594 and 1595, he thought, his father had seemed to age. He still looked well, and certainly there was nothing in his gait which betrayed his mature years, but something in his eyes concerned Diego. Holding out his hand for his father to grasp as he climbed aboard his mount, he noted that his father seemed to stagger against him, though he quickly righted himself, and with a slight boost from Diego, climbed aboard.

His sons had given Pedro the horse he was riding when the decision was made to join the New Mexico venture. It was not his most expensive horse (and his family now owned an additional 65 of like stature), but this one, a gray stallion, was his favorite. A direct descendant of one of the 11 stallions, five mares, and one foal that Cortes had brought to New Spain, it was even further descended from the North African Barb, which had originated in Armenia and been transplanted to Barbary. Although his horse was not handsome—for it was thickly muscled, strong, compact, and perhaps a bit prehistoric-looking—it was swift, exceedingly hardy, and blessed with great stamina. It looked as though it could prevail against all odds. Pedro the younger had teased his father that he had wanted to name the fiery steed Rocinante (for *rocin*, a —'hack'), but had not been allowed to do so by his brothers who said that when the spirited animal was addressed by that appellation, it had looked sad. The horse, called instead Babieca (commemorating El Cid's charger of the same name), needed bit rather than spur. It stood there pawing the ground with the remainder of the party's horses, snorting and whinnying and clamoring to get going. Amidst the yelping of dogs and the ceaseless bleating of goats and sheep, the party rode out of camp and headed north.

The men immediately knew they were in for trouble. Although Aguilar had been sternly commanded by Onate to remain hidden, he did nothing to veil their presence as they rode up the rift valley replete with spiny shrubs and smallish trees. They rode boldly and in full view of anyone who might be watching, their ancient armor gleaming in the morning sun. Pedro and others suggested they keep to the river bottom where magnificent stands of cottonwoods might shield them from view. However, Aguilar (who appeared to be attempting to live up to the pretensions of his surname which is from the Latin '*aguilar*' meaning, 'haunt of eagles') laughed this off. He wanted them to be seen and to have the Indians cower at their presence.

Cualacu, located above the stark redoubt of the Black Bluffs, was the first pueblo they encountered. It lay on the east bank of the Rio Grande at the foot of Black Mesa. Nestled in a deep valley, Cualacu was surrounded by verdant meadows that grew to the water's edge. It was Aguilar's decision first to observe the village from the *jarales* that grew heavily at the bank of the river, then, after determining the Pueblos' strength and numbers, to enter the village with a heavy show of force. The men of the reconnaissance party loudly protested this move, but despite their protestations, the impetuous and arrogant Aguilar proceeded with his plan.

"You've not requested our counsel, *capitan*," said Pedro Robledo, who had approached Aguilar at the edge of the thicket where he stood, "but the men have asked me to speak with you. They say—and this is my view also—that we should not enter this village. We've done what we came to do, explore the trail to the first pueblo. We should return as quickly as possible and tell *don* Juan what we've discovered." He hoped this argument would be accepted favorably by his superior.

"So what are we supposed to do, *don* Pedro," Aguilar asked sarcastically, "go back to *don* Juan to tell him that the Indians are here? Of course they're here! Everyone knows they're here!" he bellowed. "Of what possible use would that information be to anyone? Oh, *don* Juan!" he continued in falsetto, daubing at his eyes in an affected manner and behaving like a fop. 'The Indians! The Indians! They're here! They're there! They're everywhere!' A great survey and examination that would be—I can just see my commendation."

Aguilar paused and studied Pedro before continuing. "You're Spanish-born like myself, and sometimes we just know things that might escape the notice of others. *Don* Juan's wrong in this matter," Aguilar said, suggesting by this comment that since Juan de Onate was born in the New World, he was somehow less knowledgeable than his subordinate, Aguilar, who was a native of the city of Ecija. "The Pueblos know we're coming," he said. "They've probably known this since we crossed the river at *Las Puertas*, almost two weeks ago. Our job here is to put them on notice. They're to obey our wishes and commands and to provide us with what we need and desire. That's their only responsibility. And your responsibility is to obey my commands. You can't pick and choose which commands you'll follow and which you'll ignore, *don* Pedro. That's the manner of the army. You may, when this is over, take your complaints to *don* Juan. However, at the moment, you have no recourse but to do as I tell you."

Then with a longer pause, during which Aguilar looked beyond Pedro to the remainder of his men hidden in the *juncos*, he added "You may be the captain's standard bearer, Robledo, but you've no special standing here. I'm an old Christian, and that in itself is enough to make me a count—no ha-Levi, as is Onate who keeps his credentials at church.[4] These are my wishes, and you're to respond to them as my commands.

162

Go tell your son and the rest of the men the same." With this he moved to brush by Pedro who had unintentionally blocked his path.

Pedro, standing toe to toe with Pablo de Aguilar, said nothing at first, but he also did not move. Then, after a brief moment, he said. "You're my captain, *don* Pablo, and I must obey your commands, but I don't wish to enter the pueblo. I ask that you assign me to watch the horses. If necessary, I'll watch them alone."

Thirty-eight year old Aguilar studied Pedro, this old man almost twice his age, and it may have occurred to him to strike him. However, after some consideration, he said icily, "I'll do as you wish, *don* Pedro, and Diego will stay with you. The rest of the men, I'm sure, will do as they're told." Then standing immediately in front of the older Robledo, his foul breath upon Pedro's face, he added, "Just remember, *don* Pedro, that a lame goat never takes a nap." He then rudely brushed past the senior Robledo, returned to the thicket where his horse was tied, and rode back to where his men were hidden in the bush.

Diego and the rest of the men who had watched this encounter from their hiding place in the *bosque*, could not make out the conversation in which the two men were engaged. Nevertheless, they could tell by the postures of Pedro and Aguilar that differences of opinion were being expressed, and that Pablo de Aguilar was fuming. Diego had only once before seen his father in such an engagement, this when his father had kept a muleteer from beating one of his beasts that had fallen alongside the trail. He thought of his father as a gentle man and not one to engage in physical encounters, but his father had demonstrated in numerous ways that he was willing and able to stand his ground when the circumstances required it.

* * *

The Roman army's system, which loosely divided the day into time segments, was still observed in 1598, with daily watches rotating on the third, sixth and ninth hours, and the night's watch divided into two *quartos*, each of six hours' duration. On this occasion, and through the next night during which the vanguard would see an as-yet-unexplained flash of brilliant green light in the western sky, Diego and his father kept the watch together.

With the horses corralled in an abandoned section of the old pueblo, Pedro and Diego sat around their campfire drinking their *pinole* of toasted ground corn, and eating their meal of paper bread, or *piki*, that had been provided them by their somewhat reluctant hosts who seemed to have little to share. Although Diego had spent many days and nights on the trail with his father on their sojourns from Vera Cruz to the Valley of Mexico, he was to cherish in years to come these seven days above all others.

As Pedro sat against the stone wall attempting to light his pipe, his thoughts drifted to his grandfather and great-grandfather who, like his father and himself, had lived in their village of Carmena. He stood and removed his short coat of chain mail and pulled at his *cuero* and at his rumpled trousers until they were adjusted to his satisfaction. Then he sat down on one side of their small fire of upright sticks, with Diego on the other. Their horses shifted about as though questioning their status at day's end. While Diego and his father talked over the small flames, they could smell the smoke of pinon wood and sweetgrass with which they had kindled the fire.

Diego looked around them as if trying to get his bearings, although it was apparent in which quarter lay the west since the sun was just beginning to set behind the distant mountains. He looked down, examining the ground before them, snapping twigs and larger pieces of wood, which they had brought from the *bosque*, and laying them aside.

"You know Diego," his father said, looking off in the distance as if trying to remember something, "I wish my great-grandfather could have lived to see this. When I was a boy," he said, while taking quick puffs on his pipe in an attempt to light its charge, "I learned that my great-grandfather had been one of the tenants tied to the soil who was freed from the land by Queen Isabella.[5]

"When he left his village," he said, "he took a pair of spurs with him that he had found hidden in a niche in the city wall. He used to tell my *abuelo* that these spurs would be worn either by himself or by one of his descendants when he became a *caballero*.[6] Those were the spurs, one of which I have with me, that sat near our fireplace in Carmena."

"Why only one, Papa?"

"I buried the other one," his father replied, re-lighting his pipe with a firebrand. "You may remember this, Diego," he said, "although probably not. You were only three. It was to have been our last night in Carmena. That was the night I buried my treasures." Pedro sat quietly for some time before continuing.

"When I was a boy," he said, "I had a teacher who made me believe that the experiences we have as individuals and as a people are important and worthy of writing down. I used to keep track of everything: the color, kind, and worth of the cloth in my papa's inventory, the crops in our field. The sun. The rain. Everything. It became a habit, a way of keeping track of who we were, and what we were about. My employment as a scribe was only an extension of this need.

"When we began with our plans to leave Carmena," he said, "it seemed important to leave something of ourselves behind, something that would tell whoever might find it who we were and how we lived. I hadn't thought of it till now," he continued, while repositioning the wood in their small fire with the heel of his boot, "but, in a way, those spurs are symbolic of that history. They're not really ours and God only knows what stories they have to tell, but we're their guardians, Diego, protectors of a special thing. Whatever right we have to nobility," he said, "it's borrowed. And a portion of it remains buried and unseen, hidden on our Castilian *meseta*. Wearing the spurs was what your great-great-grandfather lived for. And if I wear the one I have, it will be to honor him.

"You know, Diego," Pedro said, again looking off into the distance, "although my papa was only the owner of an embroidery workshop, he benefited from certain rights that were attached to a profession considered particularly honorable. Yet, despite those privileges, I didn't want to follow in his footsteps, and I think this offended him. Rather than make cloth as all in our family had done I pleaded to be allowed to enter the university at Salamanca, even if this required the begging of alms to pay for my attendance. But my papa would never allow me to beg. Instead, and despite our meager resources, he arranged for me to be tutored by a brilliant teacher and by *Fray* Dominguez, a learned man and a graduate of Alcala. And you know, Diego," his father said, "I couldn't have received a better education.

165

"We used to meet at my teacher's home where he'd make us work in his garden, hoeing weeds, picking carrots. I used to eat as many carrots as I picked. You know how boys are. My basket was always empty. Then, filthy from our work in his fields, we'd meet in his *plazuela* and begin 'reading the book,' for we only had one book, Diego! We only had one book! It's hard to believe, Diego," his father went on with a laugh, "given that my teacher had almost nothing to work with, but he focused on the study of law and philosophy.

"His name was *Senor Estudiante*, or at least that's the name by which he was known, because he insisted that he was and would always remain, a student. Student or not, we used to call him *Senor Tapado*. He had this strange bulbous nose with little red veins that grew redder and wider when he became excited. And he was completely bald, except for two strands of long red hair which seemed to grow out of his left ear;" Pedro was now laughing uproariously. "He'd comb these over the top of his head to his right ear where they lay as though waiting for something to happen. We used to watch him in fascination, waiting for them to spring back to their original place, but before they had a chance to dry and leave their perch, he'd lick the palm of his hand and pat them down again! We'd laugh at him when he wasn't looking, Diego," his father said with a wide grin visible in the firelight, "but he was a brilliant man, Diego, a brilliant man!

"We only had this one ragged book, Maimon's *Guide to the Perplexed*. It didn't matter to *Senor Tapado*, though, because he used to say that 'a large library is apt to distract, rather than instruct, the learner.' Study was restricted to four thinkers, all from the Islamic center of Cordova: Seneca, Bishop Osio, Averroes, and Maimon, of course. 'Better to study a few well,' he used to say, 'than to wander at random over many.' We had to rely on him for the philosophy of Seneca, Osio, and Averroes, but we'd read Maimon over and over again, posing formal arguments both for and against a proposition: 'The king should expel all *Moriscos* from Spain,' or 'Farmers should be allowed to fence their fields,' or some such. We'd begin with a proposed solution and then argue its merits, yelling at each other and threatening to hit one another with our hoes. We were required to know as much about the other side's case as they did, and only facts and opinions were allowed as evidence, not our

166

opinions, at least not at the beginning. The only opinions allowed were those offered by our experts, Seneca, Osio, Averroes, and Maimon, judged by my teacher to be 'the finest pagan, the greatest Christian savant, the most brilliant Muslim, and the most outstanding Jew' of Spanish history. And just when we were happy and comfortable with our arguments, Diego, he'd make us switch sides. He made us learn to question and to debate, but mostly he taught us to think.

"I go back to this when I contemplate the people of these villages," he said, "and wonder if we understand their case well enough, understand what their villages allow them to claim in terms of planting fields, gathering areas, sacred places. I'm not sure we can know exactly, because we're of another culture, but I wonder what Maimon would say.

"My studies with *Fray* Dominguez were more traditional—theology and classic literature—and he prayed that some of us would go on to the priesthood. He used to tell my papa that I should be allowed to seek a more formal education, but I had a job to do.

"I worked with my papa in Carmena, Maqueda, Torijos and throughout the *meseta* selling our stitchings which decorated silk hangings, tablecloths, bonnets and skirts. It was at the wool fair at Medina del Campo that I met your mother's father, a *drapero* from Toledo. And it was your grandfather who offered me an opportunity to expand my horizons as a buyer of material for his looms. In the end, of course, I didn't follow his lead, choosing instead to work as a scribe, making copies of laws and writing for others. However, if I had it to do over again, Diego, perhaps I would have done things differently.

"You know, Diego," his father said, as he again poked at the fire with his boot, "if I have a major regret in leaving Spain as we did, it's that I was unable to provide you and your brothers with the kind of education I had. Except for me and Brother Rodriguez, there's been no one here who could give you that and I'm afraid I've been a poor teacher."

"How can you say that, Papa?" Diego asked. "You've been a great teacher. Not only did you teach me how to read, but everything I know, I learned from you."

"Yes, Diego," his father replied, as he placed more wood on the fire, "but what have I taught you besides how to read? My perceptions?

My prejudices? I may indeed have taught you a lot, but, undoubtedly, much of it will have to be unlearned."

Pedro continued like this, reminiscing about his life and the people in it, and speaking especially of his grandfather who had lived to be almost 90 years old. "He helped my papa and me build the walls of our corral," his father said, "and he could still fling a stone with a sling-shot and hit whatever he intended. He was nearly 70-years-old when I was born, Diego," his father added. "He was tall and very thin, and had white hair and a wonderful scent about him. I remember most the scent of him when I sat on his lap and played with his beard. The aroma was that of oak dust. He and your grandfather built our looms, you know," he said wistfully. "It's funny, Diego," he said. "I'd never identified the smell till now, but that's what it was. It was the scent of oak dust on his beard. He was a wonderful man, and, even now, I miss him. When he died, I saw my papa cry, and it scared me. I'd never seen my papa cry. On the other hand," he added with a laugh, "my mama used to cry for anything—and everything. My papa used to say that she could be rented out as a professional mourner, 'intoning funeral chants for the deceased of the village and crying on cue.' It's the truth, Diego. She'd cry when my papa killed a chicken! But here's something that I learned from my papa, and you from me, that you need to unlearn. Although my papa never said this to me, I think that I understood from him that men don't cry or show how they really feel. What a waste that is, Diego," his father said. "It's the strong emotions, love, anger, fear, and grief that separate us from the animals. Without them, we might as well be one of those little hummingbirds we saw— although who's to say that they don't have strong feelings? Don't be afraid to show what's in your heart, Diego. That's what makes a man a man."

* * *

As they sat in the darkness, with Diego pondering his father's words, his thoughts, like those of his father's, were also focused on Carmena despite his having little memory regarding their home there. The home which Diego recalled had been a two-roomed, white-washed, stuccoed dwelling roofed with red clay tiles. Only in exceptional circumstances in any part of Spain did a commoner's home consist of more than one room. Where the family had kept its clothes or on what they ate their Spartan meals,

168

he could not say; nor could he well remember the furniture that was composed of a roughly made table, some wooden benches, and a rope bed under which his parents had kept his *carriola*.[7] His most vivid memory was of the pair of chased silver spurs—so out of place in that simple home. They had lain in a niche beside their hearth, a place of honor that in most homes would have been occupied by a statue of the Virgin Mary. Diego also remembered days of playing in the sun and nights of falling asleep while watching the burning embers of a brushwood fire that burned in their hearth. His memories, incomplete and fragmented as they were, were of an idyllic existence. One night, though, he was awakened in his bedroom by the sound of metal against stone ringing in the darkness.

There, in the soft glow of a small earthenware lamp, with its gray smoke curling toward the ceiling, Diego had seen his father, with his head lowered and his body bent double, working in a corner of his room. His father, who had removed the coarse rush mats and several flags from the cold stone floor, was digging a small hole in the hard-packed earth. Diego remembered the scent of the cool earth as his father dug, a tang he associated with the earthworms they had obtained as a treat for their hens.

When his father had finished digging, he had put down his shovel and moved to the table in the other room on which numerous items lay in disarray. Diego had watched as his father had carefully placed several scrolls and parchments into a large clay jar. To these, he had added what appeared to be amulets and other objects too numerous to mention, but what had caught Diego's eye were the spurs. They had been removed from their place of honor and rested now among the seeds and stones on the roughhewn table. Diego had watched as his father took a lone spur, held the cold metal to his face and then wrapped it in a cloth that he had made waterproof by treatment with oil. Placing this last small bundle in the jar, he had sealed the vessel with clay and a stone lid and buried it.

Pedro had next placed the second spur within a leather pouch, and then the pouch, along with a number of other items including their house key, within a leather pack. After that, through eyes heavy with sleep, Diego had watched as his father began to write in one of his journals. As he watched, Diego dozed again. These events had held no significance for him at that time.

Although the burial of the water jar would be forever embedded in Diego's mind, he had never mentioned it to his father, nor had his father spoken of it to him. Now, however, he recalled this event and finally understood the motivation for this previously inexplicable behavior with his father's telling of the story. His father had been planning to leave the home of his birth, the home which was a symbol of continuity and family identity. It had seemed essential to leave something of himself behind, something hidden, perhaps, and known only to himself, but something that would forever remain in the house, in his dreams, and in his memory.

* * *

It was during their second night at the pueblo, with the sounds of a coot echoing in the darkness, that Diego told his father about his long-harbored fear that it was he who had been responsible for Ana's death. His father, of course, assured him that he had not been. This helped a little, but it did not completely dispel the continuing anguish he felt over this tragedy. It was a great relief, though, to unburden himself of this secret, and to share it with his father whom he trusted to a greater degree than anyone else.

Diego and his father also spoke of lost love and of Diego's propensity to shrink in the presence of women. His father assured him that he came by this naturally, that he, too, had suffered a similar affliction. "It's a fear, Diego," he said, "a fear that we won't match up, or that somehow we'll fail. I don't know where it comes from, but I've got it, too. I didn't marry your mama until I was 32, but look at the prize I got! Remember, Diego, to everything, there's a season," he said, paraphrasing Ecclesiastes. "A time to plant and a time to pluck what's planted, a time to embrace and a time to refrain from embracing. Life is yet young. Your time to embrace will come. You'll see. You're still a young man."

While waiting for Pablo de Aguilar and his men to inventory thoroughly the contents of the pueblo, and to determine the condition, number, and location of the Pueblos'* stores, Diego and his father had few responsibilities beyond those of attending to their *remuda*.[8] Periodically, they would remove the livery from those horses they kept

---

* The non-capitalized form 'pueblo,' is used for the architectural unit. The capitalized form, 'Pueblo,' is used for the tribe, for the village name, for an individual member of any Pueblo tribe, and for the culture characteristic of Pueblo tribes.

saddled and replace the horses with fresh mounts. They would then take the remaining horses out of the ruin and lead them down to the river where the herons, shovelers, mallards and pintails harvested the seeds and tubers of the moist soil plants. Here the horses could graze and drink.

Their stay at the pueblo provided them with new surroundings and experiences. The variegated stone wall against which they had established their camp was a remarkable affair, and they marveled at its construction. The stone wall appeared to be the remains of a line of walls running around three sides of the pueblo. These were approximately 467 feet in length as they paced it, and about 20 feet in height, resulting in 18,700 square feet of surface. Diego's father calculated that, on average, there were 50 pieces of blocks, slabs, and spalls within each square foot of the wall, making for over 1,000,000 pieces for the outer surface alone. The same was repeated for the opposite surface, and also for the interior and transverse lines of masonry. These millions of pieces had had to be quarried, dressed roughly to fit their places, carried to the site, and then carefully adapted to the specific spot in the wall where they were to be placed. In addition, there were massive timbers that had been cut and fitted into places in the wall, and then covered with stone. The details of the window and roof construction, and the plastering and making of ladders were new and exciting. It was all made even more incredible by the fact that almost nothing used in construction of the walls was available at the water's edge. Everything had to be brought from the distant bluffs that were composed of Cretaceous sandstone, gray and black shale, yellowish siltstone and limestone.

* * *

Sitting against the stone wall of the ancient pueblo, and conversing long into the timeless night, the Robledos spoke about New Mexico and of their prospects for the future. The land looked promising, they felt, especially here at the river. The reports given them by Juan de Vitoria Carvajal of forests and meadows in the high country intrigued them as well. They longed to be on their way and worried that men like Pablo de Aguilar would ruin it for them. Nonetheless, they were determined to hold their tongues and do as they were told, short of mistreating the

Indians. They were pleased to find the Indians cautious but friendly, and hoped to find land unoccupied by them where they could settle.

Diego's father spoke of his recurrent dream of 'a land of birds,' back-dropped, he said, by a luminous mountain with two distinct peaks. "We'll find a stream there, Diego," he said, "with hot springs and marshes and fish that'll swim into our hands. There'll be timbered canyons and grasslands as far as the eye can see. It'll be our river, Diego, with its rapids and pools, where we'll sit and dream of tomorrow," he continued as though lost in thought.

Diego looked at him—at this man he loved so much—and thought how little he demanded of the world. It was the austere things, like the petulant beauty of a spring storm that stirred his heart. *Please God*, he thought to himself as he looked at his father who sat against the stone wall, *he's sacrificed so much to make this possible for us. He deserves his 'land of birds.' Let him have it!*

It continued like this for most of the two days, perhaps because for the first time in their lives, the Robledos had no pressing tasks. On their second night at the pueblo, in the embered dark of the late evening, father and son arranged themselves in their bedding against the stone wall. Twenty-seven-year-old Diego lay there watching light puffs of smoke and an errant spark or two as these blew from the fire pit as the dark of the night totally enveloped them. Then, under one of the most glorious starlit skies he had ever seen, Diego said, seeming to have no control over the words escaping his lips, "I love you, Papa." To this his father replied in words which Diego had never heard, but which he knew in his heart, "I love you, too, Diego."

And so it went through the seven days during which the reconnaissance party advanced to the first pueblo in New Mexico, entered it against the orders given by Onate, and retraced its steps southward only to be met by the caravan a few days below the pueblo. When Onate learned what Aguilar had done he was so angered that he demanded that Aguilar be executed by garrote for his disobedience. He had put the 500 settlers at peril! The execution would have been carried out if it had not been for the intervention of some of his staff who pleaded for leniency. He relented and let the rooster live even though he knew it to have the pip. However, the secretions and scales he had observed made him believe that he would probably live to regret it.

A Time to Die

The morning of 20 May 1598 began as had each one in the two months since they had crossed the Conchos River. At first light, Pedro Robledo left his family and their ox-carts and moved to the head of the march where he retrieved Onate's standard from outside the captain-general's field tent. Soon, perhaps as soon as tomorrow, he would be leaving with Onate and a smaller group of soldiers. They were going to ease the fears of the Pueblos (now that Aguilar had told them they were there), to acquire grain, and continue on to review the site of their first settlement, the one suggested to Onate by Juan de Vitoria Carvajal. As he rode his horse up the wide high valley, the caravan lurched into motion behind him.

Across the rolling hills that border the valley, the caravan moved northward. There is, at this place, a relatively broad gap between the Caballo Mountains to the north and the San Andres Mountains to the southeast. This is the southern end of an area which would later become known as the *Journada del Muerto* (the Dead Man's March). As the vanguard neared the head of this valley, Pedro Robledo, who was riding on this occasion with his son-in-law Bartolome Romero, asked Bartolome if he would, "just for a moment," hold the standard which he had been resting upon the arch of his boot. Bartolome, of course, complied. "Is there something wrong, *don* Pedro?" he asked as he dismounted to take the standard from the older gentleman. Pedro said that he had had a piercing pain in his abdomen and in his back for some time, but it was now most severe. He then clutched his chest and began to lose his grip on his horse. Bartolome caught him as he fell and placed him on the ground where he lay moaning and half-conscious. Romero carefully removed Pedro's leather jacket but did not remove the old man's boots, one of which had a single spur attached, the second apparently lost, Bartolome thought. While Pedro's horse, Babieca, looked at Pedro with big, sad eyes, nuzzling him, and urging him to rise, Pedro's son-in-law sent back for a priest. Diego rode up with the cleric, but waved him off. He refused to believe his father was dying and in need of the last sacraments. Hurriedly, as the Robledo carts rumbled into the area where he lay, they erected a small tent made from a white canvas taken from one of their carts. Still conscious but barely able to speak, Pedro lay in the tent they had constructed for him. The entire caravan was stopped now amid the bellowing of cattle, the bawling of calves, and the sound of hoofs.

Catalina held him on her lap smoothing back the hair from his brow, kissing his fingers as she held his hand to her lips. His shallow breathing became more labored, but he was vaguely conscious of a gentle hand under his head. He lay though the day hours of Terce, Sext, and None with the family unable to do anything to ease his suffering. Through the evening hours, as his condition worsened, his family remained at his side. But in the final hour of his agony, Catalina asked to be left alone with him, for even if he could not respond to her, she felt he would be aware of her presence.

Lying with him within their open canvas, she held him on his side facing the east wall of the tent, as she knew he would want.[9] Pedro repeated, with pathetic monotony, one solitary complete phrase in which only one word—*Adonai*—could be understood. Brother Rodriguez, with the remaining members of the family kept vigil just outside the tent.

As night came on Pedro's breathing became shallower and shallower, less and less frequent. And sometime around the canonical hour of Compline, on 20 May 1598, the 60-year-old Pedro Robledo died. The end came so gently that Catalina was not aware of the exact moment. Brother Rodriguez who had entered the tent with Diego said finally, "Pedro has left us *dona* Catalina. He's gone."

Catalina held Pedro's head against her chest, kissed his cold forehead and said "*Dios. Dios. Dios!*" several times before crying. Then she wept in a manner which was painful to endure.

* * *

Catalina had begged Pedro not to die and leave her there by herself in the wilderness, for although her children would care for her in homes they were yet to establish, she felt, she was truly alone. She later refused

174

to leave his burial site and sitting on her old leather cushion, demanded to be left where she was.

* * *

"How many men will it take to guarantee them safe passage?" asked *don* Juan regarding Diego's request that he and his brothers be allowed to return with their mother to Valladolid in Michoacan. Their plan, as presented by Diego, was to return to their former home where Francisco had been born some 18 years before. Here, they would settle their mother among friends, and then, with additional soldiers as required to fulfill Onate's contract, rejoin the colonists before the end of the year.

A Time to Speak

The officers whom Onate consulted begged him not to allow anyone to leave the expedition. "In the interest of God's service and His Majesty's," they said, "anyone asking for such permission must be considered by military law to have earned the death penalty as a deserter from his captain and his flag." The more so, they added, because they were surrounded by many pueblos inhabited by a potentially hostile people.

"It would take a squad—at least a squad, *don* Juan—to see them safely to the Conchos," answered Captain Gaspar Perez de Villagra. "From there, perhaps, they could go on their own."

"Yes, we could do this, *Tio*," chimed in Juan de Zaldivar, "but why would we? We can't guarantee them safe passage, and, more importantly, we can't afford to lose them or the men it would take to accomplish this. It would be folly. And it would give bad example to the others."

"He's right, of course, *don* Juan," added Juan de Zaldivar's younger brother, Vicente. "Others will die and still others may be killed in establishing our colony. We can't break off, turn tail and run at the first instance. We must stick together!"

Thus, in the custom and etiquette of Spanish service, *don* Juan conferred with his officers, asking each in turn to give counsel regarding the Robledo request. Their unanimous decision to deny the Robledo request was as he knew it must be. The colonists had suffered their first tragedy. Other tragedies, perhaps many others, would follow. He hoped that through his leadership and the leadership of his nephews, Juan and Vicente de Zaldivar, among others, they would avoid disaster. However, he had no illusions. If they were to succeed—and they had to succeed for many had mortgaged all they had for the project—all of them, soldiers and colonists, had to make it work. They could not be deterred by the death of his standard bearer. The banner must be passed to another, and if he, too, should fall, to yet another. Disaster and bad luck, he knew, defeat vulnerable individuals but only make tough ones braver. There could be no turning back.

Therefore, Onate's decision, when rendered, was without the possibility of revocation. "She can't stay here," he stated, "and you can't go back. It's up to you to make her understand," he added as he mounted his horse after speaking to Diego, his brothers, and his brother-in-law, Bartolome Romero. "When we leave this *paraje*[10] tomorrow she must be with you." And with this he began to spur his horse but then quickly reined up, pausing for a moment as though lost in thought. "Tonight," he said, "tonight, pitch your tents so that *don* Pedro's burial place is within the enclosure. Use this as a pretext to move your mother's cushion. When you strike your tents tomorrow, I want your mother facing north." With this, he wheeled his horse and rode off to join his officers who awaited him at the edge of the clearing.

Then, as *don* Juan had asked, Diego, now the patriarch of the family, along with his brothers, Alonso, Pedro the younger, and Francisco, began to affix canvases to the wheels of their encircled carts so as to form a covered *plazuela* around a small open *placita*. They had positioned their carts so as to shield their burial arrangements from anyone who might be watching from the distant hills. They had in warm water washed their father's body thoroughly from head to foot, and, out of respect for him, had not allowed his face to look downward while they wrapped him in a burial shroud. This was handmade, of plain white linen, simple, but with fringes snipped into one edge of the garment, one fringe of which had been cut.

He was placed on a bed of intertwined reeds that his children had made for him in place of a bier. When these preparations were complete, a gold coin was placed in his mouth.[11] *Fray* Alonso Martinez, wearing a chasuble and other vestments of black, and using unbleached candles as required by Church law, sang the Requiem Mass, the opening words of the Introit hanging above the bed of reeds like flecks of dust in the sunlight. Then, with eulogies given by *don* Juan de Onate and Brother Joaquin Rodriguez, *don* Pedro's remains—attested to by Bartolome, and accompanied by Catalina's broken heart—were lowered into a shallow grave painfully dug into the floor of this ancient ocean.

What Juan de Onate said regarding *don* Pedro, whom he saw as representing the best in the colonists, was that he embodied ancient Spanish virtues. These were courage, faith, honor, and dignity, and the serenity which comes with having achieved a grand *seignior's* mastery of himself. These were qualities which were developed in answer to crushing deprivation, and which *don* Pedro had shared with many of his countrymen. He had worn them particularly well.

Brother Joaquin Rodriguez, in speaking for himself, and for the family, said that *don* Pedro was a dedicated husband and the most loving of parents who, till the moment of his passing, had shown the utmost concern for the well being of his family. As far as he was concerned, he said, there was little *don* Pedro could not do, and little he could not do better than everyone else. What he did not say was that worry had carved wrinkles on *don* Pedro's brow and that the troubles and disillusionments he had suffered on the frontier had shattered his strength and weakened his inherent capacity to overcome adversity. These, Brother Rodriguez felt, had killed him. He knew that the good name *don* Pedro had earned was worth more than great riches. What he also knew was that *don* Pedro had come to the New World to seek a new and better life for his family, and his tragedy was that he died never having known whether or not he had achieved it.

The burial had taken place within 24 hours of *don* Pedro's death, since it was considered a great dishonor to the dead to leave them unburied any longer. That night they raised a fire on the grave's fresh earth, and the next day, before leaving the campsite, they doused the fire and scattered its ashes and remaining embers with the hooves of their beasts so as to mask the location of the burial. This was done to keep potential grave robbers from opening the gravesite to obtain its funerary objects.

The family did not sleep that night, nor did they eat, although some in the camp brought them hardboiled eggs and every variety of food and drink in baskets of willow twigs.

"You must eat, *dona* Catalina," they said. "You must eat to keep your strength. *Don* Pedro would want you to."

"We cannot have you getting sick, *dona* Catalina," they said. "We need you and all your family to be with us."

Their coaxing was to no avail.

A Time to Mourn

Everyone had remained near the gravesite until the body was fully covered, and many stayed with the family until the attendant ceremony was completed. *Fray* Martinez and Brother Rodriguez offered prayers. The family held vigil through the day, as the blazing sun moved across the heavens toward the day's conclusion, finally illuminating the Dona Ana Peaks to the east while darkening the huge sedimentary bluffs to the west. Throughout the second night, friends made during the nearly four months on the trail attempted to help the Robledos accept the reality of *don* Pedro's death.

The day came haltingly on 22 May, a false dawn long preceding the morning's real light. When the sun did tip the horizon, its flat light caused the pristine atmosphere to scatter its blue and green rays resulting in the image of a bright red disk. Some of the colonists took this as a bad omen, for they knew that a red sky in the morning held portents of bad things to come.

* * *

"*Don* Juan!" shouted Onate's chief page, *Sargento* Hernan Martin Serrano the elder with a salute like that of a flourish with a foil. "They ask if you can join them at the Robledo campsite."

Juan de Onate, dressed in his *cuero* and double-soled boots of cordovan leather, sat on his horse among his point men as the caravan rumbled past. Sensing the general temperament of the grieving widow, he had anticipated the request he now received.

"Tell them that when the train has passed their *paraje*, I'll be there," he said. And then, with a swaggerous wave of his gloved hand, he added, "Tell them to be patient."

Thus, as the remaining large flocks of sheep passed the Robledo campsite, *don* Juan, riding now with Juan de Vitoria Carvajal, appeared from behind the billowing cloud of dust that trailed the train like a dusky shadow. The two men, their leather jackets flapping as they dismounted a short distance from the waiting party, began silently and unhurriedly to remove the war saddle from Onate's bay. While Vitoria Carvajal held the reins of their two beautiful mounts, Onate, supporting his saddle on his shoulder, began to walk toward the group. Once there, he placed his saddle on the ground next to Diego's mother. Except for brief words of condolence, little else was exchanged. After a brief silence, and in words hardly above a whisper, Onate said to the Robledo family, "Let me meet privately with your mother."

While the family waited, they busied themselves with the tasks of adjusting the straps of this pack and tightening the ropes of that one. Occasionally, one of them would glance at the two principals who sat beside one another in silence. Initially silent, *don* Juan and *dona* Catalina appeared to be contemplating the ground in front of them, the groups of stray sheep, and the caravan as it receded in the distance. Now and then, a member of the family who worked at the fringe of this encounter could see that their captain was now speaking, although what he was saying, no one could say. *Don* Juan knew, they suspected, that *dona* Catalina did not trust him and questioned his ability as their leader. She likened him to Pedro Carbonero, a legendary figure who had led his men into the land of the Moors where all had perished.

When Vitoria Carvajal later asked what they had spoken about, *don* Juan said, "I spoke of *don* Pedro, Catalina's children, and her grandchildren, and great-grandchildren yet to come. I spoke of new lands, and of villages, towns, peaks, and mountains that would bear their names. But mostly, I spoke of honor and duty, for in this we must all subject our own desires to the good of the kingdom."

In the end, *don* Juan and *dona* Catalina, in gestures of submission, each respectfully kissed the royal documents that Onate took from the panniers on his horse. Then, in turn, they placed these over their heads to indicate that the king's commands were above them, and that they accepted his authority. Next, *don* Juan and Vitoria Carvajal walked about the campsite, selecting stones with which to build a conical mound, as a decoy, some distance from the actual burial site. Finally, *don* Juan gave *dona* Catalina a fossilized stone containing the imprints of life of an earlier time, keeping a second for himself. They placed these atop the actual burial site. Then, with the leather cushion placed in one of their carts, and *dona* Catalina riding beside Lucia, the Robledo/Romero clan began to move forward. They would catch the rear guard before noon.

* * *

Don Juan was later to admit to Gaspar Perez de Villagra, that despite his respect for *dona* Catalina, he would have placed her in irons had this been required to ensure her compliance. For success, Onate and Perez de Villagra both knew, required a strong arm, and mighty courage. He would do whatever was required (as later events would demonstrate) to keep his colony intact. In the settling of New Mexico, as in anything else of value, he felt, the ends justified the means.

The Diary

On the morning of 22 May, Onate left his encampment and took the Robledo brothers with him. Although this seems callous and incredibly insensitive, the assignment was probably made to avoid the possibility that they would steal away in the night. This would only have required that he send someone to arrest them. Therefore, leaving them no time to contemplate their loss, he assigned them to the task of accompanying him to the North Country.

With his mother's parting words still fresh in his mind—that he and his brothers were not to eat any meat for six days and were to observe a fast on the seventh—Diego left his mother in the care of Bartolome. After packing his mother's cushion within his parents' cart, he hurried to catch up to Alonso, Pedro and Francisco who were riding up to the head of the caravan. They were to join a large party of approximately 60 individuals who were leaving immediately to establish a base of operations on the upper Rio Grande. In this group, in addition to the Robledos, were Juan and Vicente de Zaldivar, *Fray* Alonso Martinez, *Fray* Cristobal de Salazar, and an eight-year-old lieutenant, Cristobal de Onate, who was accompanying his father. Also with the group was Antonio de Godoy who was the diarist for the expedition.

As the vanguard moved up the valley, Diego took note of the enormous 5,876-foot bluff composed of sedimentary rocks. It was the greater and more southerly of two that lay across the river from his father's burial site. Antonio de Godoy also observed the Robledo bluff, austere, darkly gray, remote and silent, and made a mental note to put the *paraje de Robledo*, the Robledo campsite, on the map he was making.

In addition to the customary *harquebus* that Godoy carried and the armor that he wore, he had a plain paintbrush and paint, the tools of a mapmaker. He was to fill the entire map with information about New Mexico regarding rivers and streams, mountain peaks and ranges, and even geologic formations that marked the possible location of ore. Most important among his practical recordings were the observations he was to make regarding the flora and fauna, for he had been instructed to couch them in terms that would sell New Mexico.

The area through which the party rode, although far from bleak, is a desert somewhat less than 3,000 feet above sea level. The grass-covered valley was exceedingly hot this May, but plants impervious to the heat grew in profusion. The area of approximately 19,500 square miles is vast with mesquite, creosote, valley cottonwood, and black grama grass growing in abundance. Also present, were the acacia, agave, algerita and anemone that the settlers would learn to use for medicinal and household purposes. The acacia, a small tree or shrub, would be used as an infused tea for diarrhea, dysentery and for stopping superficial bleeding. The agave, with its spiny-edged leaves and flowering stalk, would be found useful as a remedy for indigestion, gassy fermentation, chronic constipation, gas pain, colic, and when grated into a bowl, as a decent shampoo. They would find many uses for the algerita including its use as an anti-microbial for the skin and intestinal tract, while the anemone would be used by persons afflicted with insomnia, nervousness, and 'noxious night vapors.'

As they rode up the rift valley, which glinted and rippled in the sunlight, the members of the expedition saw the western diamond-backed rattlesnake, the armadillo, the pronghorn,[1] the kangaroo rat, and hundreds of species of birds. Among the birds were red-faced warblers, sparrows, hummingbirds, and even the elegant trogon. The valley presents a route for millions of migratory birds traveling from winter food to their northern breeding grounds. What Godoy said regarding the area was that sheep and goats would find it a paradise and that it was a land made for erect shepherds and not for stooping peasant-tillers of the soil.

As Godoy rode along one of the trails[2] intent on examining his surroundings, a covey of quail suddenly exploded from a sage thicket causing his horse to bolt and him to fall in a heap of mangled armor. The accident provided amusement for the rest of the party, and he needed help to remount his horse. He was not, however, the only one to have a horse scared out from under him. Here and there, a jackrabbit would bound from a bush causing other riders to be thrown from their saddles.

Most common, was the roadrunner or chaparral. This swift-footed bird raced up the Indian path they followed as they made their way north. A large, flightless bird, nearly two feet in length, it has long legs with two toes in front and two in back. Although this cuckoo was forever out of reach and seemed to be mocking the members of the exploratory party, the settlers eventually adopted this snake killer as somehow their own.

Heard, but never seen, was the coyote, whose "yap, yap, yap" and plaintive wail filled the night air. A shaggy-haired creature with a long bushy tail, pointed ears, and a beautiful face, it is an excellent hunter, with acute senses of hearing, vision, and smell. The colonists would come to fear and to hate it. If they did not see the coyote, however, the jackrabbits, or hares, they found along the trail, were a common sight and created a great deal of interest. These rabbits would hide beneath a shady shrub or a clump of grass. Then, suddenly, they would explode from their hiding places racing in noiseless flights, from the strange creatures coming up the trail. Meetings with a hare, even when hounds were not chasing it, were seen as bad omen. Therefore, the members of the exploratory party looked for a wolf, the sight of which was considered a good omen, to counter this.

More elusive, but also ever-present, at least at the beginning, was the Gila monster, a close cousin to a related creature the Spaniards had seen in New Spain. Bony, black and beaded (although some were brown, orange or salmon in color), it was a giant lizard, enormous and deadly. With a stout body, a broad blunt head, and a stumpy tail, it roamed at night, and the colonists were ever watchful. Although the colonists were cautious, they had little to fear from the giant lizard. While this monster was a meat eater, its food was birds, reptile eggs, and small animals. Godoy was delighted with this, for these were the monsters of which legends were made.

Ojo del Perrillo

Leaving interim Lieutenant-Governor and Captain General Francisco de Sosa Penalosa in charge of the main body of the expedition, Onate and the exploratory party of 60 continued northward, across a scrubby, waterless tract. A short distance above the Robledo burial site, the river began to veer more and more to the west, with countless deep arroyos, and great gravel hills on the west side of the river. On the opposite side of the river, bare ranges of steep mountains close to the east bank made travel by cart there impossible. Thus, as he had done much further south, Onate and his party headed directly north, leaving the river and its abundant water supply far behind them.

The wide, high valley here, part of the Rio Grande Rift, was once the course of the Rio Grande River. During late Tertiary times, the river flowed almost straight south through the *Jornada*. As fault movement deepened the great river's present valley, the stream left the *Journada del Muerto*, leaving it a closed valley with bleak little washes, scant water, and no through drainage to the Rio Grande.

The next five days would be hell. Although the exploratory party carried water with them, it was not sufficient for the riders and their beasts, and all fared badly due to thirst. At each campsite, horsemen, driving loose horses ahead of them, would be sent into the hills in the hopes of finding water and forage. The riders scoured the countryside, but often returned with parched throats not having found any.

On one occasion, after the colonists had traveled a day and a night without water, a small dog with muddy paws and hind feet appeared at their camp. The dog, which may have strayed from an Indian hunting party, led them back to a water hole which otherwise would have escaped their notice. The spot, the *Ojo del Perrillo* (Little Dog's Spring), would be named for this incident. Several days later after successfully traversing the *Jornada del Muerto*, and many miles ahead of the caravan that was following them, the vanguard was back at the river.

The Pueblos

Diego had been here before. The Spaniards were back at Qualacu, where Diego had spent those two wonderful days with his father. Qualacu was the first of a series of Indian pueblos, or villages, largely divided by language groups, which the expeditionary force was to find. They extended for 250 miles along the Rio Grande River, and into the mountains, to the east and west of the river. In contrast to New Spain where there had been more than 20 Indian languages found, New Mexico provided only eight, belonging to four language families. In a cross-shaped area, following the drainage of the upper Rio Grande, and reaching out laterally to eastern and western settlements, were the Piro, Tiwa, Tewa, Towa, Tano, and Keres Indian groups. In addition, two final groups would emerge. These were the Zuni and Hopi, who were far removed from the Rio Grande Valley, and unrelated to the rest of the Pueblo Indians.

At the moment, the expeditionary force had to deal effectively with the Qualacu, the most southerly pueblo of the Piro Indians. They lived on the east bank of the Rio Grande, 24 miles south of present-day Socorro, and these Indians, whose corn Pablo de Aguilar had inventoried, eyed them with suspicion.

* * *

In the sky overhead, a red-tailed hawk glided down along the river as the expeditionary force neared the village. Pedro Robledo the younger, sitting

184

regally atop his father's horse, was there in full regalia. As Babieca pranced about, asking to be given his head, Pedro II, in ancient armor, held him in check awaiting his orders.

The armor which Pedro wore, and which his father had helped him select from among Onate's stores, was old and Pedro loved it. His coat of mail, *cuisses*, and helmet, which he had found in a mound of *cabacete*, had been part of a set of ancient armor that Onate had acquired throughout Spain. His headgear, a *barbuta*, was a flat-type Spanish military archer's helmet that had been fashioned in Europe a century before Onate brought his colony into New Mexico. Onate purchased it with a collection of secondhand armor. These pieces had been skillfully crafted by the fingers of European artists and had been ordered in large lots for the volunteer soldier-settlers who lacked some or all of their own required equipment. The headpiece was an open-faced shoulder-length helmet. It was made of one piece and had a T-shaped face opening. It was fashioned to fit well-down over Pedro's head to protect his ears, neck, and eyes, with a small slit in front to allow him frontal vision. Towards the rear of the piece, the metal plate continued beyond the nape of the neck and over his collar. This archer's helmet which Pedro II had so proudly modeled for his father, and which he likened to that of the helmet of the Moorish king, Mambrino, had been chosen by Pedro and was now his own.

Diego had inherited Babieca by virtue of his birth order, but he had given him to Pedro who loved him and who associated him with their father. Barring any objection from his brothers, Diego wanted Pedro, who was his father's namesake, to have this much beloved animal. Diego had kept for himself his father's *harquebus*, a worn, firing piece now almost 20-years-old. Although Diego had a newer, and certainly more reliable firearm, this one, repaired for his father by a Flemish soldier with the expedition, was precious to him. The ivory of its gunstock, which had been broken and lost, had been replaced with a piece of animal bone carved to depict a walled medieval city. He loved this old firing piece, so reminiscent of his father, and was taking it to his new home.

With no objections from his brothers regarding Babieca, Pedro II, with his horse and his archer's helmet, waited in the meadow at Qualacu for Onate's orders. When the order was given, however, it was not a call to arms, but rather a request that his people set up housekeeping. The advance party, containing women, children, and supply carts, in addition to its men, was told to set up their tents. The purpose of this move was not only to let the Qualacu know that they were there for an extended stay, but also to demonstrate silently that they intended no harm. The Qualacu, having abandoned their village at the approach of the Spaniards, now watched these proceedings from a distance. Seeing that the Spaniards, though helmeted and armed, showed no hostility toward them—and were even sending them gifts—they reconsidered fleeing and returned to their village. Cautious and ever watchful, the Qualacu began to confer with the newcomers. The two groups got along well, and the Spaniards determined to stay for an extended period.

Fray Alonso Martinez suffered from the dual ills, gout and fever. The colonists attributed these afflictions to a discharge of drops of humors. Martinez was in considerable pain in the joints of his hands and feet, especially in the big toe of his right foot. The skin of this toe was tense, hot, shiny, and dusky red, and the members of the expeditionary force did not know what to do. The *yerbero*, or herb vendor, among them was first asked to bring to the sick tent the cache of his *boticario*: his metal mortar, dried plants, borage water, laxative pills, rose water, and even the oil of Hypericum which was used to cure all sorts of maladies. He had medicines for low blood pressure, bad circulation, toothache, nerves, bad memory, bad liver, and dozens of other ailments. He was also able, it was said, to create a 'brew of blood, herbs, magic elements, and bull testicles' such as that fed to Isabella's Fernando by Germain de Foix to cure infertility.

Unfortunately, the *yerbero* had nothing for gout, but perhaps the medicine for bad circulation would do. The *padre's* assistant was asked to make a tea of dried leaves and to render a prayer or two to St. Andrew, the perceived healer of the gout. *Fray* Martinez, with a raging fever and an agonizing headache, was told to drink the tea twice a day, in the morning and before retiring. The expedition, meanwhile, was to stay put until he was able to travel.

In the evening *Fray* Martinez continued to experience excruciating pain which he described as "throbbing and crushing." Eventually, he became delirious. They tried rose honey, violet, coriander, rose and

186

pomegranate syrups, then processed citrus and apple paste for laxative pills. Martinez responded with tachycardia, chills, and an increased fever. They next tried the ointments: mercurial, yellow, Egyptian, white, and Apostolorum which they rubbed on his extremely tender extremities. These did no good, serving only further to punish the poor father who lay moaning in his tent. Finally, in desperation, he was bled with the conviction that bloodletting would decrease the fever.

On Sunday evening, the *yerbero* applied a poultice of flour to the *padre's* foot, and he was required to remain with one foot raised above the level of his head which was extremely painful to him. His fever increased, and he appeared to be deteriorating.

On Monday evening, the good father continued in the grip of great pain and a high fever. He was restive and drifting mentally, and it was decided that he must be 'cupped.' This agonizing procedure was a method of bleeding. An incision was made in the back of his hand over which was put a glass cup, the interior of which had been heated with a firebrand taken from their watch fire. As the beaker cooled, a vacuum was produced and blood drawn out. *Fray* Martinez was cupped everywhere including his foot. The cupping seemed to accomplish little, but they went on with it, increasing the number of cups used in the procedure.

Some suggested that various members of the camp (especially *Fray* Salazar who had insisted on the cupping) form a brigade of firewalkers as a demonstration to God of their piety and need for his assistance. They would make a huge bonfire, the coals of which would then be raked down. Barefoot men would then cross, one by one, each carrying another person on his back as they do at San Pedro Manrique on Midsummer's Eve. Since, this ritual was a preliminary to the feast of San Juan, which was to occur on 24 June, it was decided that they would have to find another way to demonstrate their faith.

It continued like this, on and on, with the good father in agony throughout the ordeal. The tea may have helped a little, perhaps assisted by additional syrups and purges, but it was probably the results of a salubrious diet [now devoid of fish and red beef], and the repositioning of the toe strap on the father's heavy sandal that helped the most. With *Fray* Martinez in great pain and unable to ride a horse or even survive the swinging of a litter, the members of the expeditionary force waited.

Probably, during all of this, the Qualacu just hoped the Spaniards would go. They had seen men such as these eight years before, as well as those who had been there with Pablo de Aguilar. The nearly decade old sighting was of the Castano de Sosa colonists, who, on their expulsion from New Mexico, had passed this pueblo on their way south. The Castano colonists had stayed for awhile, and then they had gone. Perhaps these bearded men and their women and children would do the same.

The Qualacu may have even considered hastening the colonists' departure by attacking them. How many of them were there? Not many. Perhaps they could overpower them, these men and their beasts. But no, they had been told there were more of them to the south. Best to make friends of them and to bide their time. And so the Qualacu shared what little they had with these newcomers who were camped among the quail in the fields opposite their pueblo, and waited.

Backtracking

"God, what are they arguing about now?" he asked of the messenger who had come up the trail.

"I don't know, *don* Juan," the courier replied, "but *don* Francisco asks that you come and settle the disturbance."

The request Onate received truly angered him. It wasn't as though he was being asked to ride to an adjoining *finca*, or ranch, for a welcome respite. He was being asked to backtrack across a vast wilderness, and for what? Because Sosa Penalosa could not keep these damned independent colonists in check. Onate knew these people. They were his own. Some would want to go here, and some would want to go there. Some would judge this to be the best route, while others would judge the best route to be elsewhere. All of them would be running around like chickens with their heads wrung off, scurrying here and scurrying there with no ability to see the prize when they arrived. They were great people, these Spaniards. They had already demonstrated examples of bravery and endurance and would make wonderful colonists. They were quarrelsome and anything but docile. It had been important to leave the tambourine to one who knew how to play it, and, Onate feared, he had chosen the wrong man to replace his nephew, Juan Guerra de Resa, as *Tenient Adelantado*. It seemed that, whatever his other exceptional qualities, Sosa Penalosa could not hold the colonists in check. *Don* Juan would have to go back.

Taking a small group of soldiers and a modest cache of corn, which he knew his colonists would need, Juan de Onate began to ride south. With him was Diego Robledo. He had sought this assignment for the opportunity to visit with his mother whom he and his brothers had so hastily left behind. When Diego first saw his mother, she was sitting on her old cushion next to Lucia watching Lucia's children at play. Even though he could not see her face, for Lucia and his mother were seated with their backs towards him, he was shocked at her appearance. The points of her sagging shoulders were visible through the thin clothing she wore, and she appeared spare and wan.

Rather than the straw of summer, which would have seemed more appropriate in the intense heat, she had on his father's stained and battered felt hat, the one he had worn in his garden. It served somewhat to mask the appearance of her graying auburn hair, now dull and lifeless, but gave her an odd appearance, perhaps that of an itinerant peddler. He looked at her as she reclined against the wheel of their cart. Then, as if someone had whispered his presence in her ear, she turned, and, squinting into the glare, looked directly at him. The look at first appeared to be one of non-recognition; what he could not have known was that, just for a moment, he had appeared to his mother as his deceased parent. Although at five feet, eight inches, he was slightly taller than his father had been, and with eyes of a darker blue, his mother had recently told him that he looked remarkably like his father when she had first met him. Catalina's hesitation here startled Diego, for in her look, he discerned that both he and his mother had changed remarkably.

"*Ijiko, ijiko*—my child, my child," she cried, her eyes filling with tears, "I was afraid something had happened to you."

She asked about his brothers, and whether they were well. But mostly she held Diego's face in the palms of her hands as though seeking something in his eyes. Diego, too, cried and held his mother, something he had never done before. It seemed his father's death had opened him up, and the feelings he was holding were overwhelming.

Diego spent the better part of the next three days with the caravan. When not riding with Bartolome or tending to the cattle, he sat with his mother and with the rest of his family, attending to their camp and to their carts. He could not speak of his father, so great was the pain, nor could he be with the others when they spoke of him, for, Diego sensed that 'if the ears do not hear, the heart will not break.' But grief is the price one pays for love. And Diego's only escape was through denial, not denial that his father had died, for this was too painfully evident, but denial in terms of his inability and unwillingness to speak of him. Moreover, his dreams about his father were most disturbing. Although the dreams did not start immediately after Pedro's death, they soon began to fill each fitful night. They began with brief glimpses of his father in some rather innocuous situation, but later began to take on a different and more disturbing character. Most of these dreams had the same theme. In them, his father was fragile and ill, and, although others in the family seemed unaware of this, his death appeared imminent. In these dreams, Diego feared that only he could prevent his father's death, yet he was helpless to intervene.

* * *

One of Diego's most intriguing dreams appeared to be a continuation of a conversation he and his father had had at the pueblo of Qualacu. In this dream, his father appeared to be giving him some new and important information. When they had been at the pueblo, the Robledos had seen what might have been thousands of minute hummingbirds of the *Rupus* species. They were following the change of seasons in their migration north from Mexico to Canada and Alaska. Diego's father had remarked that these tiny, hovering birds with their bright, iridescent colors required constant access to flowers to fuel their prodigious metabolism. "The young," he had in life told Diego, "do not learn this from their parents. They anticipate the change of season and follow the plants."

The dream, which appeared to take up where the real discussion left off, provided additional information which Diego could only have received from his father. He and his father were walking along a red-toned hillside resplendent with waist-high tubular blossoms that lacked scent. Fuchsias alone appeared to be the powerful magnet, but there were, also, in a blaze of red and golden flowers, nasturtiums and lobelia, petunias and nicotianas, nemesias, salvias and geraniums that the Lord seemed to have chosen with only the birds in mind. As Pedro and Diego watched these small birds flitting from flower to flower, his father again remarked that they did not have extensive food reserves and had to feed very actively through most of the daylight hours.

"They have so little reserve," his father said, "that they lose heat overnight and must rely on the warmth of the sun to revive them. However, one of these, the ruby-throated hummingbird, flies more than 1,000 kilometers (620 miles) across the gulf with no more reserve than it would require for a warm afternoon."

"How do they do that, Papa?" Diego had asked with the wonder similar to that of a small child learning something new from his father.

"It's a mystery," his father had answered, "but someday you'll know."

* * *

Slowly, with the passage of time, Diego was again able to speak of his father, and it was then, too, that the dreams began to diminish, and finally to disappear.

By the 12th of June it was time for Juan de Onate and his escort to again leave the caravan and head north.

Antecedents

The Onate colonists did not arrive in New Mexico until 1598, but encounters between earlier explorers and the Pueblo Indians affected their relationships with their Pueblo Indian neighbors. The Pueblos on the river had seen or heard of Nunez Cabeza de Vaca, Estevanico, Marcos de Niza, Vasquez de Coronado, Castano de Sosa and others who had come to their land looking for who knew what. The colonists, for their part, were put on guard by their experience with the Chichimecas, the Suaquis, and the Tehuecos of New Spain. The native people on the river had no particular reason to want the Spaniards there. The lowlands, valley and delta of this 'new' Mexico comprised but one percent of the total land area. The Indians possessed much of it. There was bound to be trouble.

Onate, of course, anticipated this. Moreover, he was the *adelantado*, or royal governor, and New Mexico, an area that extended in all directions without boundaries, was his kingdom. Onate's intentions were to be firm but fair, to be generous and benevolent, but also to do whatever was required to bring success to the venture.

Although Onate's intentions were positive, he was, perhaps, more than anything, yoked to his authority. He was ambitious, proud, headstrong and a bit arrogant, and, in times of difficulty, he came to epitomize some of the more negative traits so representative of his people. Although he could be kind, he could also be demanding, domineering, haughty, and as ruthless as the occasion demanded. And later, when dealing with traitors, he became a despot. Yet, manners change when honors come, and, although he had received little honor in his appointment as governor, he was still the 'lord of the march.' Rugged in appearance, with a long, handsome face, he had a rather prominent and slightly curved nose, and a moderately jutting chin. Tall, slim, and regally attired, he was an arresting figure. Of his acumen in military leadership there can be no doubt. The men who had served with him in the Chichimecan wars had spoken of his courage, his physical toughness, and his willingness to share danger and hardship with them. He was known for his readiness to perform whatever personal sacrifices were necessary to achieve success. In all of this, he was a good Christian gentleman, as straight as a spindle from Guadarrama. His religion and his strong convictions would serve him well in the many trials ahead.

* * *

Onate returned to Cualacu bearing gifts, not only for the Indians whose corn he needed, but also as provisions for the people of his vanguard. Two days later, and with *Fray* Alonso Martinez now able to travel, they again headed north.

* * *

As the members of the vanguard passed the day in travel, they skirted a number of garden plots far removed from Indian villages. Most of these fields were simple plains, the deltas of *arroyos* or rivulets, where ephemeral runoff from summer rains, was used for irrigation. These plots were interesting. They consisted of irregular fields of various sizes, around which were long, low banks of earth, with stone markers at various places. The earthen banks served to define the field and to contain runoff from the area's scanty rains. It was apparent, also, that vegetation, consisting of sagebrush, grass and weeds, both within and adjacent to a field, had been cleared, heaped into the middle of the ground, and burned. The ashes of the burned material had been worked into the soil as fertilizer. Some of these fields had been planted and harvested, but most lay fallow, their marking stones as lithic sentinels, awaiting another spring's planting. The Spaniards were to find these dry farms throughout the Pueblo land as they made their way up the river.

* * *

The vanguard continued to Teipana which they reached on 14 June. Onate was to rename this pueblo 'Socorro,' Spanish for 'help' or 'aid,' for the assistance this pueblo gave the colonists in provisions and for the information the people gave him about the north country. Above Teipana, things would prove to be more difficult.

* * *

One of the pieces of information which the exploratory group received at Teipana/Socorro, was about a group of pueblos which lay to the east of the mountains, accessible, they were told, though a pass which the Indians called 'Abo.' Therefore, when the advance party reached a small pueblo 20 miles north of Socorro, they halted. They were to spend a week there, holed up in some *kivas* and in tiny dark rooms at the pueblo, while the Zaldivars went through the pass of Abo to see what they could find.

The *kivas* in which Onate's colonists stayed were underground chambers which the Pueblo Indians entered through a hatchway in the roof. Men held councils in them and also used them for secret religious ceremonies. The Indians plastered the walls, and painted many with symbolic paintings in their sacred colors of black, green and yellow. These *kivas,* which were strongly reminiscent of the underground houses in which the Robledos had stayed while on their trek from Vera Cruz to the City of Mexico, had here evolved from 'pit houses.' The latter were bowl-like cavities in the earth, covered with poles and mud frames, which the Pueblos had lived in for centuries before the development of their more permanent villages which were constructed of stone and clay.

Diego and a number of the other men carefully examined one of these rooms. In addition to a stone bench that encircled the underground room, the *kiva* had recesses in its circular wall, a firebox, a fire screen, an airshaft, rows of loom anchors (twig loops imbedded in the *kiva* floor), and a small hole in the ground, the use of which the examiners could not determine. Overhead, there was a cribbed log roof, which appeared to be made of layer upon layer of pine logs or sections of logs. The logs rose dome-like from four basal pilasters to cover the circular ceremonial chamber.

The hole in the floor, the group was later to find, was a door to the underworld. It was the *sipapu,* an opening symbolic of the mythical entrance to the spirit world, which the Pueblo Indians associated with their creation and emergence from the earth's wombs or Underworld. Onate would later assign Godoy to learn more about this theology.

While the colonists waited in these *kivas*—lodged there for protection in case of an Indian attack—Juan and Vicente de Zaldivar, with a small group of soldiers, rode to the Salinas Valley to examine the pueblos of which they had been told. On the eastern side of the mountains, which Espejo had named the '*Sierra Morenas,*' the Zaldivars found the Tompiro Indians, a division of the Piro Indians, who lived in six stone villages widely separated from one another. The village of Abo, the Spaniards found, was endowed with an adequate stream, while *Las Humanas* possessed wells. Tabira and Tenabo, the other pueblos of the Tompiro, seemed to depend on rainwater storage.

Among the Tompiros, but unrelated to them, was an eastern branch of the Tiwa Indians. They were the Quarais, an Indian tribe occupying a lush, spring-fed meadow on the eastern slope of the mountains. This cottonwood-shadowed area lay just west of a forested range rich with game.

To the east of the Tompiro pueblos of Chilili and Tajique, lay saline lagoons. The salt from these lakes, which Onate was later to describe as "the universal article of traffic of all these [Indians]," was also described by him as the Indians' "regular food, for they even eat or suck it alone as we do sugar.[1] The Tompiros also used the salt as an article of trade with tribes on the eastern plains, and those far to the south in Chihuahua. Beyond the lagoons, lay desert country, inhabited by nomadic Indians, against whose incursions, the Tompiros defended.

The Zaldivar party, with Pedro and Francisco Robledo in attendance, returned from the plains with tales of the beauty of the land and stories of the enormous herd of bison they had seen in the far distance. They also related that the Indians they found lived on major trade routes. They were both generators for and agents of trade linking the Rio Grande Pueblos and the Plains' tribes. The Tompiros, the Zaldivars said, traded beans, cotton goods, *maize*, pinon nuts, squash, and especially salt for dried bison meat, flints, hides, and shells.

The large stone complexes the Zaldivar party had found—some containing hundreds of rooms—surrounded *kiva*-studded plazas. The Tompiros raised turkeys and hunted pronghorn, bison, deer, and rabbits. They wore pronghorn and deer hides, bison robes, breechcloths, and blankets of cotton and yucca. The Zaldivars were most impressed by their basket making, their weaving, and their excellent black-on-white ceramics. These pueblos, the Zaldivars said, presented many opportunities. "As soon as we're settled, *Tio*," Juan de Zaldivar said to his uncle, "you must visit these pueblos."

* * *

From the Piro pueblo where Onate's group had waited for the Zaldivar brothers (and which Onate renamed *Sevilleta*, because of its resemblance to Seville, Spain), the Spaniards moved quickly up the river. On 24 June they were at a pueblo which Onate named San Juan Bautista. Here the vanguard halted to celebrate the feast of Saint John the Baptist from whom Juan de Onate took his Christian name. They were again housed in *kivas*. To mark the feast day, they presented a sham battle for the Pueblo Indians. At this pueblo, Onate found an Indian who said repeatedly in Spanish, "Thursday, Friday, Saturday and Sunday." From the little else

Onate and his men could understand from this individual, Onate found that the villager had learned these words from Tomas and Cristobal, Indians from New Spain who lived among the Indians in the north country. Onate hoped he could find these potential interpreters, for only one among them could speak any of the Indian languages of this new Mexico. He was a lay brother named Juan de Dios who had learned Towa from an Indian taken back to Mexico by Antonio de Espejo.

From here, the vanguard came to a valley of 12 pueblos, some of which were abandoned. This was the valley which the Spaniards called the 'Province of Tiguex (Tiwa).' At Puaray, on the west bank of the river, a mile south of Kuaua, which means 'evergreen,' Vasquez de Coronado, had wintered from 1540 through 1542. In one of the *kivas* at Puaray, Onate found a mural which depicted the deaths of the Augustin Rodriguez party in 1582. Clearly represented, in addition to Rodriguez, were the Franciscan friar, Francisco Lopez, three boys, and a *mestizo* who had been left in the care of the Puaray Indians who had stoned them to death. Because the vanguard was badly outnumbered by Indian villagers, they said nothing regarding the mural and what it depicted. Departing from the pueblo as soon as they were able, they continued northward.

* * *

Leaving the Rio Grande at a Keres pueblo (which the Spaniards were to rename 'Santa Ana') and following the Jemez River northwestward, a scouting party rode through a broad, magnificent valley that wound gently upriver, and seemed to harbor two different worlds. On 29 June, this party, which was led by the Zaldivars and accompanied by *Fray* Salazar, was at the stone pueblo of Zia (from the native word *Tsia*). This was a Keresan-speaking group of Pueblo Indians who lived in a large pueblo, of eight plazas on the north side of the Jemez River, about 16 miles from the Rio Grande. The Indians' houses, which were whitewashed and painted, were better than those the Spaniards had previously seen. The Spaniards were much impressed by these Indians, who were more dexterous, the Spaniards felt, than any they had seen to this point. Above the pueblo of Zia, the Spaniards entered some of the most hauntingly beautiful land in their Northern Kingdom.

As the scouting party rode up the Jemez River, the piñon and juniper-studded lowlands gradually changed into uplands forested with spruce, aspen, and pine. Spectacular volcanic peaks soared at their northern margins. The western bluffs were the color of amber, while the cliffs to the east of the river were of red ochre, the most beautiful any of the scouting party had ever seen. Immediately beyond the red buttes, the column entered a beautiful canyon.

Somewhat upstream, and within the canyon, the soldiers found a spectacular natural formation, built up over the centuries by the deposit of calcium from a carbonate spring the soldiers found there. The river, flowing beneath a crystalline dome, was still adding to the formation. The dome appeared to be approximately 300 feet long, 50 feet high, and perhaps 50 feet wide at its base. With unrestrained power, the river was pouring through a narrow defile, the canyon walls rising majestically 1,200 feet above the canyon floor. Outriders, who scouted on the western side of the canyon, rode through compacted ash, the remnant of an ancient volcanic explosion which lay like an igneous blanket on the sandstone cliffs. As the outriders explored the canyon walls, looking down upon green cottonwood and coyote-willow groves growing below them on the banks of the river, they found the ruined dwellings of an ancient people, sheltered from the ravages of time, by precipitous overhangs and shallow caves.

Approximately 20 miles from the Rio Grande, and above the Towa pueblo whose inhabitants referred to themselves as 'the people' (hay mish/ Jemez), the canyon opened into a vast meadow. Here, the explorers found numerous greened depressions which had formed within the trace of an enormous volcanic crater. The vast depressions, which would collectively become known as the *Valle Grande*, or great valley, were 176 square miles in area. They were ribboned with streams, and replete with a profusion of wildflowers. From the floor of these '*valles caldera*,' or 'caldron valleys,' and from their volcanic rims, rose numerous volcanic peaks, two of which soared to a height of over 11,000 feet. These volcanic peaks, each of which had numerous side canyons, were bursting with intricately sculptured alcoves, shallow caves, and lush vegetation. Perhaps most remarkable to the members of the scouting party were the hot springs, and steam vents, strewn through the high meadows. They attested to volcanic activity below the surface.

On returning to Zia, the Spaniards found four bronze cannons, which had been left there during the winter of 1540-1541 by Vasquez de Coronado because they were in bad condition. The scouting party had found little of material wealth, however, and was back on the river by 30 June.

A Clash of Cultures

The pueblo of Quiqui, which the vanguard found 29 miles southwest of present-day Santa Fe, was a large one. Across the river at first light, birds would chatter in the *bosque*, and the sun, when it rose, would reveal mountains to the west rising into the blue. Now, however, it was still full night, and Onate's band approached the pueblo in darkness, silence and anxious anticipation.

The Spaniards had been told that the Mexican Indian servants, named Tomas and Cristobal, lived at the pueblo of Quiqui. It was crucial that they find them and they soon did. Left there by Castano de Sosa, they were now very much a part of the pueblo's society. These were the interpreters the Spaniards needed, and now that they had them, the Spaniards began to speak.

On 7 July 1598, Onate met with the chiefs of the seven provinces. Why they came is something of a mystery, for in doing so, they legitimized his presence and his right to summon them. Perhaps they could have ignored him—this man who wore spurs—but to have done so, would have been as difficult as ignoring a bear in their *kiva*. What Onate said was that they had come in peace and friendship, and in the hope of securing the land for their God and king. He also asked that when the chiefs returned to their villages, they instruct their people not to flee or hide, but to come out to see them. After an exchange of gifts between the Indian chiefs and Onate, the first major encounter between the Pueblo Indians and the Onate colonists was completed, and the colonization could begin.

* * *

When Onate met with the chiefs of the seven provinces at Quiqui, he exerted enormous pressure on the Pueblo Indian culture. The Pueblos were being asked to accept the new Christian God and saints into their pantheon. They were assured that this God would heed, and was powerful enough to grant, their supplications for summer rain and fruitful harvests. The Pueblo leaders, except for the leaders of the Acome, who were conspicuous by their absence, just looked at one another. After centuries of devotion to their religious customs and beliefs, they were being asked to accept a new hierarchy of gods. They would have to see.

With their council completed, the Spaniards left the pueblo of Quiqui happy in their assumption that their meeting had culminated in a successful beginning. The Spaniards had no illusions that they had imparted much regarding the mysteries of the Trinity, or that any of their theology had been understood. However, these Indians, these friendly Pueblos, seemed interested, or so they thought.

*　*　*

The Spaniards were to rename this pueblo, Santo Domingo, to commemorate the Spanish-born 13th century preacher and founder of the order of 'Friars Preacher' known as the Dominicans. After six days of meetings and councils at their newly-named pueblo of Santo Domingo, the members of the vanguard pointed the noses of their mounts directly north and rode away to find a permanent home.

The Ascent

From Santo Domingo, Onate rode north, but not before dispatching his nephew, Juan de Zaldivar, and a small escort to see how the caravan was faring. Onate judged that by this time the caravan would be entering the Piro country. Although he was not concerned that the wagon train would come under attack, he feared the colonists would find the Piro pueblos abandoned and have no means to replenish their supplies. Onate gave instructions to Juan de Zaldivar that, upon his return, he was to follow the tracks of Onate's wagons northward. Then, Zaldivar, with his escort, among whom was Alonso Robledo, headed south.

The area through which the Zaldivar party traveled was, of course, familiar to them, and they did not have the side trips to Zia and to the pueblos of the Jumano to delay their course. Thus, by mid-July, having only skirted the pueblo of Puaray as they returned, the Zaldivar party was back with the caravan.

It was during this month with the caravan that Alonso began to see and to appreciate the changes that had occurred in his mother since his father's death. Although she had always appeared frail-looking, gentle, and perhaps a bit hesitant in her manner, she was, in addition, extremely strong-willed and determined. She seemed to have become more self-sufficient than he remembered, perhaps because she no longer had his father to provide for her. But she worried constantly about Francisca and about the men whom she would meet on the trail. And she doted upon Bartolome, who, unfortunately, had been unable to escape her smothering attention because of his sense of responsibility for her.

It was obvious, moreover, that Alonso's mother had come under the influence of *dona* Eufemia, wife of Lieutenant Governor Francisco de Sosa Penalosa, an individual even more strong-willed than his mother. *Dona* Eufemia berated the men for their lack of courage, for their reluctance to do this or that, and for the speed, or lack thereof, by which they performed some task. She instructed the women in the use of the *harquebus*, and she commanded that, should the need arise, the women be able to defend themselves and their families.

Alonso's mother took to all of this; the direction provided by *dona* Eufemia appeared to be what she needed. Where Alonso's mother had previously depended upon his father for a great many things—in driving the ox-cart, in helping to replace a wheel, and in being protected—she had, through necessity, become more self-sufficient, and for this Alonso, was grateful.

Meanwhile, with Juan de Zaldivar sent back to provide an escort for the caravan, Onate, who was nearing his final destination, again left the river. The Rio Grande above the Santo Domingo pueblo flowed within a canyon through which it would be impossible to move his carts. He, therefore, decided to climb a series of steep terraces which lay on the east side of the river. After a successful ascent, and the impossible negotiation of a cliff of black basalt, he topped a rise. Far beyond a sloping plateau that flowed gently toward the north lay a beautiful range of mountains. The black basaltic cliffs appeared to be a line of demarcation between the lower and upper river. And it was up there, beyond those beautiful blue mountains which loomed into transparent skies, that Juan de Vitoria Carvajal assured Onate they would find their new home.

The First Village

A vast cottonwood forest, merging with long stretches of red, yellow, and brown sand-plains and buttes, revealed itself to the vanguard as it topped a rise and again approached the river. In the northern distance, and almost indistinguishable from the brown earth and stone of the river's steep banks, were two small Indian villages, one built on a bluff above the eastern edge of the river, the second on the western bank. The river itself was lost in the obscure shadow of trees that lined both banks. A mantle of rich, blue cottonwood smoke from hundreds of kitchen fires, hung in the air above the two villages like a protective shroud. Members of the vanguard could see many people on the roofs of their homes, and others standing in the plazas. They could also see members of a small welcoming committee playing flageolets, whistles and rasps approaching them along the river's eastern bank.

"Vicente!" *don* Juan commanded. "Break the column into two groups. Leave a few men here to guard the carts and our extra horses. I want the women and children with the guards in the trees where they'll make more difficult targets."

"Do you think that will be necessary, *Tio*?" Vicente asked. "They seem friendly enough."

Onate reined in his horse and paused, waiting for Vicente to draw up beside him, the shoulders of their horses touching. Reaching out with his left hand and grasping the reins of Vicente's mount, he drew Vicente to him, and they remained motionless, watching the small group of

Indians approaching them along the river. Then taking a deep breath and holding it for a brief moment, Onate blew the exhaled air through pursed lips before continuing. "Ah, Vicente," he said, in a tone which bespoke years of leadership, "it's at a time like this when one must attend to the old adage, that 'a man who's prepared has his battle half fought.' Look at them coming, Vicente," he said, "these simple people with their flutes of bird bones, naked, and absent of weapons. They seem to be in great joy," he said, "but don't be thrown off your guard by the seeming friendliness of your potential adversaries. While time after time that tactic may serve you well, it will eventually lead to disaster." Leaning out of his seat, he drew himself even closer to his nephew whom he now grasped at the shoulder with a gloved hand. "Remember what I've taught you regarding the art of war," he said. "You must enter each village in the same manner in which we've entered those before this one," he cautioned, "well equipped and ready for war should it be necessary. Go into each village and every situation with a heavy show of force. Make it apparent that you may easily overwhelm whoever opposes you. If you do this, Vicente, you may never have to use the force available to you. And perhaps of most importance," his uncle advised, "you must have a plan of retreat. No plan, now matter how well-devised or executed, will go perfectly, and you must have a way out. *Entendes*?" he asked, looking intently at his nephew. "Do you understand?"

"Yes, *Tio*," Vicente said, "I understand. I'll get them all into the woods."

Onate, with the remaining men of his vanguard, rode into the first and largest of the Indian villages in an audacious display of bravado, sounding trumpets, firing *harquebuses* into the air, and demonstrating feats of horsemanship which excited the Indians who had approached them. Other Indians, men, women, and children, some armed with bows and arrows, but most without weapons, came from the fields, from inside their apartments, and from the rooftops of their homes, until a large number had congregated in the largest of the village's plazas. The Indians, however, held their weapons slack, and did not appear to present a danger. Unlike many of the other Indians the colonists had encountered as they rode up the Rio Grande Valley, these Indians, who had had little contact with previous Europeans, were not afraid, and appeared exceedingly curious.

Runners, sent up the trail to this village by neighboring *caciques*, had announced Onate's coming, and, when Onate arrived, the Indians came out to receive him in peace. Standing in the village's main plaza was an elderly Indian who appeared to be the leader of the group. He approached the mounted soldiers shouting, "*Amigo, amigo!*" It was the one Spanish word he knew. He was bareheaded, wearing his hair in bangs even with his eyebrows, and tied up in a knot behind. He was wearing a cotton *manta* (blanket) over a shirt of the same material. The long shirt, with slits at the sides, from the knees to the ankles, exposed the chieftain's bare legs and the hide shoes he was wearing. A throwing stick was stuck into an embroidered towel that he wore around his waist, while a string of shell-beads hung around his neck. He looked pleased, and smiling at Onate who had dismounted from his beautifully caparisoned horse, breathed a long reverential breath of welcome on Onate's hand. Then, addressing other similarly dressed Indian males who had approached the vanguard with him, the chief urged his followers to gather around the newcomers and to exchange breaths with them.

Standing or sitting on the rooftops of the terraced homes or in one of the open plazas were many Indian women and young girls. They were dressed in cotton skirts, embroidered with colored thread. Across their shoulders, to a length just below their hips, they wore a light cotton *manta*. This was tied around their waist with a cloth like an embroidered towel with a tassel. On their feet were moccasins, the soles of bison hide and the uppers of dressed deerskin. Their hair, revealed beneath embroidered shawls, was carefully combed, and nicely kept in place by braids, one on each side of their heads. Innumerable children, some naked, and others half-clad in cotton shirts, were chasing one another about the terraced rooftops or watching the activities in the plaza below. Bob tailed dogs of all sizes barked at the hoofs of the horses which were now guarded by soldiers in the village plaza.

With Onate were three individuals whom he hoped to put to good use. Two of these were the Aztec Indians, Tomas and Cristobal, whom he had found at Santo Domingo. The third, also a Mexican Indian, was Juan de Dios who spoke Towa. The Indians standing before Onate were

Tewa, and not fluent in either Towa or Keres, but by signs and by the use of the few Keres and Towa words these villagers knew, Onate and the Tewa chief began to talk.

This village, the chieftain told Onate, was named Okhe, which Onate was made to understand, meant, 'grinding stone.' The village, which was on the western bank of the Rio Grande, was named Yungue Ouinge, meaning 'the place known as Yungue.' The two villages, a quarter of a mile apart, and separated by the Rio Grande River, the *cacique* told Onate, were occupied by his brothers, townsmen of the same nation and tongue. The chief, who had called a council of welcome, led Onate and his men to an earthen room buried in the floor of the plaza. Indians who had been members of the welcoming committee and who were now performing an *aleuromancy*,[1] sprinkled sacred corn meal where the Spaniards were to walk. Bidding the Spaniards to follow them, the Indian members of the welcoming committee entered the underground chamber through its entrance on the roof.

Onate looked at his nephew and then at his captain, Juan de Vitoria Carvajal, who, as requested, had just examined the *kiva*. "And the arrangements?" he asked.

"We left six men with the carts, horses, and people," Vicente said. "They're in the woods and well-defended. The *kiva's* clear, and no weapons will be allowed inside. Two men will guard the entrance, and Juan and I will join you within. I've sent men to the other village with instructions to guard the road here. The rest of the men will be on the rooftops, or in the plaza with the horses."

"And how did you advise them?" his uncle asked.

"I warned them not to be put off their guard by the seeming friendliness of the Indians, and to remain watchful."

"Good, very good!" Onate said, as he grasped the top of the ladder protruding from the hatchway. Followed by the two clerics, Fathers Martinez and Salazar, his two captains, and by his Indian interpreters, Onate entered the *kiva* as invited by his host.

A fire, captured in a small fire pit beneath the so-called 'sky hole,' was on the floor near the center of the room. The ceremonial fire, shooting minute tongues of flames towards the ceiling, cast dancing shadows against the white walls, lighting up the smoky rafters, and willow ceiling.

A hollowed log, across which was stretched a deerskin, served the room as a drum.

Sitting on the stone bench, which encircled the room, was the *cacique* now surrounded by his *tequitatos*, or tribal elders. All bore staffs of aspen, and carried wands of willow and yucca. They were, despite the warmth both inside and outside the *kiva*, wrapped closely in blankets. Other Indians, evidently unofficial persons, but similarly dressed, came down the ladder and dropped to their haunches, near the fire. In a stately and grave manner, several of these latter individuals approached Onate and his contingent, taking their hands and breathing from them as though desirous of drinking in their essence. One of them seated himself near the log drum and began pounding on it with a short, knotty war-club, while the others, motionless except for their heads, nodded in time to the drummer's strokes.

The Indians said a prayer, and *Fray* Salazar covered his ears so as not to hear it. As soon as the prayer was finished, great steaming bowls of venison, trays of *piki*, and baskets of melons, were brought down the ladder and placed in rows in the middle of the room. Then, an individual wearing a strange overcoat of buckskin, ornamented with seashells and flint arrowheads, began a loud prayer over the food. In a strange language of clicks and guttural aspirations, the priest rendered his incantation.

Food was then passed around the room and the chief began to speak, his speech interpreted by the three Mexican Indians with Onate.

The chief: Clicks and guttural aspirations.

The interpretation: The corn grows aged, and the summer
                     birds chase the butterfly to the land
                     of everlasting summer.

Whenever the chief spoke, it seemed as if each of his sentences, whether long or short, was said in a single breath. The interpretations were monosyllabic, or they consisted of fragments or lengthy philosophic prose no one understood. While the chief spoke, however, the Spaniards examined him and took his measure.

The chief, with deep lines of character about his eyes, was a grave man of few words, yet with a kindly expression on his face. About 60 years-of-age, he had hollow cheeks, a medium-sized mouth, and small ears, shaded with locks of soft, jet-black hair. Of medium stature, he stooped slightly when walking, yet had a stately appearance.

After a lengthy discussion in which *Fray* Martinez attempted to explain that the Spaniards were guided by peace and love and by a desire to bring the natives into the fold of the Catholic faith, more prayers were said and songs sung. Gifts were exchanged. Onate gave the chief and his *tequitatos* gifts of iron hawk bells, shoemaker's needles, and Flemish mirrors, after which the members of the vanguard were made welcome with gifts of *maize*, flour, and beans. With great friendliness, the *cacique*, told Onate that both villages were at the colonists' disposal, and, with the welcoming ceremony over, both the soldiers, and their families who had remained in the woods, began looking for places to stay.

* * *

The Indians, Onate said, are

> *settled after our custom, house adjoining house, with square plazas. They have no streets, and in the pueblos, which contain many plazas or wards, one goes from one plaza to the other through alleys. They are of two and three stories, of an estado[2] and a half or an estado and a third each, which latter is not so common.[3]*

The village Onate was standing in had a number of adobe structures connected with one another in extended rows and squares. Other structures, of two and three stories had been built on top of them, in receding terraces, like a broken flight of stairs. The honeycombed structure bristled with ladders and roof beams that protruded from the top and sides of the building like quills on a porcupine. The ladders, extending from the ground to the first terrace of roofs, were light so that they could be pulled up in an emergency. Sky holes, black apertures on the roofs through which the smoke from kitchen fires rose, had long ladder-arms protruding from them. The ladders that descended from rooftops through these sky holes and into rooms below, were heavy, and long, leaning at various angles against the roofs. No windows or doorways pierced the walls. There were no chimneys.

Of similar construction and appearance, the villages of Okhe and Yungue had below them, scattered fields of melons, pumpkins, squash, and *maize*. Beyond the villages were dark, mysterious mountains that seemingly enveloped them. Twenty-four miles to the east was Truchas Peak, standing 13,102 feet above sea level. Eighteen miles to the west, and standing behind range after range of beautiful mountains, was Santa Clara Peak at 11,561 feet. And 12 miles to the south, and rising majestically into the sky, was Santa Fe Baldy, a forested sentinel standing 12,622 feet above sea level. These mountains looked like the mountains of New Spain, which had produced much silver, and the prospects for a strike here seemed promising.

* * *

In the waning light of the long afternoon, members of the vanguard explored the Indians' terraced structures, on both the east and the west sides of the river; the unmarried soldiers at Yungue, the married soldiers at Okhe. Indian children, some carrying bows and arrows and shouting *"Aqui, aqui!"* ("Here, here!"), a word just learned from the Spaniards, pointed out apartments which were abandoned and available for the Spaniards' use. The Robledo brothers, who were looking for rooms for Francisca and their mother and for Lucia and Bartolome, were following those soldiers climbing to the rooftops at Okhe. *Kiva*-studded plazas, littered with turkey feathers and unused pine beams, provided ladders by which the Spaniards and Indian children climbed from the ground to the roofs of the first terrace. The Robledos, with other Spaniards who had ascended ladders with them, swarmed over the honeycombed structure looking for suitable accommodations.

"Over here!" yelled Pedro, whose head and shoulders were revealed at the top of a ladder protruding from a room closest to the plaza. "Check the other one," he yelled to his brothers, while motioning with a tilt of his head to a ladder protruding from an adjacent sky hole.

"I'll check it," Francisco said to his older brother, Diego. "You go with Pedro."

Diego descended the ladder, and stepping off its last rung, stood for a long moment, allowing his eyes to become adjusted to the gloom. Standing on the earthen floor, which smelled of smoke and fire, Diego looked around him, catching his breath and observing the room's makeup. The rooms the vanguard had found at the pueblo of Puaray had been large, 24 feet long and 13 feet wide on average, whitewashed and painted. The room in which Diego was standing, was half that size and was smoked with soot. Adjacent to the ladder and immediately below the room's hatchway was the remnant of a fire pit, its narrow stones, blackened by smoke, set edgewise in the hard-packed floor. A bit of the space between small rafters, supporting the roof and a pine-staved ceiling, was pierced by the small hatchway through which he had entered the room. A square doorway covered by an old blanket led into another room. Along one wall, and interrupted by three mealing troughs, was a low adobe bench which may have served as a sitting place. The floor of plastered mud was paved near the center with slabs of sandstone. It was well-swept and gave a neat appearance. Lateral walls of puddled adobe separated two apartments. These walls were pockmarked, and, except for a well-made niche in which a small bowl was still standing, bare of any adornment. Pedro stood against one of these walls waiting for Diego.

"What do you think?" Pedro asked of Diego. "We've got to make up our minds quickly before they're all gone. We're not going to find many side by side like this. What do you think?" he asked again, urging a response.

Three rooms deep, the apartment, without exterior doors or windows, faced one of the pueblo's plazas, its back serving as the rear wall for an apartment facing in the opposite direction. Small flakes of adobe rattled to the floor as Diego beat with his fist on one of the lateral walls, testing its soundness.

"Francisco!" he yelled. "What's it look like over there? Is it solid?

"It's solid enough, I guess," Francisco responded. "We'll have no trouble breaking through. I think we should worry more about bringing it all down on our heads!"

Diego looked at Pedro with whom he was standing and with a shrug of resignation said, "God, it's going to be cold in here, especially when we break through with a doorway. That might improve the draft, and perhaps the rooms will be less smoky, but if mama and Lucia have a fire in here, they'll have to leave the hatch open to let the smoke out. And if they close the hatch, they can't have a fire. But it's the best we can do," he said in frustration, "and it's only temporary . . . just until we can build our own houses." Diego stopped, and walked about the room, looking and beating on the other walls, before continuing. "You're right," he said to Pedro. "We'd better take them. Francisco!" he yelled again, "mark that one as belonging to the Romeros!"

As Diego and Pedro continued with the survey of their mother's apartment, they could hear Francisco's footsteps as he walked across the apartment's earthen roof. Each step caused a fine mist of tiny sand particles to fall on their heads. "I think we're going to have to fix the roof," Diego said, while following Pedro to a small ladder protruding from the room's earthen floor.

Below the room where they had been, they found two small earthen rooms connected by a small doorway. The ceilings, so low that they had to stoop as they walked, were made from the joists, and pine staved floorings of the rooms above them. Crawling on their hands and knees, they examined the floor, which was carpeted with a deep layer of glumes, husks, and other seed coverings, suggesting that the rooms had once been used for storage. Something unseen, and unseemly, rustled across the floor as they dug in the refuse. In addition to corn litter, the room they were in also contained a large clay jar buried in a corner of its earthen floor. Lifting its stone lid, Pedro found that it still contained several handfuls of shelled corn. Pedro said, "Mama can use this."

Their review of the apartment completed, the three brothers stripped to the waist, and began passing loads of cornstalks through the small hatchway, and into the room above, carrying it by ladder to the roof, and then to the ground where a pile was building. They swept, mounded, and carried load after load of refuse, first from their mother's apartment, and then from Bartolome's, where the rooms' make-up, arrangement, and litter were identical to that of their mother's apartment. They worked into the late afternoon, knowing that when they were finished, they would probably have to repeat these tasks at Yungue where they were to establish their own quarters.

Later, as the afternoon moved into evening, the brothers gathered on the roof of their mother's apartment to watch the activities below. Sitting on a large ladder, which leaned against a wall of the pueblo's second terrace, they could see the entire village and the Great River, partially hidden by trees. Around them were blocks of smoothly plastered roofs and adobe apartments, each as sandy brown as the bluff on which the pueblo was built. In abrupt steps, descending toward western and northern plazas, the terraced structure spread out before them in broad flats and deep courts.

Small structures of four stakes, canopied, and roofed with willows, dotted the landscape. These shelters, which were made to shield field workers from the sun, provided a resting-place for women returning from the fields with blankets of melons, pumpkins, and corn. Women at the river were washing cotton blankets or cleaning great baskets of corn, while those returning from the river carried large clay pots on their heads.

On the terraces, either intently watching or slyly glancing at the Robledos, were women who were engaged in all manner of work. A woman, her feet overhanging a roof, was decorating a pot. Another was bringing grain up a ladder to the roof and then spreading it to dry. A number of women, in small groups of twos and threes, were slicing melons into long spiral ropes, then suspending these from protruding rafters to dry. The only man the brothers saw was busy spinning with a bobbin-shaped spindle whorl. The children, screaming in delight and oblivious to the work going on around them, played in the water and on the muddy banks of the river.

The sky to the west was many shades of lemon, crimson, and gray, flamboyant in its beauty. Bullbats, made visible by a white bar on each wing, darted and swooped in dizzying flights, while crows and jays glided in the trees below them. Diego sat on the ladder's top rung, a carved slab crosspiece, more elaborately engraved than those below it. His brothers, leaning against the shins and knees of the man above him, watched with Diego as the sun slowly sank behind the western mountains. They were mesmerized by the blue shadow of Santa Clara Peak advancing across the river and through the fields, crawling up the wall of pueblo's first terrace, and then crossing the roof until it lay at their feet.

"I wish papa could have seen this," Diego said. "Has there ever been a more beautiful sunset?

The First Explorations

With the main caravan yet to arrive, Juan de Onate began to explore his surroundings. He first rode to the great pueblo of Picuris whose name, 'Mountain Gap,' describes its beautiful location on the Rio Lucia. This Tewa pueblo, with a name so similar to his own name, Onate, which means 'at the foot of the mountain pass,' lies northeast of San Juan. Onate then went to its sister pueblo of Taos, the 'red willow place.' It is located north of Picuris and some eight miles east of the Rio Grande. He was, at this point, at the northernmost permanent Indian village in his adobe kingdom. Above Taos, his realm stretched for an undetermined distance.

Onate briefly returned to the villages Okhe and Yungue before pushing on to the Indian village of Pecos, 'the place where there is water.' This was a thriving village of perhaps 2,000 souls and was exceedingly well-situated. The wide expanse of the Pecos Valley provides abundant farmland, with two year-around sources of water nearby: the Glorieta Creek below the village, and the Pecos River one mile to the east. In addition, there are numerous springs and other reservoirs in the vicinity. This was the largest of the Indian pueblos and, like the Jemez, Zia, Picuris, Taos, and Jumano pueblos, was not on the Rio Grande.

During his exploration in the mountains between the Picuris, Taos, and Pecos pueblos, Onate found signs of ore in the sands of a small stream. He was encouraged by this glint of success, but the exploring, and prospecting on his lightning visits to the northern pueblos on this occasion, had not borne major fruit.

From Pecos, Onate and his small group explored some of the small pueblos in the Galisteo basin. Here, they reviewed some small lead and turquoise mines, worked by the Pueblo Indians and discovered other signs indicating that promising riches lay in the mountains there.

From San Marcos, in the Galisteo basin, Onate rode south to Santo Domingo, to the pueblo where, on 7 July, he had met with the leaders of the seven provinces. In less than two weeks, Juan de Onate had explored an extensive field of villages in the mountains west, north, and east of Santo Domingo and felt that the prospects for finding workable mines were excellent. Promising, too, was the caravan, now composed of 61 carts and wagons, which, led by his nephew, Juan de Zaldivar, had just arrived at the pueblo of Santo Domingo. The Robledos, Catalina, Alonso, Francisca, and Lucia with her husband, Bartolome Romero, looked for Diego, Pedro, and Francisco who they hoped were among Onate's escort. They were not there, however, and it would be almost an additional month before the Robledo family would again be united.

* * *

The caravan remained at the Santo Domingo pueblo for almost a week before its final push to the villages of Okhe and Yungue. When the colonists left Santo Domingo, they went by way of San Marcos, which Onate had found would allow the wagon train to skirt the black basaltic mesa shelf which had proven so difficult to his party on their way north. He, himself, rode west to visit eight small villages of the Towa, the one region adjacent to the river he had yet to explore. He was back in Okhe by 10 August.

The Necessary Water

With the bouquet of wild things filling the air, a small group of soldiers and Pueblo Indians made its way up the Chama River,[1] a major tributary of the Rio Grande. Blackberry vines in tangles and thickets lined both banks of the stream, while hummingbirds, feeding on showy clustered flowers in pink, red, and purple, hovered anxiously.

The river, in flood from May through July, was crystalline and new from melted snow, and despite the sunshine, bone-chillingly cold. Although seldom greater than 12 feet wide, and only two or three feet deep, the stream, full of stones and boulders, was rushing along, cascading over a continuous succession of cataracts and fast-moving water, creating a vast expanse of froth and mist and shadows. Scant inches, producing stretches of white water, flowed into turbulent corners, while currents, gushing over sculptured boulders, roared noisily.

Overhanging trees, growing at various places along the banks of the river, covered thick willows, and areas of winter kill and brush, defining the margins of the stream. A number of minute beaver dams, creating boggy, inundated regions, cropped up here and there as the group worked its way up river. It was at one of these beaver dams that the group of soldiers and Pueblo Indians put down the reed baskets they had been carrying.

It was mid-August, and Onate's work group was building a rock-fill dam, or *presa*, on the Chama River above the village of Yungue. The dam, to be made of large, tightly woven, cylindrical, stone-filled baskets, was being built to divert water from the river to an *acequia² madre*, or mother ditch, which the Indians were digging for the Spaniards. By the use of their hands and stone instruments, the Indians of Okhe and Yungue began digging while the colonists built the dam. They later were joined by an even larger group of Indians who had been conscripted for the purpose of digging the meandering three-foot wide canal. The dam, which would eventually be destroyed by water and ice (the canal itself damned by beavers and riddled by gopher holes), would have to be rebuilt each year, but when it was completed, it stood as the colonists' first major accomplishment in creating their colonial villages. All that was required to bring the irrigation system into use the following spring was to open the canal's main ditch gate, and their *acequia* would be opened.

The Arrival

On 18 August 1598 Juan de Zaldivar led the caravan into the Indian pueblo of Okhe. It had been a journey of six and one-half months from the Conchos River, and it was the first time the colonists could afford the luxury of looking back down the trail to see what they had accomplished. They had added 800 miles to the *Camino Real de Tierra Adentro*, the Royal Road to the Interior, a road that was to become one of the most important in North American history. It had been a journey across immense empty distances that had required an incredible amount of stubborn will and indefatigable courage. By the use of this road, which the wheels of their wagons and carts, and the hooves of their animals had worn into the earth, the Spanish had brought 500 colonists and 7000 head of cattle, sheep, goats and horses to a new home. For centuries, the *Camino*, which would be further marked by the fertility provided by the droppings of their beasts, would be their only link with the outside world. Travelers would use the *parajes* they had established on this first journey for the next 300 years. The colonists had much to be proud of, but rather than relishing their success, some wanted to go home.

*   *   *

The discontent was immediate. Some of the colonists who had so painfully worked their way up the river now planned to desert and return to New Spain. They hated this place, moreover, the silver Onate had promised them did not exist. Involved in this mutiny were 45 officers and soldiers, more than a third of the men in Onate's army.

Again, one of the malcontents was Pablo de Aguilar, and again, he would be sentenced to death. But also, again, the soldiers and the friars would plead for leniency, and, again, it would be granted. The friars had warned Onate that it was probably better not to stir the rice even though it was sticking, for their concern was that the disorder would spill over and create an even greater mess. Onate had sworn to Perez de Villagra that if Aguilar drew his sword against him he "should throw away the scabbard." But the friars were probably right, for Onate could ill afford losing Aguilar and the other two men he judged to be the ringleaders of those planning to desert, nor could he afford sowing further discontent among his dispirited colonists. So, aware that the spark of this fire remained hidden in the ashes, Onate banked the embers. He would, he knew, eventually have to deal with Aguilar and with these other people who sought to destroy his colony, but he would wait.

The immediate manner in which this situation was calmed, was to stage a religious ceremony in which the perpetrators could seek spiritual guidance to atone for their sins. In a sermon of tears, *Fray* Cristobal de Salazar and the remainder of the priests led the colonists in a prayer service after which, at least for the moment, things were measurably calmed. Two days later, the colonists began work on a missionary chapel for the San Juan Indians.

214

Chapel and Kiva

As Godoy exited the *kiva*, he looked back at the Indian elders with whom he and the Spanish clerics had met, and knew there was going to be trouble. He was appalled by the rudeness displayed by some of his Spanish fellows and dismayed by their seeming unwillingness to understand what the Indians had been trying to explain. He hurried across the Indian plaza, climbed a ladder to a roof and then down a hatchway into the semi-darkness of *Fray* Martinez's quarters.

Seated with the other clerics against one of the walls of the small room was *Fray* Cristobal de Salazar, Onate's cousin. He was laughing at the way in which the Indians' hair was cut. "*Trasquilen a cruzes*," he laughed. "Crudely and unevenly, the manner in which the hair of fools is said to be trimmed."

Most of the other clerics laughed at the picture *Fray* Salazar had drawn regarding the Indian elders. However, Brother Rodriguez, who had refused to join them in their laughter, said, "Not greatly different from my own." The others looked at him, cleared their throats, or began staring at the hard-packed floor while awaiting *Fray* Martinez, who was doing something in an adjoining room.

When *Fray* Martinez joined them, he was carrying a copy of Onate's contract in which were repeated some of the ordinances for new discoveries, conquests, and pacifications. Now almost a quarter of a century old, these were made by the king at the Bosque de Segovia on 13 July 1573.

"Fathers," Martinez said, "your behavior and the attitude you displayed at our meeting with the old people of the pueblos suggests to me that some of you do not fully understand the conditions under which our ministry is to be conducted in New Mexico. I'd like to read you something that will help to more completely explain our roles here." He cleared his throat, took out the feather which identified the specific spot in the text where the statement was to be found, and holding the *cedula* before him, read:

"Expeditions of discovery and settlement . . . eh . . . . gentle persuasion . . . eh . . . justice and security . . . and so on, and so on, and so on . . . Ah here it is.

" 'In order to do this'—its speaking here, of our responsibility for converting the Indians to Christianity—'they' (meaning us) 'will not begin by rebuking them for their vices and idolatries or by taking from them their women or their idols so that they are offended or become hostile to Christian doctrine.' Rather, Fathers, 'they,' the Indians, 'must first be taught and after they are instructed, they will be persuaded of their own free will to abandon that which is contrary to our Holy, Catholic Faith and evangelical doctrine.' "

Taking his spectacles from his sunburned nose and placing them as a book mark within the document from which he had been reading, *Fray* Martinez smiled happily at the tonsured clerics who were sitting in their habits of milled serge and *picote*,[1] against the walls of the earthen room. "This is a nice room, isn't it?" he said, looking at the clerics of his custody. "Eighteen feet by seven feet, the exact measurements of the Holy Sepulcher! A good room. A holy room," he said, as he pulled at his tunic. Looking older than his 40 years, his face seamed and weather-beaten, he looked around the room again, before continuing. "I've read you this," he said, "to remind you that we're working under specific obligations regarding the Indians whom we've found here."

"With all due respect, Father," said *Fray* Cristobal de Salazar, who prided himself on being well-versed in Spanish laws and ordinances, "I'm not sure I understand what you've read." His ample chin hidden by the cowl of his habit, *Fray* Salazar continued, "I thought the Church was to be seen as the ruler and authority over all the world, and that the Indians were to have the Holy Catholic Faith preached to them whether they like it or not. According to the *requerimiento*, (requirement)," he said, referring to an old Spanish document of 1514, "the Indians were not to be compelled to turn Christian unless, when informed of the truth, they should wish to be converted."

"And how is that different from what I read, Father?" asked *Fray* Martinez, with a note of annoyance toward this cleric who seemed constantly to be questioning his directives.

"Because the *requerimiento* also states that, if the Indians refuse to have the Holy Catholic Faith preached to them, we're to take their refusal, as permission to forcefully enter their country, and to make war against them in all ways and manners that we can. And that we're then to subject them to the yoke and obedience of the church." Smiling broadly at the clerics who were attempting to follow his discourse, his fair skin appearing red in the diffused light, *Fray* Salazar leaned back against the wall and waited for *Fray* Martinez' response.

"We're far beyond that, Father, far beyond that," *Fray* Martinez said in exasperation, his lips stiffened in rebuke. "We now see our roles differently. The Indians are to be taught and persuaded to become Christians," he said, "nothing more." *Fray* Salazar looking around him in apparent disgust, pulled his hood over the crown of his head and said nothing further.

Fray Martinez waited for *Fray* Salazar to respond, and when he did not, *Fray* Martinez continued. "Soon," Martinez added, addressing himself to all of the men in the room, "you're to be assigned to the pueblos, and you're to go there with the chiefs who will soon be meeting here with Onate."

"Are we to place them in *congregaciones*? (congregations)"[2] asked *Fray* San Miguel, regarding the Pueblos Indians about whom they were speaking.

"Although that would have been our expectation," *Fray* Martinez replied, "it won't be necessary since all of the Indians we've seen, and those *don* Juan has found up and down the river live in pueblos. They have their own governments and *acequias* and raise the crops they need for their maintenance. In many ways," he said laughingly, "they've done our work for us.

"I meet with you," he continued, speaking solemnly, "to explain your roles here, and to remind you that the Indian leaders I met at Santo Domingo have already been placed under obligation to the crown. Those that we are soon to meet here will also be made vassals of the king. They and their people are to be treated with consideration. Patience and persuasion are to be our only tools for conversion.

"There was a time," *Fray* Martinez laughed, "when we thought that the Indians were descended from one of the 10 lost tribes of Israel, and, that the *kivas* in which they hold their ceremonials were *estufas* (steam rooms or hot houses) for winter. How is it Espejo described them, eh? 'Houses built underground, very well sheltered and closed,' with 'a great quantity of community wood, so that strangers may gather there,'[3] is how he put it. We now know a great deal more about them and about their religion. They are, like us, descended from the original pair, and from Noah through Ham," he said with assurance. "Most importantly, my friends, they're fellow humans, children of God, and are gifted with an immortal soul. They're pagans, to be sure," he said, "but people who should be brought to Christianity."

Antonio de Godoy, who was the chronicler of the expedition, and who had been assigned the task of understanding the Pueblos' origins and theology, asked, "And how are we to understand their origins, Father? For example, they call themselves 'Winter and Summer' people. What are we to make of that?" he asked, looking about the room at the clerics who sat against the wall. "The pueblo of Yungue, is occupied mainly by the 'Summer People,'" he said, "Indians who are chiefly responsible for ceremonials linked to the domestication of plants. And the pueblo of Okhe," he said, "is occupied mainly by the 'Winter People.' They are, the Indians tell me, responsible for ceremonials associated with the fertility of animals, both wild and domestic."

In response to Godoy's question, *Fray* Martinez began to relate his understanding of the story the Indian's had told them.

Godoy and the clerics had just come from a discussion with the Pueblo Indians regarding their culture, origins and theology. Using Tomas and Cristobal as their interpreters, Godoy and the priests had met with the elders of the Tewa Indians to ask them to relate their stories, so that Godoy might make note of them.

Although the villages of Okhe and Yungue acted in concert with one another, the Tewa elders said, each village had its own highly organized social and ritual life involving the ceremonial *kiva*, *kachina* and *sipapu*. The Spaniards had seen these rituals at Sevilleta, San Juan Bautista and Santo Domingo. Not much given to warfare, they said, they were nevertheless under constant threat from nomadic tribes who pressed in upon settled areas in search of stored corn.

The description the Pueblo elders provided the Spaniards regarding their unusual relationship with the nomadic tribes reminded

Godoy of the unique relationship which the Narrow-Leafed Yucca has with its solo pollinator, moths of the genus *Tegeticula*. These moths pollinate the plant while laying eggs inside the flower. Developing moth larvae feed on the yucca seeds, yet they always leave enough to insure the survival of both species. Here, too, at the pueblos of Okhe and Yungue, the nomadic tribes took just enough corn from the Indians to insure their own survival, while leaving enough seed for the Pueblos to sustain themselves and to assure both with abundant harvests.

When asked to explain their concept of the Summer and Winter People, of which the two villages were composed, the Indian elders provided a fascinating description and explanation. "The earth," one said, "is round and flat, but it's also thick like a cake. Within the earth, near a sand lake that lies underground, there are four wombs in which people grow and live. This world, the world we now inhabit, is the fourth womb. The other three wombs are down below, inside, one beneath the other."

"At the *sipapu* (the pit in the floor of a ceremonial chamber), another elder continued, "the people came out upon the world, but it was cold and dark. Then the great sun rose in the heavens. In the sun, *Payatyama* dwells, and on it, he rides around the world in one day and one night. It is day and light, and night and dark. We also," he said, "have summer and heat, and winter and cold. And for this reason (because there are two different major principles in the world, but not in opposition as in good and evil) there are Summer People and Winter People—some who like to live when it is cold and others who like to live when it is hot. Every tribe of the Tewa has some of both kinds."

"It was cold at *sipapu*," a third Indian said. "Toward the south, it was warm, and bright, so the Summer People, led by their mother, the Blue Corn Woman, went south along the Great River. The White Corn Maiden, mother of the Winter People, led them south also, but far around by the east, over the plains where the great bison roam, where the wind blows, and where it is cold and dry. Our people, the Summer People and the Winter People, were told to come together in the mountains here at the river, and to live here in peace, each one getting food for himself and for the others."

These concepts might have been difficult for the Spaniards to understand, but the Indians' description of their creation was incomprehensible to them. The leaders of the Tewa spoke of fetishes, and seeds, and how from these, life emerged. They spoke about the origin of their clans, how the earth had been born of a clot of blood, how the gift of fire had been given to them by the gods, and how animals had come to populate the earth. But mostly they spoke about spirits and of the proper manner for rendering prayer. The spirits, they said—the *kachinas* whom they venerated as rain deities—were supernatural persons, ancestors of human beings, who visited the earth during the winter. During the other half of the year, the *kachinas* were in the spirit world, their appearance from, and departure to, the spirit world were occasions for ceremonies. Most importantly, the Indians said, the *kachinas* brought corn, rain, and melons, and they gave their masks to men so that they might accomplish benevolent acts through impersonation. In all of this, the Pueblo Indians spoke of their need to promote harmony and order in the universe, for if harmony and order were maintained, the spirits would ensure abundant game and provide sufficient rain for crops.

Each of the clerics who were in attendance at this discussion had his own opinion regarding what he had heard in their meeting with the Indians in their *kiva*. Godoy, again speaking to *Fray* Alonso Martinez, asked, "What do you make of this, Father?" to which *Fray* Salazar responded rudely, "I think that they were trying to tell us that there are two kinds of people in this world, those who believe in their creation myth, and those who do not. And, of course," he said rather matter-of-factly, "you know my view in this matter."

"May I speak, Father?" asked Brother Joaquin Rodriguez of *Fray* Alonso Martinez, who nodded his assent. "There's probably something important here," Rodriguez said, "something we should respect and try to understand. The Tewa appear to have bits and pieces of the true God, but it's lost in all of this gibberish. However," he added, "if we understood their beliefs, it might help us to reach them and show them the way. Perhaps," he said, "there's even something we could learn from them."

"I agree with Brother Rodriguez," said the ancient *Fray* Francisco de San Miguel. "We must remember what we learned in New Spain those many years ago. There, when we found them, the natives baptized their infants. They used purifying water. And they took communion as bits of Eucharistic bread from one of their gods."

"Yes," Brother Rodriguez added eagerly, "they even called the host *teoqualo*, meaning 'god is eaten,' and," he added, "they had priests who heard confession and who extended absolution as you do."

The religious, San Miguel and Rodriguez, continued, recounting the similarities between their own religion and that of the natives of New Spain. The Indians of New Spain knew of the Trinity, a member of whom was born of a virgin. They knew of the flood. They had a tower of Babel at Cholula. And the enigmatic Quetzalcoatl lived in the minds of many of them as the expected Messiah. Most importantly, San Miguel and Rodriguez insisted, the people of New Spain knew of the cross, which they believed to be of great spiritual importance, even before the arrival in New Spain of the Spaniards.

"The people of these villages speak of a serpent which bred selfishness and competitiveness among their people," Rodriguez said. "Perhaps there's something there we can use. And may I make a plea, Fathers," he said, speaking to the entire group. "I have an urgent request regarding the idols of which the ordinance spoke. Those human effigies and idols, of clay, stone and wood which we found reverently displayed in the aumbrys of their *kivas*, are important and must be preserved. It's clear from the ordinance as read by Father Martinez that we're not to take these idols from their owners, but I beg, also, that we treat these objects with care and respect. I say this, especially, about the stone slabs we found, particularly those painted and decorated with the Indians' many figures. They may be of great value to us. They may contain information about their makers and about other matters, information we don't possess."

Fray Martinez nodded in agreement, first at Rodriguez who had spoken these words, and then at the entire group. "The request by Brother Rodriguez seems reasonable enough, Fathers. We will not rebuke the Indians for their vices or for their idolatries, nor will we provide offense. So be it?" he asked of the group.

"So be it," they replied, with only *Fray* Salazar abstaining.

"As long as their idols are in their *kivas*," *Fray* Salazar said, "I'll not conduct services there."

"But you will preserve their idols, and will find other places to hold your services until your church can be built. Is that right, Father?"

"Yes, Father," *Fray* Salazar said, "I'll do as you ask in that regard. And may I say something further, Father Commissary?" Salazar asked, using Martinez's complete title. "While there may have been many similarities between our rites and doctrines and those of the Indians of New Spain," he said, "such similarities were, I'm sure, perversions and profanations promoted by the evil one. So it is here," he said. "Whatever these people of the vowels believe," he said, referring to the language speakers of Tiwa, Tewa, and Towa, "it's an abomination, and I'll have none of it!" Gathering his cassock about him, *Fray* Salazar stood and asked of *Fray* Martinez, "Now may I be excused Father?" Getting *Fray* Martinez's permission to do so, he ascended the ladder and disappeared through the sky hole.

The clerics did not know, that the cross was used as a religious symbol by the Chinese, the Buddhists, the Egyptians, and by the American Indians, among whom it may have symbolized the four winds, the active or passive components of the phallic in nature, or the hammer. And they did not care that the cross was used as a symbol of punishment and suffering long before the time of Jesus. These Indians the Franciscans had come to save, said *Fray* Salazar, must to come to know God in *Fray* Salazar's way, and that was that! Martinez assigned him to the pueblos of Okhe and Yungue where he could keep an eye one him

Vassalage

"It must be placed against the east wall," *Fray* Salazar said of the Eucharistic table that his assistant, a Mexican Indian '*donado*,' trained as a catechist and 'donated' to the friars by his people, was constructing inside the poor chapel. "There's a reason for everything," he said as he whacked the young man on his bare legs with a sprig of green willow. "Tradition must be followed," he said, emphasizing the must.

222

"But it looks odd there, Father," the young man said, gathering his abbreviated habit about him. "It's blocking the door. The wall opposite the entrance would be better."

"Well you built the chapel wrong," Salazar said in annoyance, "the door facing the east! You'll just have open another wall as the entrance!"

The missionary chapel, built on the southern edge of the village of Yungue, was a mean structure of *jacal*, close-set, vertical posts set in a trench in the nature of a palisade. It was plastered inside and out with mud. The structure, roofed with mats of mud, willows and rushes, provided protection against the sun, but little else. The friars loved it and hoped to have the structure completed and ready for its dedication by the first of September.

* * *

The chapel was dedicated on 8 September 1598, and the following day, the Spanish residents of the two villages, along with their Indian guests, assembled cheek by jowl for the first service. Following High Mass, at which all 10 friars assisted, Onate gave religious responsibility for the kingdom of New Mexico to the Franciscans. Then, having previously conferred with Commissary Alonso Martinez, Onate assigned the friars to the various pueblos.

The next day, Onate asked the leaders of the central and northern pueblos to meet with him in the main *kiva* at Okhe. Then, as he had done at Santo Domingo in early July, Onate, who spoke with the assistance of Tomas and Cristobal, told the assembled leaders the reasons he was there. He stated that he had come to this land to bring them to the knowledge of God and the king in which lay the salvation of their souls and a safe and peaceful life in their republics, sustained in justice, secure in their properties, and protected from their enemies. He stated further that he had not come to do them any harm.

Although it was ordinarily cool in this gigantic *kiva*, the temperature rose as Onate spoke. The leaders of the Tiwa, Puaray, and Keres looked around at those who sat on the stone bench that encircled the earthen room. The leaders of the Zia, Tewa, Pecos, Picuris and Taos looked back at them and at each other. They were not totally sure what was being asked of them, nor did they understand the theology being expressed: one God with the Roman Pontiff and Spanish King as his servants, and Onate and the Franciscan priests as their representatives in New Mexico. What did it all mean? Whatever their confusion, there was one thing Onate made abundantly clear. They were to take the assigned missionaries to their villages and obey them, and if they failed to heed their friars, or harmed them in any way, they and their cities and towns would be put to the sword or burned alive. Onate stated, however, that he wished these men to render allegiance to God and to Spain because they understood the correctness of the world he, Onate, represented. He wished them, of their own free will, to become vassals.

Thus, in turn, each of these old men of the Pueblos made himself Onate's man. Kneeling before Onate and placing his hands between his, each of the chiefs swore an oath of fidelity to Onate. This created ties of dependence, but also of mutual obligation, and the Pueblos were his.

* * *

These events initiated a weeklong celebration of the colonists' arrival. Most prominent in this celebration was a sham-battle between the Moors and the Christians, a play enacted on foot and on horseback, in which a Moor deceitfully pretended to accept Christianity while plotting to steal a cross. The week ended with a crescendo that culminated in the firing of volleys of *harquebusiers* and artillery with a full complement of powder but no shot. The Indians were greatly impressed by the noise but could see that these instruments caused no harm. This was to be a deciding factor in their future behavior.

Mutiny and Desertions

The festivities during the first part of September had been staged for the purpose of healing some old wounds. On 12 September, however, the wounds were opened anew. Onate, already overburdened with cares and duties, was sitting in his quarters at Okhe when one of his officers, Captain Gaspar Perez de Villagra, strode in with disturbing news. Four men, the brothers, Juan and Matias Rodriguez, and two Portuguese colonists,

Manuel Portugues and Juan Gonzalez, had stolen some horses and were on their way south. These were four of the men who had been involved in the plans for desertion quelled earlier and Onate was furious. "Get Marquez," he said, strapping on his sword and dagger. When Perez returned, Onate, who was to mark this day with a black stone, was saddling his horse and readying himself to pursue the evildoers. His men, however, convinced him that his place was here where further desertions might be in the offing. His men asked for their orders and Onate returned to his quarters where he hurriedly composed a brief message to the viceroy in which he informed him that he had directed Perez and Marquez to pursue the perpetrators. What he did not write, but what he told his men, was that, when the deserters were apprehended, they were to be killed. With these incomplete orders in hand, Perez and Marquez, accompanied by three additional soldiers, swung onto their horses and rode out of the village.

It was anticipated that Onate's men would overtake the deserters somewhere within the southern boundary of the kingdom. However, the runaways, who had stolen some good mounts, were constantly ahead of their pursuers as each group rode its horses to exhaustion for many hundreds of miles. When Onate's men finally caught up to the deserters, the two parties were on the Rio San Pedro in *Nueva Vizcaya* in the kingdom of New Spain.

Although Perez and Marquez had no jurisdiction in New Spain, they could not leave the deserters unpunished. Therefore, using the authority provided them by Onate's honor and need, they offered the deserters safe conduct and proceeded with their murderous assignment. After receiving the royal immunity, and, incredibly, relying on the laws of honest engagement, the four allowed themselves to be taken. When it became obvious that a promise pledged to deserters would not be honored and that the Portuguese soldiers, at least, were to be executed, the Portuguese begged to be allowed to have the priest at the nearby mines of Todos Santos hear their last confessions. This was denied. Instead, each of the two, in the savage manner of the day, had a knife plunged into his throat and his head severed from his body. In addition, the right hand of each of the executed men was chopped off and pickled in salt to be carried back to Onate as proof of their deaths. Because the Rodriguez brothers

225

were friends of Perez, he apparently allowed them to escape, for they were not killed—Perez later explaining to Onate that the posse had been unsuccessful in their capture. Perez and Marquez with their three comrades rode south to Santa Barbara to replenish their supplies and to send a letter to Viceroy Monterrey. In this letter, carefully sealed with Spanish wax, Perez emphasized the goodness, richness, and fertility of New Mexico in an attempt to buy Onate time, for although the colonists had only been in New Mexico for five short months, the discontent and threatened desertions of some of the colonists told them quite clearly that they were in trouble.

* * *

In the meantime, things were also not going well in Spain. King Philip II in his *Real Monasterio de San Lorenzo de Escorial*, awaited his death. *El Escorial* (The Slag Heap), built in thanksgiving for Philip's victory over the French at Saint Quentin in 1557, is a colossal monastery-palace of stone. It stands in a small valley in the midst of the mountains that crisscross the Castilian plateau. Here Philip II, who had built "a cell for himself and a palace for God," occupied a small, austere monastic chamber near the choir where, through a small shuttered window, he could hear the priests say Mass. As he weakened, he was unable to leave his room, the virulent malady which he had inherited—like Spain—from his father, slowly killing him. He lay in bed or sat in a special chair with one gout-swollen foot raised above the other. Here, he listened as the priests rehearsed his funeral. For months, he lingered between life and death. Finally, on 13 September 1598 (the day after the Onate desertions), King Philip II, who had reigned during the zenith of Spain's Catholic empire, died, never knowing (or probably caring) what had happened to his New Mexico colony.

* * *

The colonists did not know of Philip's death or of the coronation of his 20-year-old son, the Prince of Asturias, as Philip III. What they did know with utmost certainty was that they were stuck in the middle of nowhere with seemingly no way out.

Hunting

The mountains, granitic contours against a pale blue sky, were still burdened with winter's snow, lying in protected east-slope serrations, plainly visible to the residents of the valley below. A bank of fog, spilling over the ridges of mountains to the west, brought with it the scent of ambergris, chaff, humus, and duff. The Indians on the Rio Grande, told the Spaniards that the misty cascade of condensed water vapor was commonplace but rarely reached the valley into which it now slowly poured. And the cataract was early, the Indians said, the result of cooler than normal air on the eastern slopes of the mountains. The fog lasted but a few short hours. Eventually it began to evaporate, and from the bottom of an extensive cloud which had the appearance of bone lace, it began unraveling upward, slowly retreating up the forested slopes.

For a brief time, warmth returned to the Rio Grande valley. During this period, thermals from the valley floor continued building pillars of immense clouds miles into the sky. Easterly drifting clouds, producing thunderheads and trailing diaphanous rain showers, spilled into the valley below. One could often see as many as three such thunderstorms—called 'male rains'[1] by the Indians—rumbling simultaneously: one over the eastern plains, another obscuring mountains to the west, while a third, building an enormous tower of black, flat-based, cumulus clouds, trailed curtains of gray rain over the mountains to the south.

In early September, Diego awoke to autumn coming through the sky hole at his quarters in Yungue. Although the day was bright and sunny, he could smell the scent of fall in the air. Red-winged blackbirds in the towering cottonwoods made a row as he ascended the ladder from his room and emerged onto the roof above his apartment. Mist, lying in a brumous haze, hugged the mountains to the west. The atmosphere was frosty and hard, the leaves on the valley cottonwoods beginning to fall.

The forest was alive with birds: bluebirds, chickadees, woodpeckers, and sparrows. Though reluctant to let the summer go Diego was invigorated by the chill air which was now flowing into the rooms below. Returning to his quarters, he retrieved his brother, Pedro, with whom he was to hunt.

Riding their best horses and trailing a mule, Diego and Pedro rode out of the valley and toward the eastern plains where they hoped to bag some game.

The land through which they traveled, replete with dry waterbeds and gulches, led across an elevated plateau and toward 'Rock-Horn Mountain,' (Truchas Peak) the name used by the Tewa, in reference to the upward-projecting rocks on the mountain's 13,000 foot summit.

The mountain, only 18 miles from their quarters in the Rio Grande valley, loomed before them, but the hunters had no intention of going that far. Although it was becoming increasingly difficult to find game close to the villages of Okhe and Yungue, deer and pronghorn fed at dawn and at dusk. If the hunters were unsuccessful in making a kill on their way out during the early morning, they hoped to make a kill on their way back.

They rode through a vast expanse of sagebrush, relieved on occasion by groups of stubby pine growing in pure stands or mixed with junipers and scrub oak. They rode east, then north, and finally west, generally following the outline of the plateau they were on, and ultimately making their way back towards the river. Behind them, the towering clouds of an autumnal storm were growing, spreading out at the top, and extending ahead of the main clouds which appeared to be immediately over Rock Horn Mountain. To the north, additional clouds were building columns high into the sky. Azure foothills were on the horizon.

Making a large circuit of the area to the east of the river, the hunters dismounted occasionally searching for fresh tracks. They found the spoor of both pronghorn and deer, but none of the tracks or trails were of recent making. Then, preparing to return to the river, the Robledo brothers rode down through a dry waterbed, obscuring their view of the land on both sides of the gulch. When they finally emerged from the gully, Diego and Pedro were startled to see a pronghorn buck and several does grazing in the distance. They dismounted, left their horses in the *arroyo*, and crawled up the steep bank of the gap, lying down just before its crest, hoping the pronghorn would come their way. Hidden among the rocks, sagebrush, and juniper trees lining the *arroyo's* banks the brothers felt a chill breeze playing upon their exposed arms and faces.

Overhead, a flock of swallows competed with one another in dizzying flight, while the hunters waited for the graceful pronghorn to come to them.

"You know, Pedro," Diego whispered, "we could wait here forever. Maybe we should go to them."

"That's impossible," Pedro replied with the assurance his previous hunting successes had given him. "We could never sneak up on them, Diego. They'd see us coming, smell us, or sense our movement. I've never seen such skittish creatures. They're beautiful, and seem to have a sixth sense. And if we get one," Pedro said, "it'll be because they came to us. So we'll wait."

They remained there for what seemed like hours until they saw, silhouetted against the hills on which luminous daylight remained, two of the slender and graceful creatures which had moved within striking distance. The moon, as conspicuously colored as a Valencian orange, cast highlights of rust on the flanks and necks of the pronghorn, and on the white fur of their under parts. A small number of bats and nighthawks joined the swallows in their aerial display, while killdeer, with their loud shrill cry, shrieked about them.

"Diego," Pedro whispered, "take the one on the left. On my count . . ."

Diego listened for the count, and on 'three,' raised from a prone position to his elbows as the pronghorn bounded away. The sound of the two weapons exploding simultaneously was deafening. A great plume of smoke rose in the moonlight. Pedro's animal ran for a short distance and then collapsed, while Diego's, and the remainder of the small harem, continued on, finally disappearing over the distant dunes.

"Damn it!" Diego said, slapping himself on his head with his gloved hand. "I missed again! What's wrong with me?"

"You're not leading them, Diego," Pedro responded. "You're shooting where they were, and you've got to shoot where they're going to be! Look," he said, demonstrating with this weapon. "Sight along the barrel like this with your eye and the muzzle of your *harquebus* on the shoulder of the animal as it runs. Then, squeezing the trigger, continue your motion until your barrel is ahead of the animal. Fire! Both the pronghorn and bullet will get there at the same time. Try it. You'll get the hang of it."

New Promises

Good news is good in any season. And if ever an individual needed some good news it was Onate. He got a bit of this in early September when he found an Indian named Jusepe who wandered into his command center at Okhe. He was an Aztec Indian, he said, who had been with the two Spanish soldiers, Francisco Leyva de Bonilla, and Antonio Gutierrez de Humana. They, with a small party including himself and additional Indians from New Spain, had been sent out to punish some rebellious Indians in *Nueva Vizcaya*. Having accomplished this, they continued north. Somewhere upon the featureless plains, Jusepe said, Gutierrez had quarreled with Leyva over the command of the expedition and had killed him. Jusepe said that he was so frightened by this mutiny that he had escaped and retraced his steps to New Mexico. He was later captured by a group of Apaches from whom he also escaped when he heard there were other Spaniards on the river.

There were a number of things about this story that intrigued Onate, and he began to craft a plan. The viceroy had ordered him to capture Leyva and Gutierrez for their illegal incursion into New Mexico, and there was now, in addition, a charge of murder against Gutierrez. In addition, Jusepe's description of the bison plains suggested to Onate that he could replenish his dwindling supplies with a hunt. This would give his men something important to do and get them out of the villages of Okhe and Yungue where they might only create additional difficulties. Therefore, on 15 September 1598, Captain Pablo de Aguilar, Juan de Pedraza, Juan de Olague, Rodrigo Zapata, Juan de Leon, Diego Robledo, and Vicente de Zaldivar, with 56 additional men, rode out of the pueblo of Okhe heading southeast. They first went to the pueblo of Pecos where they left the ancient *Fray* Francisco de San Miguel and lay brother, Juan de Dios. Then, through wooded mountains, soft green meadows, and under a brilliant turquoise sky, great with white billowing clouds, they headed northeast following the same route that Jusepe told them Gutierrez had traveled.

Eleven leagues from Pecos, Godoy recorded, in a meadow replete with pale blue irises, they came to

> *a small stream carrying but little water but containing a prodigious quantity of excellent fish, pilchard, sardines, prawn, shrimp, and matalote. That night 500 catfish were caught with only a fishhook, and many more on the following day.[1] At that place, four Indian herdsmen came to see him [Zaldívar]; they ordered that the Indians be given food and presents. One of them arose and with a loud voice called many Indians who were hidden and they all came to where the Spaniards were. They are [a] powerful people and expert bowmen. The sargento mayor gave presents to all and won them over. He asked them for a guide to the cattle and they furnished one very willingly.[2]*

The Indians the Spaniards had encountered were the Plains Apaches. This was an Indian group also known as *querechos* or *vaqueros*, whom Vasquez de Coronado had labeled the 'People of the Cows.' The Spaniards, riding through a vast meadow in which cold air flowed about the legs of their beasts like a viscous medium, set out east, following these Indians into the vast unknown.

The central plains, on which the *querechos* lived, were often a parched grassland with isolated patches of wild flowers, but now were responding to a year of wet snowfall and abundant rain. The yucca, or beargrass, was blooming to such an extent that they were no longer able to support their blossoms. *Playas*—wide open spaces on the plains—were full of the white and yellow blooms of jimson weed, buttercups, and poppies, while horsemint and clover filled the air with the aromatic scent of their blossoms. The tall stalks of goldenrod and purple penstemon, intermingled with Spanish bayonet and sagebrush to create a kaleidoscope of color against the blue horizon which Godoy described.

"A soldier can lean down from his saddle and pluck flowers without dismounting—seven varieties within reach of his lance. The air is serene, and the sun shining in all its glory. The birds are singing sweetly, warbling their songs, as they stake out their territory or advertise for mates. Nature seems to smile on our expedition. Everything seems to encourage us onward."

The Indians who were camped within this forest of wild flowers on the plains east of Pecos had a large quantity of hides which, when wrapped about their bodies, served them as clothing. Since the weather was hot, however, the men were nearly naked, and the women only clothed from the waist down.

Godoy also recorded what he had learned about the Indians' reliance on the bison:

"In addition to providing food and clothing the bison serve the Indians' every need: axes and hoes from their shoulder blades, fuel from their dung, glue from their boiled hooves, red paint from their blood, ladles from their horns, fly whisks from their tails, battle shields and coracles from their tough hide, hair to stuff pillows and mattresses, ornaments for their clothing, bone needles, bow strings, warm robes, tallow, and leggings. To get these, all Indian members of the tribe participate in the hunt, with both men and women using the bow and arrow with which they are quite skilled."

One of the villages which the Spaniards encountered was composed of 500 tents made of extremely well-dressed hides in red and white. The tents were round and shaped like a pavilion, with buttons and buttonholes used to fasten them. They were large, with branches (tent poles) an *estado* and a half in length placed in a circle. Some of these tents were large enough to accommodate four mattresses.

Most impressive, Godoy observes, were the tanned skins of which the tents were made.

The tanning is so fine that although it should rain bucketfuls it will not pass through nor stiffen the hide, but rather upon drying it remains as soft and pliable as before.[3]

Cutting a piece of hide from one of the tents, Vicente de Zaldivar soaked it in water and dried it in the sun. It remained as soft as if it had not been wet. He bought a complete tent (which most remarkably only weighed about 50 pounds) and took it with him.

232

To transport their tents, tent poles, and other goods from place to place in their search for bison, the *vaqueros* used medium-sized shaggy dogs in place of the more usual draft and pack animals which were unknown to them. By means of a harness, the Indians attached two poles to each dray dog, with the poles that were trailing behind the animal used to support the baggage. The Spaniards estimated a single dog could, in this manner, transport at least 100 pounds of material.

The *vaqueros* roamed the open grasslands in search of bison. One of the groups provided the Spanish soldiers with a guide to lead them to the herds, and late in September 1598, the Spaniards found their first herd of 'wild cattle.'

The Zaldivars had seen an enormous herd of these animals in the far distance on their initial visit to *Las Humanas*, but this was the first opportunity the Spaniards had to really see, and to appreciate, these majestic animals. On the Spaniards' approach to the main herd, which roamed in the vast distance, they caught sight of a smaller group of bison running anxiously across the plains. The bison, whose primary instinct is to run in the face of danger, were being pursued by a pack of wolves that ran alongside of them, looking for a vulnerable animal to cull from the herd. Two small calves running with the herd had instinctively placed themselves in the middle, where the mass and ferocity of their elders shielded them from attack. Although the calves could run as fast as the adults, one ultimately tired, dropped behind the herd, and became surrounded by the wolves, who pulled at its ears and tail in an attempt to bring it to its knees. The Spaniards watched in admiration as a large adult male left the herd, and returned to where the calf was struggling with its attackers. They then watched with further appreciation as additional adults, including the calf's mother, returned to assist in the rescue. With lowered heads, and flying hooves, the magnificent creatures were successful in liberating the small yellowish calf, which the adults then took with them as they returned to their run across the plains.

Although the Spaniards viewed these animals with awe describing them as "terribly obstinate, courageous beyond exaggeration . . . cunning . . . " and "remarkably savage and ferocious," they were also amused by their appearance. Godoy described them in detail.

*Its shape and form are so marvelous and laughable, or frightful,
that the more one sees it the more one desires to see it, and no one
could be so melancholy that if he were to see it a hundred times a
day he could keep from laughing heartily as many times, or could
fail to marvel at the sight of so ferocious an animal. Its horns are
black, and a third of a vara long, as already stated, and resemble
those of the buffalo;[4] its eyes are small, its face, snout, feet, and
hoofs of the same form as of our cows, with the exception that both
the male and female are very much bearded, similar to he-goats.
They are so thickly covered with wool that it covers their eyes and
face, and the forelock nearly envelops their horns. This wool, which
is long and very soft, extends almost to the middle of the body, but
from there on the hair is shorter. Over the ribs they have so much
wool and the chine is so high that they appear humpbacked,
although in reality and in truth they are not greatly so, for the
hump easily disappears when the hides are stretched.*

*In general, they are larger than our cattle. Their tail is like that of
a hog, being very short and having few bristles at the tip, and they
twist it upward when they run. At the knee they have natural
garters of very long hair. In their haunches, which resemble those
of mules, they are hipped and crippled, and they therefore run, as
already stated, in leaps especially down hill. They are all of the
same dark color, somewhat tawny, in parts their hair being almost
black. Such is their appearance, which at sight is far more ferocious
than the pen can depict. As many of these cattle as are desired can
be killed and brought to these settlements, which are distant from
them 30 or 40 leagues, but if they are to be brought alive it will be
most difficult unless time and crossing them with those from Spain
make them tamer.[5]*

These creatures the Spaniards had encountered were truly awesome.
Large bulls could be as long as 12 feet from the tip of their noses to the
ends of their tufted tails. They could measure as much as six feet at the
shoulders, and weigh as much as 3,000 pounds. There were untold

millions of them thundering across the western plains, and now the Spaniards wanted them too.

There was no question that there were enough to go around—two enormous herds, one above the Arkansas River, the second below it. Everywhere, the prairie was alive with bison, dotting the distant swells like black specks. Filing in long lines to drink at the river, the bison were wading, plunging, and snorting in the water, and climbing the river's muddy banks. They could be killed, and the members of the exploratory party intended to do this, but the Spaniards also wanted to know if these wild cattle could be domesticated and become part of their livestock.

Zaldivar[6] hoped to corral a multitude of these beasts. He ordered his men to build an immense winged stockade, constructed of large logs of cottonwoods within which he intended to enclose 10,000 head of bison, but this proved impossible. The animals were so wild, quick-tempered, and unmanageable that the soldiers were unable to accomplish their confinement. They were successful in capturing several of the three-month-old calves, but the calves, whose instinct to flight contained a terrible fear of restraint, became so hysterical with fear that they died of shock. The Spaniards determined that these wild cattle could not be domesticated unless they were captured as newborns. The exploratory party was successful, however, at killing a large number of these cattle for meat.

The meat, which the Spaniards considered superior to that of their cows, was prepared for long storage by cutting it into thin slices called *cecinas* (jerky). Salt was added to protect it from the swarming insects, and the slices were hung on lines, braided by hand from the hides of the bison. This meat, equal to the most tender veal or mutton, was dried in the sun or over a campfire. When prepared in this manner, it was safe for use all winter and was still nutritious.

The preparation of the meat as jerky made it light in weight. The hunters could, therefore, carry large amounts of the meat, suet, hides, and tallow back to the villages on the Rio Grande, and keep these for later use. The colonists were going to need it, for the Pueblo Indians had told them that it was going to be a long and rigorous winter.

235

Mills and Creatures

Meanwhile, back on the river, the Spaniards remaining there continued to build their villages, now renamed San Gabriel (Yungue) and San Juan (Okhe), and often referred to, collectively, as the villages of the San Juan. The Spanish colonists had arrived at the site of San Juan on 23 August 1598. This was the site where Onate planned to build his capital of 'San Francisco de los Espanoles,' or St. Francis of the Spaniards. However, even by early September, reality had begun to rear its ugly head. There was to be no palace, and the regal carriages, which the captain-general had so laboriously hauled to his Northern Kingdom, would be of no use to him here. What the villagers really needed was a mill with which to grind the grain they would harvest the next year, and so while Zaldivar was off hunting, the villagers began to build one.

Using millstones shaped from blocks of black, porous lava rock that the Spaniards obtained north of their villages, a team of settlers began the construction of a horizontal waterwheel or *molino* adjacent to their main irrigation canal. The horizontal waterwheel, which may have originated in the mountains of Armenia (c 200 BCE), was an extraordinarily useful piece of machinery. Although seemingly a primitive device, the technology was suited to streams with a small volume of water such as could be obtained from an irrigation canal or from the Chama River. The mill employed a horizontal, paddle-armed wheel attached to the bottom of a vertical axle. The axle, extending upwards through a platform-placed stationary stone and through a rotating millstone, had an iron spike driven into its bottom. An iron plate fastened to a timber which lay across a pit below the mill, had a dimple in it on which the spike rotated. The *molinero*, or miller, could adjust the clearance between the millstones by the use of shims, thereby accurately controlling the fineness of the flour. The mill needed no gearing and was easy to build, and although it relied on fragile wooden parts, it was also easy to maintain and to repair. The settlers affixed a chute from the main *acequia* down a steep incline to a spot below the main canal. Water from the *acequia* was directed onto cupped blades where power was derived from the impact of the water's velocity. Once the water passed through the mill, a secondary ditch returned it to the fields for use in irrigation. Nothing was wasted.

Achieving the power of two horses, the mill could provide up to 400 pounds of meal a day. All that was required to bring the so-called '*Molino de San Gabriel*' into use was to open a small gate at the entrance of the chute, and the mill would be operational.

Additional millstones quarried near the village of San Gabriel would be used at a second mill the settlers were building. This village, to be known as the *finca de San Pedro*, was being built by Captain *don* Alonso de Sosa Albornoz, to replace the estate he had sold in New Spain. It was while looking for suitable material for these millstones that they found the skeleton.

*   *   *

Late one afternoon, during the fall of 1598, a lone horseman rode into the village of San Juan looking for his leader. He had been among a party of six men who had been sent to scout for suitable stone from which to carve millstones. In their search, the scouting party had discovered an almost completely exposed skeleton which they at first identified as that of a small horse (one of Castano's they thought). The skeleton, embedded in the slope of a gulch, rather than near the surface where a more recent skeleton should have been, was remarkable. Approximately three meters in length, its hind limbs were elongated and bird-like, and its hands, one of which was completely exposed, had three clawed fingers. Making the find all the more grizzly and frightening, were the bones of a creature, much like its parent, within the adult's body cavity. The adult had apparently eaten it. The men of the scouting party were beside themselves. The bones of this devil—for all were sure that it was a devil—meant that it was truly dead, and perhaps could no longer harm them. But who knew the extent of its powers? They retreated to the head of the gulch, unwilling to wait at the outcropping while they awaited Onate's arrival.

Told of the find, Onate came well-armed. With him was Juan de Vitoria Carvajal who, Onate thought, might be able to identify the being as something in Castano's troop. Onate and Vitoria Carvajal, carrying mining tools they had brought with them and accompanied by one of the men of the scouting party, strode up the gulch, while the remainder of the scouting party waited at what they considered to be a safe distance. The examination, by Onate's small party, confirmed what they had already been told. The skeleton was not that of a horse, nor were these the bones of any creature now living or known to them. These were the bones, they determined, of a creature long-dead, a relic of the distant past. They did not know how long it had been dead, or how long ago long ago could be. It was, however, a strange and monstrous creature, and, yes, perhaps a devil. It probably could not hurt them, but there was no reason to take any chances. Preoccupied by signs and portents, as individuals of this era were prone to be, the Spaniards were convinced that one had to take safeguards against evil spirits, especially—as was the belief—at the change of seasons. The creature must be reburied. Therefore, with great tumult (for the surest safeguard against spirits was noise), the entire group worked to detach and topple a portion of the outcropping above the creature, so as to bury it. When they were through, the entire group rode out of the gulch and through the dark valley below, each of the soldiers knowing, that even if commanded, he would not return.[1]

Salinas Province

In early October, with the countryside ablaze in crimson and gold, Onate, with 34 soldiers, among whom were Bartolome Romero and Hernan Martin Serrano the elder, left the pueblo of San Juan, and journeyed to some Indian villages lying east of the Rio Grande River. These villages were located on the east side of the Manzanos, an almost continuous range of mountains east of the Rio Grande Valley, and on the edge of the Great Plains. The villages were of the Tompiro or Jumano Indians, which Onate's nephews, Juan and Vicente de Zaldivar, had visited in late June 1598, and which they had encouraged him to visit as soon as he was able.

Cueloze, was the first pueblo Onate visited. Its location on the ridge of Chupadero Mesa provided its villagers with a 360-degree panorama of rolling pinon- and juniper-forested meadows. The village, composed of numerous building complexes constructed of pale gray stones, had hundred of rooms, one on top of the other, honeycombing the entire ridge. The buildings and rooms housed a like number of people, making the combined village one of the largest in the Southwest.

The site was impressive. Although there was little water in the immediate vicinity, the surrounding meadows were terraced and irrigated via an elaborate water catchment system. On these irrigated meadows, the Pueblo Indians raised beans, *maize*, melons, and squash. These vegetables, and a diet rich in deer, quail, rabbit, and bison meat, allowed the Indians villagers to live on a site that would have otherwise been uninhabitable. The Indians at Cueloze also raised cotton. In addition, the salt they obtained from dried lakebed deposits, provided them with a trade specialty. The copper bells, mother-of-pearl jewelry, and parrot feathers which Onate found at the site, provided documentation that these Indians were part of a vast trade network which stretched from the Mississippi River to the Pacific Ocean, and from central Kansas to New Spain and Central America.

What Onate was looking for at this site, and at each of the pueblos that he visited, were natural products which could be shipped to New Spain, Europe, or China, and sold at a profit. What Onate found were briny lakes similar to those that may still be found in Northern Castile. The dry lakes extended for many leagues and contained what was seemingly an infinite amount of excellent white salt. Collecting some, the Spanish soldiers wrapped it in cornhusks and took it with them. This was a valuable commodity, which could be used in the smelting of silver and in world trade. At last, Onate had found something he could use. Although he did not have any immediate intention of establishing a mule train to haul the commodity south, he did have a salary.

But Onate remained a man possessed. There had to be a way to make this land really pay, and he had yet to find it. When he devised his plan to journey to the South Sea is unknown. At some point, however, while he was looking over the Great Plains at Cueloze he decided to journey to the Southern Sea to "examine the harbors." Without any clear idea about how far the South Sea might be (for it was believed that New Mexico was a peninsula extending northward between Newfoundland and China), Onate got on his horse and headed west, but not before composing a note to his nephew, Juan de Zaldivar, with clear instructions. In this note, Onate told his *maese de campo*, who was still at San Juan, to wait there until his brother, Vicente, returned from the bison plains. Juan was told that when Vicente returned, Juan was to follow him with 30 men. With this, Juan de Onate, who knew that great exploits are reserved for great men, rode down the hill at Cueloze, and under a magnificent azure sky, full of hopes and dreams, headed northwest and towards the pass of Abo.

The Bitter Season

On 12 October, the first snow fell on the villages of the San Juan. It stayed but for one chilled morning, and then it was gone, the remnants of the brief fall clinging to tubular flowers besieged by hummingbirds. After this dusting, which had covered the land with a crystalline glaze, came a period of mild and warm weather followed by a heavy frost which destroyed the corn plants and vines.

Towards the end of October, snow fell softly again, a filmy white veil settling over the mountains in a translucent haze. It was apparent that winter was taking place over the valley, and soon, the snow, which had begun as a slight taste of the bitter season, began burying the San Juan villages in rime.

* * *

Pedro awoke to the faint sound of horses being ridden through the village and toward the corral, an enormous enclosure of posts and rails to the north of the village of San Gabriel. It was not yet dawn, the countryside illuminated by a brilliant heaven. Pedro lay in his blankets listening to the sound of the riders and trying to guess their number. *If they were Vicente's men,* he said to himself—*perhaps those of Vicente's vanguard, which would be preceding the expedition's carts—each man would be mounted on one horse, while leading an additional two.* Pedro listened, but he could not make out the number of riders. Therefore, he remained in his blankets, hoping to hear Diego's horse, Durandal, who would be waiting at the corral to welcome his master.

Durandal was not happy. Only scant days before Diego's departure to the bison plains, Durandal had challenged a stallion new to the corral, boxing with his front hooves, and trying to grab the withers and forelegs of the new animal with his teeth in an attempt to cripple it. Both horses had been injured. With shrill screams of indignation from Durandal, and despite Diego's desire to take his favorite horse with him on his hunt, Durandal had been left behind. This opinionated and impatient horse now awaited Diego's return.

If Pedro could have observed Durandal from the roof of his quarters, he would have seen an animal in a high state of alert—his weight placed squarely over each of his legs, his head up, muzzle elevated, ears pricked, nostrils flaring—long before the sound of hoof beats were audible to human ears. The vibrations of the earth, caused by the trample of the approaching animals and transferred to him through his feet, were being carried to Durandal's brain where they registered as sound. He listened intently until he discerned that the hoof beats were some he recognized. His initial calls were of a low whicker, followed by a loud and sustained whinny. Then, amid a cacophony of neighing by the horses in the corral, as well as those approaching it, Durandal's squeals and snorts could be heard above the cheerful greetings of the other corralled horses as they galloped around the railed fences waiting to view, and to inspect, the new arrivals. As Durandal trumpeted his knowledge of Diego's return, Pedro stirred the ashes of his fire pit and kindled the morning fire.

"I'm glad you're back." Pedro said to Diego as he appeared at the top of the ladder. "We're going hunting."

"Tomorrow, Pedro, or maybe the day after," Diego responded as he descended into the fire lit room. "I just got back, and I've got to see mama."

"You can see her when we get back," Pedro responded. "It'll only be for a few days, Diego. We need the food, and when I get back, Francisco and I are going with Juan de Zaldivar to act as *don* Juan's rear guard. This won't wait," Pedro said, "and I want you with me."

"Where?" Diego asked.

"To the west of the valley," Pedro responded. We're going to do well there," he said with his usual optimism. "We'll bring back enough meat for the whole camp. I'll get the horses while you eat,"

* * *

The day was bitterly cold, and snow covered the fields and the banks of the Rio Grande as Diego and Pedro rode out of the village of San Gabriel and up the Chama Valley. This area was 'a paradise,' the San Juan Indians had told Pedro. It had been previously occupied by Tewa-speaking ancestors of the 'Summer People,' and much game could be found there.

Fog, hugging the highlands to the west, cast a dreary tone to it all. The riders, listening to the sound of the wind moving through the canopy of the trees, rode up the southern bank of the Chama River, their beasts struggling through waist-high drifts. Jagged cliffs, cloaked with pine trees and rising up majestically from the stream's austral bank, kept the riders close to the river where there was less wind.

The tracks of deer and of other animals were apparent in the pinewoods, but they rode through the morning without seeing any game. Later in the day, the hunters emerged from the forest and entered a beautiful canyon through which a stream was flowing. There was a haze in the air, so that the sun, hanging just above the canyon walls, cast everything in a dim light. They rode up the riverbank following the margins of the stream as it ran between thick forests of pine on both banks. The snow, clinging to bark and to branches, softened the lines of the trunks and limbs, creating delicate new shapes and making the valley appear to be a fairy land replete with gnomes and elves.

Late in the afternoon, without having seen any game, the riders entered an even narrower canyon where they could hear the river rippling over rocks in the icy stream. An overcast sky, which only moments before had been clear, darkened and snow began to fall. Tussocks of expiration hung in the still air as the riders and their beasts moved up the valley. Snowfall, in soft, light flakes, masked the canyon walls. The snow built up on the heads and rumps of their horses, while covering their pack mule in white.

The river ran leaden and murky in waves with the sheen of watered camlet, hunching over veiled rocks and then sinking into troughs. And, although it was blowing miserably on the heights above the canyon walls, there was little wind on the river, just a light snow continuing to fall in a white mist. "It was a paradise," Diego later said. "There were birds everywhere, chickadees, jays, and nuthatches feeding in majestic evergreens."

The stream in the canyon was dark from melting snow. The hunters came to a broad, flat pond, tapering into a stretch of riffled water. The

242

pool's, dark waters were quiet with an easy snow falling. A water bird moving in advance of them led them up the stream, while a belted kingfisher, sitting on a branch above a rivulet, watched for small fish to swim by. These birds provided a backdrop for the sheldrakes and sawbills the hunters saw. The tracks of mountain lion, bobcat, and deer were in mud, and along the banks of the stream were markings where playful otters had been wrestling, romping, and sliding down the icy riverbank. The Robledo brothers dismounted, took water from the stream and decided to camp.

"I say we camp here," Pedro said.

Diego who had thrust his frozen hands into his armpits agreed. "Do we make shelter or hunt?" he asked of his younger brother.

"We'll do what we came to do," Pedro responded, removing his *harquebus* from the sheepskin in which it was sheathed. "It looks like the cats were following something, probably deer. Maybe we'll get lucky."

"Let's get some wood before we go," Diego said. "We can start a fire as soon as we get back."

In their search for firewood, they found a shallow cave in the canyon wall, its entrance nearly hidden by the trunk of a fallen tree. They decided to make their camp there, with Pedro gathering dead fall from the forest floor and Diego placing their gear in the cave well out of the snow. Then, leaving the animals saddled and tied beneath a large tree, Diego also got his *harquebus*, and the brothers began walking up stream.

The sky was dreary and gray and seemed to hover just above the tree line. Snow continued to fall, the pine needles drooping with its weight. When it stopped, a thick fog settled around them, and the only thing clear was that the day was quickly failing. They continued walking without speaking, the brook noisy at their feet.

They rounded a bend in the river and came upon a small group of deer, some silhouetted against the trees, others with only their heads and shoulders showing, fading into a forest of pine. Holding up his closed fist, Pedro motioned for Diego to stop, and both sank to a knee in the abrupt manner of English reverence.

"How many are there?" Diego whispered.

"Two in the open, and at least six, maybe eight, in the trees," Pedro responded quietly. "Check your load."

Then they did what they had trained themselves to do: apportion their targets and fire. The explosions from their weapons dislodged snow from branches of the tree behind which they had knelt, the cold of its crystal fall on their heads and necks filtering down the gap of their collars, and momentarily blinding them.

"Did we get them?" Diego asked eagerly as they ran into the clearing.

The two deer they had hit had not gone very far before collapsing. Taking their knives from their sheaths, Diego and Pedro slit the throats of their deer, cleaning their catch of blood so as preserve the meat. The blood pooled in the snow beside them as they worked.

"Go get the mule," Pedro directed.

"We won't have time to get them both back," Diego responded.

"I'll be damned if I'm going to leave one here for the cats," Pedro said. "Damn it, Diego! Go get the mule!"

Diego ran, falling down several times before reaching the animals which were tied beneath the tree where he had left them. The pool, beside which they were tethered, was quiet, the bodies of the beasts reflecting clearly in the quiet stream. Night was approaching as Diego, his fingers frozen from the cold, worked to loosen the mule's reins.

"*I'll never make it back in time,*" he said to himself. "*We can't make two trips. We'll just have to leave one there.*"

The mule was difficult to move, and its actions seemed uncertain, wobbly, and painful. Grabbing the reins of the poor animal, Diego retraced his steps up the stream bank and shortly came upon Pedro, stumbling and struggling with a deer on his back. Unwilling to remain with the deer while awaiting Diego's return, Pedro had eviscerated both animals. Then, carrying a carcass on his back and walking a short distance down the path they had carved in the virgin snow, he had dropped the first carcass and returned for the second. Using this odd relay, Pedro had moved both carcasses down the trail for some distance where Diego found him. Placing a deer on the back of their mule—and refusing Diego's request to carry the second—Pedro placed the second deer over his shoulders and carried it to the cave.

Returning to the campsite, the hunters found their horses looking wet and miserable in falling snow. Diego's horse, Durandal, looked dejected, his head dropping, and his breathing irregular and accompanied by the noticeable movement of his nostrils and chest wall. Diego checked his ears and then his lower legs. Both felt extremely cold. He made the same examination of Babieca, adding, in addition, a check for heaves, by placing his hand on the flanks of Pedro's horse, and feeling the rise and fall of his breathing. Babieca seemed well, but Diego was extremely concerned about his own horse. He looked at his beasts, and at the sky, and could sense that the temperature was dropping. Left where they were, Diego felt, the animals might be dead by morning. Releasing their reins from the tree, he led the animals to the back of the cave. After removing their saddles, he spent a long time stroking the three animals on their backs and on their rumps and rubbing them down with a dry blanket, starting on the upper part of their legs and finally working over their entire bodies. He spoke to them quietly, reassuring them of their safety, and spread corn for them to eat.

"*That'll have to do,*" he said, more to himself than to Pedro who was working to build a fire. Taking only salt and a metal pot from their gear, Diego filled the latter at the stream and returned, pouring water into the cup of his hand, giving each animal water to drink. Within minutes, Pedro had a warm fire burning at the mouth of the cave where the brothers squatted and readied their meal.

Although the cave was shallow, there was more than enough room to sit, to stand, and to move around in. The floor, thick with dry leaves and duff, was mostly flat, but with a raised portion in the back where Diego had put the animals. Nosing around in the back of the cave while checking on their beasts, Pedro had brushed scratchings of dirt and twigs from the floor, revealing worked stone, and two fine projectile points which he and his brother now examined in the firelight. "Summer People," Pedro said, and Diego nodded in agreement.

Spreading sheepskins, and wrapping themselves in blankets, the brothers sat against the cave's one flat wall and feasted on dried *piki*, corn mush, *condumio*,[1] and deer meat, washed thoroughly of blood and cooked on a Cross of Lorraine.[2] When the meat was hard and crisp, they rubbed salt on it, cut it into thin strips, and ate it with gusto.

"Too bad we don't have some of mama's stuff with us," Diego said. "Oh, what we could do with some garlic and onions. That would make this a perfect meal!"

"Why don't you just wish for some tomatoes and peppers while you're at it?" Pedro asked.

"And some vinegar and olive oil, too," Diego added, before allowing Pedro to finish.

"Let me know when you get back from Tembleque," Pedro said, using an expression often used by their father and addressed to a long-winded story teller. "If we had all of that, we could make some *gazpacho*[3] or an *olla podrida*."[4] They both laughed. "No, Diego," Pedro said, "this is perfect just the way it is. And it won't be long before we're gentlemen and will have to use toothpicks."

The brothers talked as they ate. "How are they?" Pedro asked about their animals.

"Babieca's fine," Diego said, "but I'm worried about Durandal. He's weak and seems sick. I'm going to have to stay up all night to make sure he doesn't lie down. If he lies down and casts[5] back there his weight will cause him to suffocate."

"He'll be fine by tomorrow," Pedro said of Diego's horse. Babieca has a special sense about this sort of thing. They're nibbling at each other's withers back there now, and Babieca won't let him lie down. You'll see. That Babieca makes all kinds of good things happen!

"You know, Diego," Pedro said. "I knew we had a winner when we bought him. The man we got him from said that Babieca and his mother were kept in a small corral away from the other horses, but almost from the day he was born, he was a *maneruelo*,[6] leaving his mother to make friends with any passing stranger. And if the person petting him sat down on the ground, Babieca would lie down and stretch out his neck to be stroked like a dog. He'd even rest his head on the knees of the person petting him, and wouldn't get up until he was forced to do so. Most horses don't do that!" Pedro said. "They only put up with us because we feed them, and because they have nothing better to do. You'd think that with his affection for people, that he'd behave like a *cabestro*,[7] rather than the stallion we know him to be. I knew papa would love him—and that he'd love papa—and that he'd miss papa when he was gone."

"And now he's yours," Diego said to his brother.

"And now he's mine," Pedro responded, smiling at Diego.

"Well, you're good for each other," Diego said, "and with a short rest at San Gabriel when we get back, we'll all be ready for another hunt." They sat quietly for awhile, watching the falling snow, and listening to the moan of the wind in the heights above the canyon walls. "This hunting is getting harder and harder, Pedro," Diego said. "Every time we go out, we have to go farther and farther from San Juan to get the same amount of meat. I think we're driving the game away."

"You're probably right," Pedro responded, "although there was probably never a lot of game right on the river anyway. But Tomas, the interpreter, told me that, even at Santo Domingo, where there's less forest than here, there had been enough game on the river for the Indians who lived there. Now, though, with our thousands of livestock, we're taking wood, and forage for miles around. I can just hear what papa would say if presented with this problem. 'It's the axes,' he'd say, or 'It's the noise' – you know, in that way he had of breaking things down to their simplest elements."

"It is the axes," Diego responded. "The Tewas had only stone, but they managed to find enough wood from dead fall. And look at us with our steel blades! We're cutting down everything, cottonwoods, junipers, pinions for cooking, for warmth, for charcoal, and even for fodder for our beasts. Without our mules and horses, we'd have to carry the wood back from the mountains on our backs. You know, I'm sure I sound like a Perogrullo[8] prophesizing the obvious, but the Indians are going to start thinking that we're more trouble than we're worth. They're not going to want to feed us forever. We may soon have to see whether it's true . . . that only Catalans can wring bread from stone."

Pedro agreed. "The Pueblos are complaining that our cows are eating their corn and trampling their seedlings. We'll have to build our own villages away from theirs, Diego. Maybe on the plains where you went with Vicente de Zaldivar?"

"I don't think so," Diego responded, "I don't think any Spaniard could be happy there. No Spaniard really feels at ease unless he can see a mountain, and there are no mountains there. Nearer the pueblo of Pecos, however, where there are both mountains and plains, the land is beautiful. You should have seen the plums, Pedro, like those of the *Almonacid de Toledo* that papa used to bring home for us to eat when

Lucia and I were children. There were millions of them, enormous, and sweet, and warmed by the sun. We ate so many that we could barely sit our horses the next morning, only going but a league, before our stomachs were rumbling, and we were looking for bushes."

Pedro laughed at the thought of this, and Diego continued.

"Two days from Pecos," Diego said, "we found Indians. They were very different from the Pueblos here. They appeared to be a powerful people and expert bowmen. Most of the men were naked, but some were clothed with skins of bison, and some with blankets. They came to us demanding food and presents, but offered their friendship by extending the palms of their hands to the sun, and then bringing their hands down on the person whose friendship they wanted. We gave them what we had and quickly made friends of them."

"Did they take you to their camp?" Pedro asked.

"Not then," Diego responded. "Zaldivar sketched out a plan for visiting their village in which he would have a van and a rear guard, and soldiers in-between. But in the end, he went alone, taking only Jusepe as an interpreter. He returned that night, having gained much respect among us for his bravery since the Indians could easily have killed him. They asked for his assistance against the Jumanos, a tribe of Indians who, Zaldivar was made to understand, paint themselves after the manner of the Chichimecas."

"And when did you see these Indians?" Pedro asked.

"We saw them the next day. They live in hide tents. The women wear trousers made of buckskin with shoes of the same. They came out to meet us bringing *pinole*, and we gave them presents also. They provided us with a guide, and we continued on our way to discover the main herd of cattle."

"Were those the only Indians you saw?" Pedro asked, anxious to hear more about the Indians and the bison.

"No. There were more. A lot more," Diego said. "Several days later we found another Indian encampment of perhaps 50 tents, bright red and white in color, and bell-shaped. And the bison, Pedro . . . Oh my God! We found and killed a lot of scattered bison along the way, but then we found an enormous herd, greater than anything you can imagine. There had to be at least 100,000 cows, Pedro. The plains black with them. We built a corral within which to capture them, but it was impossible. We killed many, however, gaining at least 80 *arrobas* (a ton) of tallow. And the meat, Pedro, the meat of the bull is excellent, superior to that of our cow, while the meat of the cow is equal to our most tender veal or mutton. I want those cattle for our herds," Diego said, "but I couldn't live on the plains."

A person could live here in this cave," Pedro responded. "You could have bison and deer and elk and this would make a great place to make a home. How far back do you think it goes?" he asked of his brother, regarding the cave.

"I don't think it goes very far," Diego responded, "although that small hole back there could be enlarged and used for storage."

"There's kind of a shelf back there, too, that could be used for something," Pedro said. "You know, Diego, it wouldn't take much to turn this into a home. A wall here at the front. Bring in some dirt to level the floor, and you'd have a proper house."

"Don't forget a fireplace and chimney!"

"Hell, yes! It would be better than anything we've got at San Gabriel!" Pedro said. "Let's make ourselves a promise, Diego, that we'll come back in the spring . . . . that we'll come back at every season to see what its like."

"Hunting and fishing?"

"Hunting and fishing! A promise, Diego?"

"A promise."

The snow sputtered as it fell into the fire, and it was clear that the temperature was dropping. The fire heated the cave walls about them, a measure of its radiated heat reaching into the back of the cave. Each man loosened the 'point' of his trousers, the tie or string with an aglet in front which held up their breeches. And to their *gabans*, their greatcoats, which had a hood to cover their heads, they now added *papahigos*, a half-mask that covered their faces as a protection against the cold and the wind. Wrapped in their blankets and holding their *harquebuses* across their chests with their gloved hands, they were as warm as they might have been sleeping in their barracks at San Gabriel.

Diego stared into the fire, contemplating Pedro's words and thinking that he, Diego, didn't have the ability to accept the simple ride and tide of life, as shown by Pedro and by their father. He envied Pedro, so full of life, boisterous, loving, excited about everything, yet, like their father, demanding so little of the world.

"Pedro," Diego said quietly, "maybe this is your land of birds."

There was no response, and Diego could tell by Pedro's breathing, that he was asleep.

Home and Hearth

A threatening sky, dark as a slate roof, served as a backdrop for the pueblos of the San Juan. Clouds of a darker gray filled the sky to the west. The wind blew intermittently through the crown of the trees, bending and then breaking them, as an ice storm moved into the valley. The storm, which moved across a brooding landscape, pushed snow ahead of it, each tiny six-sided crystal reflecting light and moving silently upon unseen currents of air. The storm of ice pellets and long needles, was being driven with quiet fury into the wind-tossed stream which now became one with the turbulent sky.

Diego, clutching his greatcoat about him, climbed a notched beam to the roof where he walked to the center of a square opening out of which protruded a ladder. A wisp of blue smoke came from the aperture, and it stung his eyes as he descended into his mother's apartment.

He stood at the bottom of the ladder allowing his eyes to become adjusted to the veiled light. The room, which served Francisca and their mother as a kitchen and storeroom, smelled of pine and cedar, of dust and clay, the scent sifting through the ceiling, the walls, and the floor. The small chamber, its walls, whitewashed with burnt gypsum, had leather wall hangings, or *guadameciles*, to ward off the chill.[1] The floor of plastered mud was covered with a coarse matting called *jerga*. Wool blankets were rolled up along one wall. A doorway covered with a woolen blanket was in the back wall. It led into a second room, and beyond it, into a third.

A woman looking spare and wan appeared in the doorway between the two rooms, an air of misery clinging to her like an ethereal veil. Diego smiled, and reaching out, grasped his mother hand. He wanted to hold

250

her, but their relationship had never allowed for an easy display of affection. He unrolled a couple of the blankets from their place against the wall, and they sat down upon them.

* * *

"And how is that land?" his mother asked of Diego who had recently returned with his brother Pedro from the valley of the Chama. "Is it like this one?" she asked.

"It's beautiful, Mama," he exclaimed, "a sheltered valley with lots of game. You should have seen Pedro, Mama," he laughed. "He was in seventh heaven. I practically had to drag him back. If he wasn't going exploring with Juan de Zaldivar, I think he'd still be there. He's happy to be in San Gabriel because the four of us are there together, but he'd rather be off hunting.

"And San Gabriel?" his mother asked in her soft, sweet voice. "Have you boys made a home there?"

"There's not much there, Mama," Diego responded somewhat dejectedly as he sat cross-legged on the floor in front of his mother, the knees of his long legs supporting his elbows. "It is, in many respects, a ghost town," he said as he sipped at the contents of the vessel his mother had offered him. "We were told that a number of the people at Yungue moved here to San Juan several years ago. And," he added, "if we're going to take over that village as *don* Juan has said, I think that a lot more of the Indians will be coming here. That appears to be the way of these Pueblos," he continued, scratching his newly trimmed beard. "They seem to build and abandon their villages for many reason. They don't seem to have the same attachment to their homes as do we."

"Would you like to have something to eat, Diego?" his mother asked. "I don't get to feed you anymore and I miss that."

"No, Mama," Diego responded quietly. "I came to tell you of some plans." He stopped, sipped broth from the cup he was holding in his hand and said, quite deliberately, "The *maese de campo* is making plans to join *don* Juan in search of a port. It's an important assignment," he added "but I can't go. He's taking Pedro and Francisco, Mama," Diego said, glancing at his mother to gauge her reaction. "Maybe because they're younger?" he asked, as though answering his own question. "Anyhow, I drew the long straw, and I'm to stay here."

"Is it a scout?" his mother asked, with a note of concern clearly registering in her voice. "How far is the sea, Diego? Three day's ride? Ten day's ride? Where is it, and why are we going?" his mother asked as she placed her outstretched hand on his wrist. "What have we to gain, Diego? You're to become *hidalgos*. Why do they have to put you further at risk?"

Diego told his mother that Onate had been told that the South Sea was but 15 days' journey, and reminded her, that men face risk primarily out of a sense of their own honor, and not to gain advancement in the world. "Even if there was nothing to gain, Mama, we'd have to go," he answered, moving to grasp his mother's hand in a gesture of protection, as well as affection.

"We've got a responsibility here," he told his mother. "We have to hold this land for our children—for Lucia's children. We've got to hold it at all cost. You should see it, Mama," he continued with enthusiasm. "It's beautiful almost beyond compare. Only 11 leagues from Pecos, on the other side of the mountains, there's this place—'a land of birds'—which must surely be the 'Land of Promise' or '*Sobradisa*' of which papa dreamt. It has this small river, which leaves its beautiful canyon there, to emerge upon the plains. Behind the canyon, up in the *sierras*, there's a luminous mountain of purple and rose with two distinct peaks. The mountain, which some called the *Cerro de Tecolote* (Owl Mountain), marks the spot and provides water for the stream."

"Near Pecos?" his mother asked. "Where's that?"

"Not far from here, Mama," Diego responded. "To the south, perhaps a day or two. And then around the mountains. A day or two more."

He stopped, measuring his mother's reaction to all he had told her, and with even more enthusiasm than he was actually feeling, he continued.

"Directly behind the cliffs that guard the entrance to the canyon," he said, "there is what papa would have referred to as a '*cirque*,' an oval amphitheater. The river flows around the south side of it. In this basin," he said, cupping his hands and demonstrating for his mother, "there are hot springs without number. Hot springs, Mama! You can bathe in hot water to your heart's content!

"After the river leaves its canyon," he went on, trying to paint a picture of the site for his mother, "it flows through vast green meadows that continue in a broad valley as far as the eye can see. We camped in the *vega*—the fertile plain—below the canyon and fished for two days. It was incredible, Mama," he said with delight. "We'd throw our lines into the stream and pull out fish as quickly as we were able. No bait. Just bare hooks. As many as we wished on one line. We took forty *arrobas* (a thousand pounds) in less than three hours!

"The area immediately to the east of the river is surrounded by acres of marsh and water, timbered canyons and streams, and grasslands extending into eternity. They provide shelter and food for the millions of animals in the area including pronghorn and deer.

"We saw grebes and herons and ducks without number. And in the sky overhead were bald and golden eagles, harriers, falcons and an autumn migration of hawks. And I don't know what they're doing there, Mama, perhaps it's proof of the nearness of the sea, but there were pipers and gulls mixed in among the doves, larks, swallows and jays.

"The crows, of course, complained that we were taking too much," he laughed, "but your favorites were there, too, Mama, the bluebird and robin, bidding us to stay and take whatever we wanted. As soon as you're able, Mama, and it's safe to go, I'll take you to see this land, which is some of the most beautiful I've seen here. We may not be able to go this year, and perhaps not in the year to come, but I think I've found our home, Mama, on the *vegas grandes en el rio de las gallinas*.

* * *

The evening before Pedro and Francisco were to leave with Juan de Zaldivar, they met with their mother and with all members of the family as they did on many nights when not playing cards, dice or other *jugandos a las tablas* in their barracks at San Gabriel. Without Bartolome, who was with Onate, the family sat around their fire for a parting meal. The meal, served on tin-glazed, colorful, Mexican-made, majolica ware, was not as lavish as it might have been on most important occasions, but the best sauce is hunger.

"I wish I was going with you, but I've got a job to do here," Diego said to his brothers, ignoring the fact that he had not been chosen for this assignment. "But you've got some good men with you," he added, trying to put his mother's mind at ease, while scooping beans from his dish with a folded tortilla. "They're some of our best. Geronimo Marquez, Gaspar Lopez Tabora, Las Casas, Escalante, and Nunez. They're some of our best," he repeated. "I don't think you could do better."

As the Robledo family sat around their open fire, its blue smoke curling towards the ceiling, they spoke about the upcoming holy season (Christmas, the Epiphany, and, most importantly, the full moon of February, for which they would keep a three-day fast).[2] These would be the first holy days they would have in their new homes.

While they ate, the occupants of the small room could see the starlit sky through the open hatchway. As the evening progressed, heavy clouds moved in to shield these stars from view, and minute snowflakes, like jeweled points of light, began to tumble out of the evening's sky, some of which drifted silently into the fire-lit room.

Below the hatchway, and wearing his cherished archer's helmet, Pedro modeled Bartolome's large buckskin jacket and some ragged pelts which he had found, and which he had tied around the ankles of his boots. They all laughed uproariously as Pedro did a *zapateado*, a clog dance in which he struck the soles of his boots with the palms of his hands and lumbered about the room like some armored walrus. He continued like this, stomping on the earthen floor in great delight, until he suddenly broke through into the room below.

"*Dios Mio!*" his mother said, first holding her hands to her chest, and then covering her face in uproarious laughter. "Oh, my God! Pedro, what have you done?"

Pedro, with only his eyes visible within his metal helmet, extracted his foot from the small hole, knelt on the floor and with great solemnity, peered into the chasm below. Taking a firebrand from the small fire and holding it beside his metal cheek, he again looked into the room below. "You know, Mama," he said, "this could be useful. If you don't fall through while you're cooking, or while walking around up here, you could use it to check on your supplies without going down the ladder."

They laughed until they had to stop, so sore were their stomachs from laughter.

Diego and Alonso covered the small hole with a flagstone taken from the center of the room. And, after a wonderful evening of fellowship, and with the recognition that the younger Robledos would be gone for an undetermined period of time, the family said its goodbyes. Then, the young men mounted their horses for the short ride across the freezing waters of the river to their barracks at San Gabriel where their comrades awaited them. Tomorrow, 30 of them, a quarter of the colony's forces, would leave to join Onate in his quest for the South Sea.

*   *   *

And so it was, that at mid-day, on 18 November 1598, with the cold brisk wind of a tramontane blowing out of the north, that Juan de Zaldivar and his men rode out of the village of San Juan and headed south.

Acoma

Onate had already been here. He had obtained shelter among three enormous sandstone buttes which solemnly guard the approach to the 367-foot stone tableland rising out of a level plain. After leaving the Salinas Province, and stopping briefly at Puaray on the Rio Grande, he journeyed to Acoma,[1] the cornerstone and most firmly rooted of Indian villages in his adobe kingdom.

The site presented an impregnable position and was rated by one of Onate's men as the best-situated Indian stronghold in all of Christendom. Antonio de Espejo, and Francisco Vasquez de Coronado before him, had also been here. Vasquez de Coronado had marveled at the three-and four-story dwellings made of rock and clay, and at the site which he judged to be one of the strongest ever seen. He noted that the homes, which were built on the high rock, faced south to absorb astral warmth during the winter, and featured impenetrable boreal enclosures as a shield against freezing winds.

Onate carried with him the description of Acoma that Espejo had provided in a document sent to King Philip II during October 1583. In part it read:

> In the very rock stairs are built by which [the Indians] ascend to and descend from the town, which is very strong. They have cisterns of water at the top, and many provisions stored within the pueblo ... They gave us liberally of food and of all else which they had. [2]

Although Onate was also cordially received at this mesa-top village to which he and his men had so painfully climbed, he was shrewd and wary enough not to enter the one *kiva* into which he was invited. He was later to find that assassins had awaited him there. After conferring with the Indians, he and his men returned to the plain, but not before repeating the ceremony of vassalage. Each of the leaders of the Acome, Coomo, Chaamo, and Ancua in turn knelt before him, placed their hands between his, and swore an oath of fidelity in which they stated that those who vow obedience can never again withdraw their allegiance under penalty of death. Then the Acome watched as Onate and his men left the base of their mesa and continued westward.

As the Spaniards rode away from the base of the mesa, snow began to fall. The flakes some of the largest the soldiers had ever seen. The weather throughout the journey was cold and dismal. Along the way, they ran into a snowstorm, lost some of their horses, and were generally in rather pitiful condition when they arrived at Zuni.

At Zuni, where Onate and company were also cordially received, they found crosses—still treated as revered objects—that had been left there by Vasquez de Coronado. Here, Onate sent the trustworthy Marcos Farfan de los Godos, his captain of the guard and of the horses, to look for a great salt lake which the Indians told him lay some nine leagues to the south. After finding the lake, Farfan and his four companions returned to Zuni with what Farfan hoped would be received as a favorable report. "Nowhere in Christendom or elsewhere," said Farfan, "can such a wondrous thing be found. Nor does our king possess such salt."[3] Again, salt! So far, this was the only thing of real value they had found. There had to be more.

While waiting at Zuni for Farfan's return, Onate sent three of his men to find the horses they had lost in the snowstorm. Instead, they found a half-dead Perez de Villagra who had raced ahead of Geronimo Marquez and the other soldiers to report to Onate the outcome of their murderous assignment. At Puaray, Perez learned that Onate had passed through there on his way west and Perez decided to catch up with him. Changing his course from north to west and crossing immense, lonely distances, he continued alone with his beloved dog as his only traveling companion. Nearing Acoma, he spied in the distance a small contingent of Indians guarding the trail and waiting like so many crouching tigers ready to pounce upon anyone approaching their village. He managed to avoid them by leaving the trail, and rode through the afternoon and waning light of evening.

Toward nightfall, however, Villagra found that neither he nor his mount could go any further. Prostrating himself upon the mean earth, he slept fitfully but awakened in the spent quarter of the night to discover himself cloaked in a mantle of white. Fearing he would freeze to death if he remained where he was, he mounted his horse and continued in the fresh dawn.

The Acome, who had failed to lure Onate into their *kiva* where assassins had awaited him, now hoped to ensnare any Spaniard who sought to follow him. Disturbed by the report they had received from their spies who had observed the ceremony of vassalage conducted by Onate at Okhe in early September, the Acome had decided to kill or to drive from their country the Spaniards and all Indian members of the pueblos who had welcomed or fed them. In the middle of the trail, they had dug a pit within which they placed sharpened stakes. Then they covered the whole with brush and earth. The pit was now additionally blanketed with snow which further hid its presence. Riding along this trail, Perez and his horse fell into the pit and his horse was impaled. Perez was lucky enough to survive uninjured, but he was now without a mount. Although a seeming tragedy, this was perhaps a godsend, for it would have been difficult for him to remain hidden if accompanied by a horse. In the middle of nowhere and with a snowstorm approaching, Perez began walking west.

Throwing aside his helmet, armor, *harquebus*, and shield, Perez kept only his sword and dagger. Then, wearing his shoes backwards so as to fool anyone who might attempt to track him, he continued westward in the direction in which he knew Onate had traveled. Incredibly, Perez survived this ordeal in freezing temperatures, without food, and hiding where he was able. Half-dead with cold, thirst, and exhaustion, he wandered in a westerly direction for four days until the chance encounter with the men who had been sent out to look for the lost horses.[4]

On Sunday 8 November, in a blinding snowstorm (and on the same day that Vicente de Zaldivar returned to San Juan), Onate left Zuni for Hopi where he was very cordially received. After reviewing the Hopi pueblos, which he judged to be very poor, Onate dispatched the extremely reliable, Farfan de los Godos, Bartolome Romero, Hernan Martin Serrano the elder, and six additional soldiers on a scouting expedition. What they were looking for were the Cruzados, Indians who, according to the Hopi, painted their faces with the bright colors of the earth. Perhaps these colored soils suggesting silver ore held a clue to the mines Onate was looking for, and Farfan and the others were sent to find out.

* * *

With his brother Vicente now returned to San Juan from the bison plains, Juan de Zaldivar, who had been left in command of Onate's headquarters, was free to leave San Juan as commanded by his uncle, *don* Juan de Onate. Therefore, with 31 men, some of whom had recently returned with his brother from the *Llanos de Cibolo*, he left San Juan on 18 November 1598. The group backtracked along the trail the expedition had blazed from the Province of Tiguex to San Juan, and at Puaray, the Zaldivar party turned west and headed toward the Pacific. As they rode away from the Rio Grande and its thick stand of denuded cottonwoods, the country through which they traveled became undulating grasslands with regions of pinon and juniper.

Days later, as Juan de Zaldivar and his men rode through vast stretches of bare, rough country and drifting snow, the treeless earth opened out before them. In a broad valley to the west, they saw what appeared to be an enormous butte, the clay and stone terraced structures on top indistinguishable from the rock on which they were built. As they rode closer, they could more clearly see these structures and the people who inhabited them now scurrying about on the edge of the cliffs. A marvelous conglomeration of abrupt escarpments made up of mighty pillars, rugged, cavernous clefts, and scores of crags, the cliffs were more than fifty *estados* [5] in height. Approaching, the men observed that they were not only perpendicular, but actually overhanging.

Thirteen days from San Juan and approximately 60 miles from the Rio Grande, Juan de Zaldivar was glad to be where he was. Correctly guessing that his uncle had been there before him and knowing that Espejo in 1583 had been given *mantas*, deerskins, strips of bison hides, and provisions of *maize* and turkeys by these people, he sought to barter what he had for the same. It was 4:00 p.m. on 1 December 1598 and storm clouds were billowing in the west.

"Geronimo!" Zaldivar shouted into the wind that whipped at his clothing. "Take six men and find a way to climb to the pueblo. Take these beads, mirrors, hawk bells, and hatchets and ask the Indians to give us some water and firewood, for there's none here. Use the hatchets in barter for flour. Bring back as much as you can carry." Then walking with Marquez to where the horses were tied, he told him of his plans. "We'll set up a temporary camp here to get us out of the wind," he said as Marquez and the others mounted their horses. "We'll have to find a better camp when you return. Work fast, Geronimo," he added, holding Marquez's mount by its reins. "We've got to find better shelter."

With this Geronimo Marquez and his men rode the short distance to the base of the mesa. Indians were now descending from the top which was a league in circumference. The Acome showed them the ladder trail on the northwest side of the mesa and encouraged them to climb. This trail consisted of two flights of steps cut into the solid rock. The first flight was composed of 200 steps that could be ascended without much difficulty. It was followed by a second flight of a 100 more steps, narrower and more difficult than the first, which continued to a location approximately 12 feet from the crest. The final 12 feet were the most difficult. Here, Marquez and his men had to ascend by putting hands and feet into holes pecked into the rock face. Once he reached the top of the mesa, Marquez discovered a great pile of stones that the Indians kept to hurl at an approaching enemy. Marquez presented the hatchets and hawk bells to individuals he determined to be the leaders of the village. The Indians agreed to provide the water and firewood he requested and while doing so, gave Marquez and his men a tour of their village.

While the Spaniards waited—for the Indians appeared to be in no hurry and perhaps even reluctant to comply with his requests—Marquez took note of what he saw. The village was built on an irregular but nearly level mesa of approximately 70 acres. He noted that the great rock was almost cut in two by a savage cleft that effectively divided its surface into two mesas, north and south. There were no homes on the south mesa.

On the north mesa, the homes appeared to be part of the sandstone itself, and, although they were not hewn out of the solid rock, they appeared to be as much fortress as home. Marquez found three parallel lines of approximately 500 houses made of stone and clay.

Each group of houses was approximately a 1,000 feet long and 40 feet high running from east to west and separated from one another by *calles* or streets. It appeared the *calle* between the middle and south row of houses had been purposely left wider than the other street to provide a plaza for open-air ceremonials. He estimated the number of individuals in the village to be approximately 1,500, mostly Acome, but other Indians were also present who were not of their tribe.

Each of the structures consisted of three or four stories built in terraces such as the Spaniards had found at Okhe and Yungue. The lowest story was from 12 to 15 feet high and access to it was gained from the roof above it. Also, as at Okhe and each of the pueblos they had visited, the lowest story was used exclusively for the storage of supplies—enough, Marquez guessed, to withstand a long siege. The Acome, therefore, entered their houses by ladders from the ground to the second story. Unlike the other pueblos, however, where access to the third story was also gained by ladder, here at Acoma, the third and fourth stories and the roofs were reached by steps and narrow stages built into the division walls. He noted, also, that most of the ladders leading to the roofs had been withdrawn.

In the one home which Marquez visited, he saw the standard three corn-grinding troughs found in the family units at each of the pueblos. Hung from the *vigas* (roofing timbers brought, he was told, from the blue *Sierra de San Mateo*, almost 25 miles away) were bundles of dried herbs and roots: pig weed, wild pea, bulrush and yucca. Between the *vigas* and their pine-staved ceilings were beautifully painted and plumed prayer sticks, made to be hidden and presented on an altar. Below them, suspended from one of the *vigas*, was a smooth pole upon which hung blankets and articles of clothing. Hanging from pegs, which were affixed to the walls, were quivers, bows, war clubs and throwing sticks. On the floor were water jars and a black cooking pot. Reed mats, which were covered with blanket rugs and robes, were folded against the walls.

Marquez took note, also, of the people who appeared to be silent and wary. They were, like the other Pueblos, small of stature but strongly built. The men wore their coarse black hair loose or in one or two braids fastened with bright-colored lengths of cotton. On their foreheads, their hair was cut in a fringe even with the line of the eyes. They wore bands around their heads but left the crowns uncovered.

The water, for which Marquez was waiting, was being scooped from two great natural reservoirs that he saw on the north mesa. He was told, also, that there was a similar cistern on the south mesa, but that access to this was severely limited because of the cleft. Additional water, he was assured by the Acome, could be found at their summer or farming village which lay some six miles distant from the mesa. This was water that ran along the bed of a stream the Acome used to irrigate their fields. Marquez took special note of this, for that was where he would tell Zaldivar they should camp.

Eventually, the Indians provided the Spaniards with the water and firewood—but not the flour—they requested, but they did not appear happy, and even appeared to be arguing amongst themselves.

When Marquez and his men returned to camp with the firewood and water, Marquez suggested the Spaniards guarantee compliance with their request for flour by detaining the chiefs he had brought with him. Marquez said, "There's no more work to be had out of a person after he's been paid for it." Zaldivar refused, wanting to assure the Indians they would not be harmed in any way.

Although his present location did not provide his troop with either water or sufficient shelter, Zaldivar set up camp, hoping to obtain the flour he needed the next day. The next morning the Acome came back to his encampment with several *piki* and three or four *fanegas* of *maize*.

The *maese de campo* asked them again for some flour for the journey as he had, through Marquez, already given them articles of trade for it with promises of more trade goods. The Indians merely repeated their suggestion that Zaldivar go to a place some two leagues from the pueblo where there was water. There, Zaldivar and his men could wait until the required flour which they were to receive from the Acome was available to them.

Therefore, Zaldivar ordered his men to break camp, pack their baggage, and move to the stream they had been told about. There, adjacent to an extensive marsh, they found fields on a medium-sized river whose waters the Indians tapped for irrigation purposes. It was there that Espejo had found bushes of Castilian roses (later to be used as a small pox preventative) and Castilian onions (used by the Acome for food and seasoning). Espejo had noted that the roses and onions grew wild in this country without planting or cultivation. There, too, the Acome gathered mushrooms, rock cress, bamboo and reed (from which they made flutes), spearmint and horsemint (which they chewed while hunting), wild celery, sandbar willows (from which they made their baskets), wild potato, clover (which they used as chewing gum), and cattails. These were items they used as food or for utilitarian or medicinal purposes.

With his bivouac now established, Juan de Zaldivar, with 12 soldiers, rode back to the mesa, climbed to the pueblo, and was escorted throughout the village where he, too, was encouraged to descend unaccompanied into one of their *kivas*. Like his uncle, he also declined the offer. The purpose for this second visit was to strike a bargain with the Acome for the flour he needed. Offered in exchange for this flour were many metal articles, including knives, little silver hawk bells and more than 15 hatchets. The Indians reiterated what they had previously told him. They did not have an adequate amount of flour on hand, but they would grind it. He was asked to come back in two days. Zaldivar gave the Acome those items he had with him and promised to bring the rest when he came for the flour. With a bargain thus struck, and carrying handfuls of *piki*, he and his men descended the mesa and returned to the arroyo where they were camped.

That evening was one of the strangest the men had ever experienced. With the descent of the sun, the golden tint on the clouds first changed to bronze, then to carmine, and a dull red, this last finally turning into a pale yellow which blended imperceptibly into the darkness of the night. Then the sky, great with black billowing clouds in the west, darkened so that no stars were visible. Most remarkable was the awesome silence. The atmosphere in its purity re-echoed the slightest sound. Only the crunching of feet trampling the crisp, crystalline snow relieved the stillness. There appeared to be an infinity of separation between themselves and all living creatures. The night was exceedingly cold and, as the men huddled in their tents, they became aware that even the horses had been silenced by the heaviness of the night.

On 3 December 1598, the day dedicated to St. Francis Xavier, Bernabe de las Casas, who had been detained at San Juan, rode into camp where Zaldivar and his men had been hunkered down against the cold. They were about to leave on a scout as Zaldivar knew that he could not let this opportunity to explore the area escape him. Therefore, he sent men in all four directions and into the marsh to determine what the area held. Those who rode north and east found additional springs, while to the west, there were ruins. To the south were a rock pinnacle and a *pinon* mountain but little else, and all returned to their encampment cold, wet, tired, hungry, and eager to be on their way.

* * *

The three, Pedro and Francisco Robledo, and their friend, 19-year-old, Juan de Olague, one of four Olague brothers with the expedition, sat just within the entrance of their tent facing one of the fires which the group had kindled near the bed of the river. Olague noted that Pedro, the most animated of the Robledo brothers, was strangely silent. "You seem a million miles away. What's with you?" he asked as he blew into a *churumbela*, a wind instrument he had made from a hollow reed. "I've never seen you so quiet."

"It's this place, Juan," Pedro Robledo answered, "but not in the way you'd think. I was thinking about my father and how he never really had a chance to see our land. He would have loved it. My papa, more than anyone I know, really appreciated beautiful things—my mother, beautiful horses, beautiful country. He especially loved beautiful places like this marsh with its green grasses, running water, and wild things. He saw beauty where others only saw desolation. He would have loved this new Mexico."

* * *

The morning of 4 December 1598 was bitterly cold, and snow covered the ground. Twenty-eight-year-old, Juan de Zaldivar, who was to lead the group to the pueblo conferred with several of his men as he sipped the contents of the steaming vessel he held in his hand. With him at his campfire were some of his most trusted officers and soldiers, Geronimo Marquez, Bernabe de las Casas, Gaspar Lopez Tabora, Diego Nunez de Chaves, and Felipe de Escalante. To each, he was about to give an assignment.

"I'll be taking 24 men, including four servants," he said. "These should be enough to guard the horses, make the climb, and bring back the amount of flour we need." Looking around at the men of the encampment busy at their chores, Zaldivar said. "We'll take four squads. Felipe, you'll be responsible for Arujo, Velazquez, Camacho, and Perea. And you, Diego, you take Riveras, Sarinana, Ramirez, and Rodriguez. Gaspar, you'll be responsible for the Robledos, Pedro and Francisco, Olague, Caso, and Zapata. And Bernabe, you'll go with us. But I want you, Leon, Segura and Gonzales to stay with the horses." Then with a broad grin, he turned toward his great friend, Geronimo Marquez. "And you, Geronimo, *me bon compano*," he said, "I need you here. If, God willing, it appears we can secure the flour and leave today, I'll send one of the men back to instruct you to break camp. If you've not received these instructions by 4:00 o'clock, I want you to make provisions for another night's stay. Yes?" he asked, directing his question to all, but to no one in particular.

"Yes," they answered as of one voice.

"To work, then, for, as the wise man says, there's danger in delay."

Then amid the rattle of sabers and spurs, the men of his group donned their *cueros*. This was a leather jacket similar to a *brigandine* but without the small plates of metal stitched inside. It was made of as many as six layers of heavy buckskin fashioned into leather plates only partially secured and made to deflect an arrow from its true course. Over his *cuero*, each placed his coat of chain mail and then the remainder of his armor, his *cuisses*, helmet, and *bevor*. Each captain strapped on his sword, to which he added a small dagger that hung to his thigh, and each man secured his *harquebus* with all its accouterments. To this harness, they added leather pouches within which they now carried the additional hatchets they had promised the Acome in exchange for provisions. Soon, if all went well, they would replace the hatchets with flour and be on their way.

* * *

The ride from their encampment to the mesa was without incident, but misfortune comes when one least expects it. As they rode in the immense stillness, Francisco Robledo riding beside Pedro's bridle, wished he had listened to his brother when he had suggested he wear an arming cap. This was a small quilted cap worn under a mail *coif* that offered protection from blows and from the friction of mail against the head. Instead, he now suffered with each stride as the motion of his horse caused his helmet to ride up and down over his ears with much discomfort. His helmet was ill-fitting, but it seemed better than nothing at all, especially since it would serve quite well to protect him from the stones. However, he swore to himself that he would not complain, for to do so would only give his older brother, Pedro, further reason to think him an unseasoned soldier.

When they reached the base of the mesa, Zaldivar, as planned, asked 25-year-old, *Alferez* Bernabe de las Casas, native of the Island of Tenerife, to remain there with three soldiers to guard the horses. Indians who had watched them approach, descended from the mesa top and were there to meet them. They went first to the horses to take their perspiration and, then in a rite similar to that of a *taurobolium*,[6] they rubbed their bodies with it, conferring upon themselves invincibility in battle. They were friendly and offered to carry the soldiers' leather pouches and other items to the top of the mesa if the soldiers wished. Zaldivar gave the Indians permission to place the trade goods within their burden baskets, the tumplines of which freed the Indians' hands for climbing, but he declined their offer to free the Spaniards of their other equipment. It was going to be an exceedingly difficult climb, encumbered as they were by the dead weight of their cargo, but with their *harquebuses* now strapped to their backs in place of the leather bags, 16 of these men, with three additional Indian servants, began to climb.

Eighteen-year-old Francisco Robledo readjusted his *harquebus* as members of his squad moved past him on the stone trail. With him near the front of his group were his 20-year-old brother, Pedro, and Francisco's friend, Juan de Olague, each of whom now immediately preceded him. As he climbed, he watched the heels of his friend, Olague, who felt for the best foothold upon each narrow step.

The first 200 steps were not so difficult, although the *harquebus* Francisco carried continued to slip from its place on his back. More difficult was the second flight of 100 more which had been pecked from the cliff face and which were much narrower than the first. Most difficult, however, was the traverse they had to accomplish across the face of the cliff before they reached the top of the mesa. Francisco thought, and even said to Juan and to Pedro who preceded him, that this was a hell of a place. If they fell from here, there was nothing to stop their fall for many hundreds of feet. The perspiration on his brow, and which he felt running down his muscled arms, was as much from anxiety as from exertion. He was exceedingly happy when they reached the top of the mesa, for never had he felt so vulnerable.

When they reached the summit, with each of the men singly exiting the ladder trail, Juan de Zaldivar sought to regroup. "Gaspar," he said to Lopez Tabora, "take six men and gather the flour. Try to stay together as much as possible. We don't want to get separated. And make sure that you pay for everything."

With this, Juan de Zaldivar gave the Acome the remainder of the trade goods for which they had bargained. Then, in three groups rather than four as originally constructed, and with Captain Gaspar Lopez Tabora leading the way, the men began their collection.

There were many Indians on the mesa top, but Francisco could not guess their numbers. Each group of Spaniards was being followed by a contingent of Indians, with the largest group, he noted, following that of his *maese de campo*, Juan de Zaldivar. Zaldivar's men tried to stay together, in so far as they were able, with the soldiers and their servants moving down the same *calle* and walking among the same group of houses as they worked their way down the parallel line.

In flour, they received a scoop here and a pat there, but nowhere did they receive a substantial amount. Becoming frustrated by what he perceived to be the Indians' dawdling in providing the flour—for he had already paid for it—Zaldivar sent Captain Diego Nunez de Chaves, native of the town of Guadalcanal, with an additional six men to get the rest of the provisions. When they did not return, he sent Lopez Tabora to find out what was going on. When found, Nunez told Lopez that the Indians would not give him anything. He asked that Lopez return to Zaldivar to ask him for more men to help them persuade the Indians to comply, for it was getting very late, and they had accomplished little. Zaldivar responded by sending Lopez with three additional men to complete the task. He asked Lopez to gather flour from homes on the other street as well, and to finish quickly.

With this, Zaldivar's forces at the top of the mesa were effectively divided into three groups: Nunez with six, Lopez with nine, and Zaldivar with two, with each group being led like unsuspecting lambs from one small plaza to another. At the bottom of the mesa, Bernabe de las Casas watched the return of his Indian servant who had ascended the mesa with Zaldivar. He carried corn and instructions that the three soldiers with Casas were to ascend the mesa and assist with the provisioning. At that moment, on the top of the mesa, Lopez heard shouting from where Nunez and his men were gathering flour. One of the men with Nunez, Martin de Riveras, was holding a turkey in his hand and an Indian woman, who seemed quite upset, was yelling at him. With this as a pretext, the mesa top became alive with its villagers whose limited plan appears to have been to kill the shepherd and scatter his sheep. If this was indeed their plan, they were to be successful far beyond their wildest expectation.

With the woman's shouts as their signal, the Acome rose from their hiding places and began to beat the Spaniards with sticks, stones, and clubs, and to shoot arrows at them, not only from the ground, but also from the terraces with both men and women participating in the attack.

The situation for the Spaniards was desperate. Faced with many hundreds of Indians harrying them—much as a knot of blackbirds follow a hawk—Zaldivar and his men now found themselves in a very narrow place at the edge of a high cliff. Although they were being beaten into the ground by enormous stones and pierced by arrows which the Indians were shooting at them from their rooftops, Zaldivar ordered his men to shoot into the air and not at the Indians. He hoped only to frighten the Indians and intended to placate them with good treatment and kind words. However, the Spaniards never had an opportunity to speak.

The Robledos, Pedro and Francisco, with Juan de Olague, crouched against a wall on one side of the *calle* restricting, somewhat, the missiles which could be directed at them. With the whine of arrows moving though rarefied air and the dull thud of each as it embedded itself into flesh, wood or the surrounding clay, the Spaniards fought to the edge of the cliff. Martin de Riveras was already on the ground, as were Juan de Segura and Diego Nunez, when Juan de Zaldivar, who wore an embossed corselet, chased and inlaid with an unusual design, felt an excruciating pain in the back of his thigh. Embedded deeply and still quivering from its short flight was an arrow with little more than its feathers and a short shaft protruding from a minute wound. Zaldivar fell to one knee as he attempted to extract the arrow. Failing in this, he broke off the short stub and attempted to rise. As he struggled to his feet, an Acoma warrior, Zutucapan, struck him a great blow to his forehead with a massive war club. His helmet crushed like a wilted leaf, Juan de Zaldivar fell in a heap among some rocks where other Indians crushed his skull with stones.

Meanwhile, Casas, who waited alone with the horses at the bottom of the trail, heard muffled shouts from the top, as did the numerous Indians with him. Inexplicably, the 60 or so Indians who were with him did not attack him, as one would have expected. Rather, the Indians retreated to the cliff trail which they began to climb. Soon, Casas began to hear the sound of *harquebuses* being fired on the mesa. Following the shooting, Indians came down the narrow path to kill him and to take his horses.

Casas, the lone soldier waiting at the bottom of the trail, was able to hold off the Indians as he watched his comrades fight to the edge of the cliff. He saw Zaldivar fall and cried that he was unable to help him. He then watched as several of the men, beaten with rocks and struck with arrows which bounced off their armor, prepared to jump to their deaths. Two of those he saw were Juan de Olague and Pedro Robledo whom he implored not to jump with his whistled language of the Guanche that imitates spoken Spanish. He fired his *harquebus* in the direction of the Indians, hoping to drive them from the edge of the cliff. This, he hoped, would allow his comrades to regroup. His shot, however, fell short, and Juan de Olague and Pedro Robledo jumped rather than suffer being beaten to death.

The badly bruised Olague, whose fall had been broken by scree and by fine aeolian sediment that had drifted against the base of the mesa, hit the top of the detritus which collapsed beneath him, while Pedro Robledo, with whom he had jumped, struck an outcropping. Robledo fell end over end like some rag doll, hitting the cliff face at several points during his fall. His helmet and armor were torn from his body, and he was dead before he hit bottom.

They were not the only ones to jump. Francisco Robledo who had become separated from his brother and from Olague, had, like Olague and two others, fallen into fine sand which was steeply sloped against the cliff face. He now lay in a heap, in an exposed place, conscious, but badly hurt and unable to rise. His singular thought was for his brother Pedro. "Please, God, let him be alive," he prayed.

Meanwhile Casas, who was at the base of the ladder trail, was in a rather precarious position, for the process of loading and firing a single ball from his *harquebus* required 10 or 12 steps. In ordinary circumstances, he and the remainder of his squad (referred to as a 'battle,' and often standing 25 ranks deep) would have fired. They would then have moved to the rear of the group and been replaced by a second rank. The soldiers would have continued this process with each rank firing and then withdrawing to the rear to reload. On command, each rank would have gradually moved forward by successive volleys until its turn came again to fire. The larger group would thus have been able to maintain a limitless exchange. However, alone and with no one to hold off the Indians while he reloaded, he quickly placed powder in the pan, rammed home both the wad and multiple bullets, and raised the ten-pound implement to his shoulder. When he fired, ignition came from the blow of flint against steel, with the sparks directed into the priming powder in the pan; if his mark was good, he hit his target. He continued like this for some time, getting off several shots. He fired up the trail at anyone foolhardy enough to place himself in such a vulnerable position until no one else came down the rock hewn path.

Then, as soon as he was able, Casas, whose main responsibility was for the horses, began searching for some of the others who had jumped from the cliff. In his search, he noticed that the Indians had blocked the two narrow places by which one could climb to the top. The first man he found was Juan de Leon, a native of the port of Cadiz. A 19-year-old Leon had, on 29 April 1587, stood helplessly on the wooden bridge at Santi Petri as Francis Drake executed his brilliantly successful raid. On that occasion he and his fellow townsmen had escaped injury while Drake sank more than 20 sails. Now, however, he had become separated from his servant and was badly injured. He had been smashed in the face with a boulder and had some bad arrow wounds in his head the blood of which now mingled with the red of his beard. Leon told Casas that he had seen Sebastian Rodriguez de Hinojos, with whom he had first escaped to a rooftop, killed by several arrows which had pierced his body.

A fourth jumper, who had miraculously been able to reach Casas and the horses on his own, was 25-year-old Juan Velasquez de Cabinellas. Riding one of the horses he had obtained from Casas, he now dismounted and placed Leon on another horse.

Casas also found 18-year-old, Alonso Gonzales, who, after leaving Casas, had joined Zaldivar's group of which his uncle, Juan del Caso, was a member. Somehow, Gonzales had been able to slide down the cliffs. Although alive, he was bruised and had been badly beaten. In addition, Casas rescued 30-year-old Gaspar Lopez Tabora who had somehow escaped the mesa top. The Indians had hurled so many stones at him that he was stunned and had been forced to abandon the *harquebus* and sword with which he had defended himself.

Casas continued the search. Found a short time later was 24-year-old *Sargento* Rodrigo Zapata from Azuaga in Castile, who had escaped, although badly mangled, with four wounds which were bleeding profusely, and with painful bruises all over his body.

And thus they took roll. Among the survivors were Casas, Lopez, Olague, Francisco Robledo, Velasquez, Leon, Zapata, Caso and Gonzales. Were there more? They searched for others but could find no one. They had left 13 or more on top of the mesa but not for long, as the Acome began hurling over the side of the cliff the bodies of their fallen comrades. The faces of some had been pounded with clubs or stones and were now grotesque masks of grumous blood encrusted with grit. The bodies lay in several contorted heaps at the base of the cliffs where the village dogs went out to eat them. Casas considered retrieving them but gave this up as futile for the Indians continued to pelt them with rocks and to subject them to a shower of arrows. His major responsibility, he felt, was to get these injured men back to the relative safety of their camp at the river.

Pimps, Cuckolds and Cry Babies

With the Indians shouting insults at them from the top of the mesa, calling them bastards, murderers, and '*aputos temiquiz*' (whore mongers) in the Aztec language, the beaten and shattered Spaniards who had escaped the savage attack retreated. As they limped away from the mesa, Casas could see several Indians standing at the edge of the cliff or jumping from crag to crag. They were wearing the metal helmets and carrying the swords of his fallen comrades. He cursed them for their infamy as he rode away to rejoin Marquez.

* * *

About half an hour after sunset, an Indian servant of Juan del Caso arrived at the Spanish camp with a naked sword in his hand. He came with devastating news. Their leader, the *maese del campo*, was dead, and with him, many of the men in his troop. Marquez, with the 11 soldiers who remained in camp, considered mounting a rescue expedition but was advised by the servant that this would be futile. They could do nothing in the dark. Besides, any who had escaped the initial attack would surely have been killed since they had been set upon by many hundreds of Indians. Later, two or three hours after dark, Bernabe de las Casas, arrived at camp with the wounded soldiers, and with the horses, including the again-orphaned Babieca who had been left in his care.

With sentries posted, 45-year-old Captain Geronimo Marquez and his men spent much of the night in prayer and waited for first light. While waiting, they used the cover of darkness to bury a cache of extremely valuable iron goods including two small field pieces which they knew they could not carry while on their rescue mission. Unfortunately, they were not successful in hiding the burial site, for once they were gone, the

Indians dug it up and carried away a number of iron bars, some mining tools and quantities of iron which the Spaniards had planned to use for horseshoeing.

On the morning of 5 December, while Marquez searched for survivors, four men led by the royal *alguacil*, Gaspar Lopez de Tabora, native of Lisbon, left camp. They went to report the disaster to Onate who was in the provinces of Zuni and Hopi. Hampered by a blinding snowstorm, they were unable to find their way to Zuni and returned on the 6th. On the 7th, with the storm now abated, Bernabe de las Casas set out with six companions on the same mission. As they traveled, the Acome came out to attack them at a bad pass, killing one horse, wounding another, and challenging them to return to Acoma where their small army would be destroyed. Escaping the assault by some skillful maneuvering, Casas ignored their taunts, and continued on his mission. Geronimo Marquez, those men he had retained at his camp and their wounded friends in slings contrived from canvas tents, began their long, sad journey back to the pueblo of San Juan. They had been unable to retrieve the dead for proper burial as Francisco Robledo had begged, but Marquez swore they would be back.

*   *   *

Onate wondered where they were, his nephew Juan de Zaldivar and his men. He wondered what had detained them at San Juan, for surely Juan's brother Vicente had, by this time, returned from the bison plains freeing Juan to act as his rear guard. Onate had reached Hopi where he had dispatched Marcos Farfan de los Godos to search for the Cruzados and the mines which they were reputed to have. Concerned about his *maese de campo*, who had yet to arrive, he decided to return to Zuni and await him there. Ultimately, however, Onate decided to return to San Juan. He left Zuni on 12 December and, following a natural corridor, which took him by the *Ojo de Agua Fria*, reached *El Agua de la Pena* at El Morro the following evening.

El Morro, the headland or bluff, which looms 230 feet above the 7,200 foot upper Sonoran plain, is a great triangular rock made of light-colored sandstone soft enough to be cut with a knife or sword point. This bluff, and the life-sustaining pool at its base, Onate felt, would provide him with the water and shelter he needed while he and his vanguard awaited his nephew. And it was here amidst an ocean of sagebrush and a pine and juniper forest that Onate received the grave news.

Under an endless sky, gray and unforgiving, Casas told Onate of Juan de Zaldivar, his captains, Nunez, and Escalante, his soldiers, Perea, Arujo, Camacho, Ramirez, Segura, Pedro Robledo, Riveras, Rodriguez and the two servants. He told him of the valor with which they had fought and the means they had taken to defend themselves. They were overwhelmed, Casas said, by a treacherous and premeditated attack, and they were unable to withstand it.

Stunned by the news, Onate retreated to his tent and no one could approach him. Later, in a snow shower that blanketed the ground before him, he asked his *procurador-general*, Gaspar Perez de Villagra, to make him a cross and simple rosary. Perez, lacking the galls of a cork tree by which to accomplish the latter, made the rosary from a strip of his own clothing with 11 knots tied in it, one larger than the rest. Then, through the night, Onate cried pitifully, the strain of the past year and the grief of losing his most trusted nephew and stalwart soldiers, almost too much to bear. The next morning, with his grief now purged from his soul, he asked to meet with his men. He said that they had suffered an irreparable loss in the death of their *maese de campo* and his companions who had no equal. His fallen soldiers, he said, had had to submit to God's will without knowing exactly what it was.

"They were beaten and torn to pieces," he said, "and they died like martyrs. They died in the service of God and their king. Their work is done. Now our labors must continue."

In a numbing snow shower that slanted out of a white-chalked sky, Tomas, the Indian interpreter, was sent back to Zuni to retrieve the seven soldiers Farfan had left there. Tomas was directed to tell them to skirt the area of the Acome and to return to San Juan in the greatest haste. With this, the sad army, in complete battle attire, its van and rear guards posted, packed its baggage, decamped, and began its seven-day journey. They had to inform their people of the tragedy that had befallen them.

We Meant Them No Harm

On the morning of 15 December 1598, a picket who stood sentry on a snow-swept bank of the Great River watched in apprehension as a lone horseman, driving his spurs to the knobs, rode through cottonwoods and bare cornfields on his approach to San Juan. Everything about the armed fighter suggested his ride was crucial: his mud-encaked military wraps, his laboring horse, and the reality that he rode alone. He came with devastating news. His group had been attacked at Acoma and his leader, Juan de Zaldivar, and many others had been killed. Behind him, lay a swath of bare fields, the worn trail he had followed, and beyond that, devastation.

The people of the two villages received the news with great sadness and many tears. There were many devastated families. Juan de Zaldivar had left his brother, Vicente, as well as his uncle, *don* Juan de Onate. Hernando Ruiz de Hinojos had lost his brother Sebastian Rodriguez de Hinojos. Captain Diego Nunez de Chaves was survived by his wife and by his comrade-in-arms, his father-in-law, Alonso Sanchez. And Pedro Robledo, whose father was the first colonist to die in New Mexico, left a large, devastated family consisting of his mother, Catalina Lopez, three brothers, Diego, Alonso, and Francisco, sisters Francisca and Lucia, and brother-in-law, Bartolome Romero.

Of these, perhaps the most devastated was Diego's widowed mother. Although she had always had misgivings regarding the New Mexico venture, she had also felt the expedition and colonization had offered her family much promise. However, now in the space of less than seven months, she had lost two of her most cherished family members. The deep depression she had suffered at the deaths of her children Ana and Luis now returned. And throughout the Christmas season she lay on her pallet in a dark corner of her room, required the assistance of others to dress and to care for herself, and, both physically and mentally, slowly drifted away.

Some in the village agonized over the fact that their loved ones had died without having received the last sacraments, but Catalina's agony arose from the realization that her beloved child had died alone and remained unburied. She could not be reconciled to the facts of the tragedy and seemed unable to survive it. She knew that, even if the soldiers were successful in retrieving his body, he would not be returned to San Juan. She had left her husband alone along the trail and knew that her son would also rest in a place that was not his home. However, he must be buried and her children promised that somehow he would be.

Onate returned to San Juan on 21 December 1598. Early the next morning he asked to meet with his clerics. He asked them to study the events at Acoma and to render an opinion as to what conditions were necessary for him to wage a just war against the Indians. He also asked what reparations and damages could be exacted from these people and from their village. *Fray* Alonso Martinez and his group agreed to undertake the Court of Inquiry but asked that they be allowed to wait until after Christmas.

* * * *

Christmas 1598 was the saddest any of the colonists had experienced. Winter had come early with its freezing wind and driving snow. The villagers at San Juan were besieged by frost, sleet, hail and snow and the small villages were deep in the throes of winter. It was almost as if the earth was becoming colder. The freezing temperatures in the high mountains (where current annual snowfalls average more than 26 feet) enabled large amounts of snow to build up and turn into ice so that valley glaciers began to form. The Rio Grande, which had begun to ice up with a thin rim of hoarfrost along its banks in mid-November, now provided a solid, if extremely slippery, surface by which the people could cross from one village to another. The colonists spread the ashes from their life-sustaining fires upon the surface of the ice to provide traction for their beasts, but the transit remained treacherous.

* * *

On 28 December, the clerics, led by *don* Juan himself, began hearing testimony regarding the disaster at Acoma. However, Onate fought to keep an open mind and asked the friars to keep him honest. He knew that, if left unchecked, his personal biases would skew the results. The testimony Onate received was both conflicted and confused because of the shroud of battle: the noise, the fear, the confusion, made any complete report an impossibility. Nonetheless, with the rod of justice lowered so that each witness in turn might place his hand upon the cross and take his oath, the men provided their testimony. The picture that emerged, although fragmented and ill-formed, became clearer as each man spoke.

The Acome, his men said, had shown much satisfaction and gladness at seeing Zaldivar and his men who had gone to the village to barter for provisions. It was known among them that Alvarado and Espejo had been given cloaks of cotton, skins of deer and cows, turquoise, fowl and other food by these people. His men said these people had made a present to a previous expedition of a large number of turkey cocks with very big wattles, much bread, tanned deerskins, *pinon* nuts, flour and corn. Onate himself had received *maize*, water and turkeys here, so it was not too much to expect they would be well-provisioned by the Acome. It had occurred before.

Marquez thought that, although the Acome had given them water and firewood for which the soldiers had paid, they had not given it willingly. "There was a problem from the start," Marquez said. "There was something else going on there."

Marquez noted that he had brought down two or three Indian chiefs from the mesa top and had suggested to Juan de Zaldivar they be detained at the campsite to make certain the Indians furnished the provisions. Zaldivar, however, refused Marquez said. He wanted to assure the Acome they would not be harmed in any way. "He thought that, in this manner, as the Indians gained confidence in us, they would furnish the provisions more willingly, so he let the chiefs go."

Had Riveras paid for the turkey? They didn't know. Perhaps he had not yet paid for it, but he would have. Each of the men had been given his own items of barter and had been admonished to pay for whatever they took. Moreover, the response and retaliation for the theft— if it had been that—was far out of proportion to the incident. "No, it was a pretext! The attack was done treacherously and with premeditation."

"But was it premeditated?" *don* Juan asked. "Did the Indians of the village plan and demonstrate sufficient intent to commit a criminal act?"

"They were waiting for us on their roof tops and had pulled up their ladders so we could not ascend," said Juan de Leon.

"They were armed and well-hidden," said another. "Both men and women engaged in the attack. They never had any intention of giving us the flour. We were only being led to a place on the cliffs where we could not defend ourselves."

In this, there was only one major piece of exculpatory evidence. Why had the 60 Indians with Casas at the bottom of the mesa not attacked him? They had retreated to the ladder trail when the difficulty on the mesa first erupted. Surely, they could have overwhelmed him, with some returning later to kill him and to take his horses. Did all in the village know of the scheme?

"Perhaps they did not know if the attack would occur, or when it would occur, or whether it had occurred," said Casas. "Perhaps they went back to see what was going on, and only then did they discover that the signal for the attack had been given."

"It was a treachery and an outrage they so unjustifiably perpetrated," shouted another. "They had entrenched themselves and blocked the path to the pueblo. They intercepted our soldiers, shouted insults at us, called us scoundrels and challenged us. And they killed and wounded some of our horses with arrows."

"Do we have ties of dependence and mutual obligation with the Acome?" asked one of the clerics, directing his question to *Fray* Alonso Martinez.

"They rendered due obedience to our king and lord," answered Martinez "and they unanimously swore to this. They declared that they wanted to accept the evangelical law and an affidavit of obedience and vassalage was drawn up and stamped with my seal."

They Are Watching What We Do at Acoma

Thus Onate took testimony from Gaspar Lopez Tabora, Bernabe de las Casas, Rodrigo Zapata, Juan de Olague, Juan de Leon, Juan Velazquez de Cabanillas, Alonzo Gonzalez, Antonio de Sarinana and all in the Zaldivar camp. Geronimo Marquez stated that he was "at the pueblo and saw that it was so impregnable that the Indians living in it—and those who might seek refuge there—could defend themselves and escape punishment for their misdeeds. This witness is sure," he said, "that if this pueblo is not leveled and its inhabitants punished, there will be no security in all of New Mexico, nor can New Mexico be colonized. The natives of the other pueblos are watching what we do at Acoma and whether we punish them."

Others expressed the same determination, saying that unless the pueblo of Acoma was punished for the treachery and outrage committed, there would be no safe place anywhere in the kingdom, nor could New Mexico be settled. The village, they said, must be destroyed and made permanently uninhabitable and the Indians must be severely punished for their infamy. The Indians of the other villages are waiting, they said. They want to know when the people of Acoma will be punished.

It continued in this manner for two weeks with each man in turn providing his testimony. There were, to be sure, many unanswered (and probably unanswerable) questions regarding the debacle. Had the soldiers done anything to provoke the attack? How many soldiers and servants were on the mesa when the attack occurred? And how did these few who survived manage their escape? In the end, however, the general picture was clear. The attack at Acoma had been unprovoked and 13 innocents had been killed. The Acome, the clerics decided, had acted with treachery and premeditation. They were vassals of the king, and, as such, had placed themselves under royal law. These Indians, the clerics said, must be given an opportunity to sue for peace, but if they declined, all three conditions for a just war as set forth by St. Thomas Aquinas had been met.[1] War was justified, the friars said, but only for the purpose of preserving the kingdom. Those who refused to surrender, determined the clerics, were at the mercy of the victors.

On 10 January 1599, the 113 remaining soldiers of Onate's small army mustered before his headquarters to express their views regarding the best method for chastising Acoma. The charges against the Indians and the testimonies taken during the two weeks were read in minute detail. Following this, Onate offered many reasons both for and against carrying out the punishment. In the end, it was decided that they would attack and destroy Acoma as soon as possible. The reason given for this decision was to discourage the other pueblos from forming a league with the Acome. Such a league, it was feared, would doom their colony to extinction. Thus

278

it was that the fate of Acoma was sealed. Both sides had now to prepare for war.

* * *

During the late afternoon of 11 January 1599, Diego and his brothers, Alonso and the badly injured Francisco, met with their mother in her darkened room at the Pueblo of Okhe. With the sound of hailstones beating against the adobe roof, the young men arranged themselves around their mother whose bed, usually covered with a rough woolen rug, was now further covered with her one bedspread of crimson taffeta trimmed with lace. There, in these cave-like surroundings, and in a chill that struck to the bone, they waited, hoping she would acknowledge their presence.

There was little verbal exchange among them as they held a thin hand or stroked her auburn hair, now considerably grayed and caught in a gilt hair net. There was not much to say, for both Diego and Alonso were going to fight, and all of them knew that their mother would not survive the loss of another child. Yet they had a job to do, and one does not contemplate killing, unless one is ready to die. They knew that to avoid risk is to avoid life, and they had to secure the colonization.

Their mother had remained mute throughout their visit, but, as the young men rose to leave, their mother, all skin and bones, turned, and in a voice as muted as the whisper of a breeze in the cottonwoods said, "Diego, *mi ijiko*. Bring me his helmet. We'll bury it here to honor him."

A Rage of Cannonballs

On the bitter cold morning of 12 January 1599, as war clouds darkened the winter sky, Onate, with his 40 remaining soldiers, watched as Vicente de Zaldivar, with 72 men, rode out of San Juan. With him, in full armor, were seven captains, five of whom we have met before: Marcos Farfan de los Godos, Gaspar Perez de Villagra, Geronimo Marquez, Alonso Sanchez and Pablo de Aguilar. Onate had wanted to lead the expedition himself but was finally convinced that his place was here. Should the assault at

Acoma fail, he had been counseled, he might be needed to lead the remainder of his colony out of New Mexico. Therefore, he reluctantly gave responsibility for the expedition to Vicente de Zaldivar, brother of the slain Juan. He cautioned Vicente to act prudently and provided him with explicit instructions regarding the undertaking. He was to use his interpreters, Tomas and Cristobal, to offer the Acome generous terms for surrender, for he knew that nothing was more disarming to an opposing people than a proposal of generosity. If they would relinquish their weapons, accept the authority of their ruler, and hand over those people who were guilty of the treachery, they would be spared. The Acome would be removed from their mesa and their pueblo destroyed. If they chose to fight, Vicente de Zaldivar was told, he was to consult with his officers and take the best course of action for defeating them. However, his uncle warned him to "make more use of clemency than severity" if he determined that these Indians acted out of lack of reason rather than malice.

"May God hear and sin be deaf," Onate said to his nephew by way of wishing him success in the venture. "Forward, in God's name."

One must have a mind of winter
To regard the frost and the boughs
Of the pine trees crusted with snow;

And have been cold a long time
To behold the junipers shagged with ice,
The spruces rough in the distant glitter

Of the January sun; and not to think
Of any misery in the sound of the wind,
In the sound of a few leaves,

Which is the sound of the land
Full of the same wind
That is blowing in the same bare place

> For the listener, who listens in the snow,
> And, nothing himself, beholds
> Nothing that is not there and the nothing that is.

> —Wallace Stevens

At Acoma, a *Kahera*, or town crier, was going about his rounds on the wind swept mesa. Clad in a scarlet blanket and jingling small copper bells, he walked down one *calle* and up the next assuring the villagers of their security.

> "All is well," he intoned, "All is well."

However, both he and the other people of the Acoma village, who could hear the faint rumble of the oncoming storm, knew their peace would be short-lived. For weeks they had been gathering from the Sawtooth and Datil Mountains, and from among their stores, *cholla*, sunflower, rabbit brush, cliff rose, apache plume, Mexican locust, chokecherry, firewood, tons of rocks and all manner of food. They gathered *cholla* since they feared they would need it for the wounds they probably would suffer. Sunflower[1] would be used for a salve to stop bleeding. Rabbitbrush, cliff rose, apache plume, and Mexican locust were to be used to make arrow shafts, while chokecherry was for bows. Additional plants—alder, aster, and western wallflower among them—would provide salves for sores, swelling, and burns. The Acome had to be ready to fight and to withstand a siege of unknown duration.

* * *

The army, riding through knee-deep snowdrifts and fighting high winds, arrived at Acoma on 21 January in the fading light of that winter afternoon. In the deepening twilight, and with an icy rain falling, they struggled to set up camp. After a forced march of nine days over mountainous terrain, they were exhausted, muddy, and frozen to the core. Reaching the foot of the mesa on this, the feast of *Santa Inez*, Vicente de Zaldivar circled it three times as much to determine the pueblo's defenses as to offer terms of surrender as dictated by his uncle, Juan de Onate. The Acome merely laughed and jeered. Who did this tribe of people think they were, these men who wore spurs? Just let them try to climb to their mesa. Their horses would be useless in an assault. And with stores hidden in underground passages that undermined the rock, the Acome could, they assured themselves, withstand a siege of limitless duration. They answered the Spaniards with a shower of arrows, spears, countless stones and jagged pieces of ice that fell harmlessly to the valley floor.

In his reconnaissance, Zaldivar noted that there were no trails over the sheer precipices to the east and none to the south, except, perhaps, one toward the southwest, although he could not be sure of this. However, not far to the east of the ladder trail there appeared to be a dangerous north trail which he felt might provide him with a postern gate. He may have wished he had a siege engine constructed as a combination tower and battering ram mounted on wheels. The battering ram itself may not have served any purpose here, made as it was in the form of a pointed arm to be used to pry out the stones of a city wall, but it would have provided his men with a stage from which to fire, had the platform above it been high enough.

Unfortunately, Vicente did not have a siege engine. What he did have were two brass *pedreros* or siege cannons which had been provided to his uncle, *don* Juan de Onate, at government expense. These were not the famous lombards, 12 feet long and capable of hurling 165 pound balls of iron and marble, but stone-throwing guns, which were used in siege and navel warfare. However, unlike a *trebuchet*, which could have been assembled in the field, the cannons had to be carried from San Juan to Acoma, even as they had been carried from Zacatecas to New Mexico. In some circumstances, two wagons in line could have provided a form of articulation, but this contraption often overturned. Therefore, since they wanted the cannons at Acoma, they had to carry them aboard ox carts, and to successfully bring them into battle, they had to be set up on a frame or trestle for firing. This generally resulted in a mediocre effect, but they hoped for better than that.

Later that evening, in falling snow, Vicente de Zaldivar met with his men. He told them that, although the village appeared impregnable, it could be conquered, for to will is to be able. An effective blockade, he noted, would be difficult without a far larger body of troops than he had, and, although an encirclement and blockade of the village might eventually result in success, a siege was out of the question. Although a *camisado* (*camisa*, or nightshirt over armor: a night attack) might be considered, they were not going to wait in the snow while the Acome slept beside warm fires. The Acome's bowstrings would be wet and thus less efficient, and the Spaniards had asked God to punish the Acome and to 'let the crumbs freeze between their hands and their mouth.' But they could not hesitate, because their honor as Spaniards depended on their attacking and defeating the Acome. And Zaldivar had a plan.

His plan was the classic tactic of a feint in one area followed by an attack from a different quarter. To the east of the ladder trail, he noted, there was another trail that appeared even more dangerous than the former. They would make a frontal assault there as a diversion to pull everyone on the mesa to its northern face. With the forces of the Acome positioned there, they would place a smaller group of men on the south wall to make a climb. Once they had achieved the summit, he said, they would bring up the *pedreros* and more men.

"In the name of Roque," Vicente said, rendering an oath of determination, "it will be done. It will be from the south mesa that we'll make our attack."

Therefore, on Friday the Feast of *San Vicente*, about three in the afternoon, with the tasseled heads of the prairie grasses rolling like swells upon a white foamed sea, Vicente opened the attack. With a warning to the Indians on top of the mesa to prepare themselves for battle, his small army began its assault at the north trail where he did not have to worry about the proper placement of the combatants with regard to the sun. Amid the blare of trumpets, shouting, and the firing of *harquebuses*, the Indians were drawn to the northern face. They answered with a shower of stones, spears, and arrows, none of which did much damage as the overhang of the cliff face shielded the Spaniards from the attack.

With this feint, and amid the tumult, the fully armored Vicente de Zaldivar with Gaspar Perez de Villagra, Pablo de Aguilar, Diego Robledo, and eight other *escalanados*, or wall-scalers, climbed the high walls of the immense mass of stone to reach the top of the mesa. They climbed unnoticed, but as soon as they reached the summit, their presence was known. Attacked by a massive group of Indians, they became engaged in some hand-to-hand fighting with Diego and the others getting their first taste of blood.

Dispersed and defending a wide area, a powerful Indian wielding a short mace, charged Diego who defended himself with his sword. Running with his mace held menacingly over his head the Indian attempted to strike Diego who thrust his weapon upward using both hands. Run through from breast to back, the Indian dropped his mace and, using only his fist, struck Diego with a great blow to the side of his head. Knocked senseless, Diego fell in a heap. Seizing Diego by a leg, the mortally wounded Indian whirled him around in a series of circles above his head. With the great strength he possessed, the powerful Qualco threw Diego two men's lengths towards the edge of the cliff before falling to earth. Recovering himself, Diego stood there trembling, hesitant, noting how narrowly he had escaped death.

Both groups secured their positions.

For 12 gloomy hours, the Spaniards huddled on the desolate rock, without food and eating snow only to slake their thirst, without shelter, and without any means of getting warm or dry. Incredibly, the 12 men were able to hold their ground. Sleeping on their weapons, they spent the bitterly cold night alone, exposed, and watchful.

Who Loses the Morning Loses the Afternoon, Who Loses the Afternoon Loses Life

The next day, which was the feast of *San Ildefonso*, the weary, hungry and shivering men again shouldered their weapons. At first light, the men at the top of the mesa began to receive their reinforcements. In addition to the armaments that were secured to their bodies, they brought several small pines that grew to the south of the mesa. These pines, which were to be tied together and used as a bridge, had, under the cover of darkness, been cut, dragged down across a trench-like valley, and then up the perpendicular walls to the top of the mesa.

With their bridge thus constructed, the men immediately began their attempt to reach the Indian village. Four men who had been chosen to carry the joined timbers rushed forward. Under the cover of *harquebus* fire provided by their comrades, and with cries of *"Santiago y cierra Espana,"*[2] they threw the timbers across the chasm where, miraculously, they lodged on the other side. Then, using the timbers as a bridge, the men began to cross. Thinking to use the bridge further ahead, however, some of the men picked it up, thus stranding themselves on one side of the cleft where they were set upon by club-wielding Indians. In a feat that has become legendary, 44-year-old, Gaspar Perez de Villagra, seeing these men trapped on the other side of the chasm and being unable to reach them, leaped across the fissure and replaced the bridge. This allowed reinforcements to reach the stranded men and the assault continued with the Indians using shields of buckskin, bows, and flint-tipped arrows, war-clubs, and helmets made of bison hide. Then came the *pedreros.*

The siege cannons, which had originally been equipped with gun carriages, axles, and iron-rimmed wheels, had been transported on carts from San Juan to the scene of the battle. Here, absent their wheeled equipage, the cannons had, by superhuman effort, been hauled to the top of the mesa. It was late in the afternoon when they arrived, but valued as they were for the shock of their impact which brought down large pieces of walls, the cannons were immediately put to work.

Lacking gun carriages, which would have permitted the muzzle of the gun to be raised or lowered, and would have also served to absorb some of the recoil, each cannon was tied to a trestle made of small pines. An artillery man ran his hand through the powder to test its dryness while a second, holding a match impregnated with sulfur, blew on the smoldering slow fire, waiting for orders to place its glowing red head to the touch hole. Then, with appropriate prayers rendered to *Santa* Barbara, patroness of gunners, the bombardment began. The cannon leaped backwards against its lashings as a long red flame spewed from its mouth and as a backfire from its vent. Hurling stone cannon balls, which were, in many respects, superior to cast-iron projectiles (despite the variability provided by 'windage,' the difference between the diameter of the shot and the bore), the Spaniards began destroying the village. Many of the Indians retreated to their fortress-like homes. However, a like number of these brave and tenacious people, with arrow and sling, continued to respond to the *harquebus* fire while, with report after report, a rage of cannonballs screamed across the mesa to splinter wood and stone and to crush the puddled walls of which the village was constructed.

The noise was deafening, the air thick with dark smoke and the taste of gunpowder, adobe dust, and flames, of blood and burned flesh. Godoy, who may have been borrowing the words of Fernando del Pulgar, Isabel's court secretary and historian of her reign, in recounting the siege of Ronda says, "The children, terrified by the fire and the shock of the cannons, screamed and wept and, with their shrieks and sobs, the leaders of the Acome were driven out of their senses and lost all ability to help either themselves or their people." He continues:

> It was miraculous that so great a number of the enemy were killed
> without the loss of any of ours; and that the air was extremely
> favorable, for it was so cold that the harquebuses did not become
> heated, although the firing was continuous through the entire time.
> It was all the more miraculous considering the small number—less
> than 50—who were on top of the rock, for the balance who made
> up the total of the 70 [three] who went to this war, guarded the
> base of the rock on horseback. [Therefore], on the top of the rock
> there were 10 of the enemy to each Spaniard.[3]

On this day, the Indians of Acoma saw an apparition of *Sant' Iago* the impetuous fisherman who had, by stupendous metamorphosis, been transformed by Spanish legend into a valorous knight. And on this day, Asencio de Arechuleta, accidentally shot his comrade-in-arms, 23-year-old, Lorenzo Salado de Ribadeneira, a red-bearded native of Valladolid in Castile. Salado, the 'abandoned wretch' (for he was thus referred to by his comrades for not having gone to confession and Communion as offered by *Fray* Alonso Martinez from a portable altar that accompanied the expedition), was the only Spaniard to be killed in the three-day assault.

The death of Salado, the governor's chamberlain, occurred in this manner. In preparation for the placement of reinforcements on the south mesa, the men below were told to ready their *harquebuses* to fire the instant they reached the top. Therefore, 27-year-old Asencio de Arechuleta, with mailed glove, poured powder down the muzzle of his weapon, placed powder in its pan, and rammed home multiple balls in readiness for the assault. During the climb, Salado, who was beside Arechuleta and on a slight ledge, began to lose his footing. In a hopeless attempt to arrest his fall, he reached out for Arechuleta but grasped the *harquebus* now reversed which was strapped to Arechuleta's body. He caught his finger in the lock, released the flint, and the weapon fired with a dull thud which Arechuleta described as seemingly an explosion within a cave. Four heavy lead balls that pierced Salado's body mortally wounded him. However, despite this new burden of lead, which he carried in his vitals, he managed to reach the Spanish camp and made his last confession before he died. As Salado toppled from the ledge, Arechuleta, whose black beard was now covered with bloodied ice, attempted to retreat to where his friend had fallen but was forbidden to do so, for he was needed on the mesa.

The battle continued with report after report resounding from the smoke-shrouded *pedreros*—now disgorging great stores of small shot—and being dragged through the streets of the village to provide more advantageous positions from which to fire. The carnage was shocking. The fire that swept the Indians' homes killed many, and many killed themselves and family members rather than give themselves to the Spaniards as a vanquished people.

Late in the afternoon, with the boom of the *pedreros* still resounding in the sharp, cold air, Diego and five others were selected to retrieve the badly charred bodies of their fallen comrades who had lain on a funeral pyre for 51 days. Although the temperature during this nearly two-month period had been exceedingly cold, and the desiccated bodies of the soldiers were now buried under several feet of drifted snow, the retrieval of the bony scarecrows of corpses remained a grizzly task. Found first was Diego Nunez whose remains consisted of a charred liver attached to a piece of backbone, a skull shrunk to the size of a melon, a bare foot burned down to just above the ankle. They wrapped his remains in a bison robe, placed him on an artillery cart, and continued with their sad detail.

The retrieval of the barely recognizable men continued with *Alferez* Perea and then Sebastian Rodriguez next to be found. And so it went: Escalante, Arujo, Camacho, Ramirez, Segura, Pedro Robledo, the *maese de campo*, Riveras, and the two servants, a *mulatto* of Damiero and a Cochuelo Indian. While retrieving his brother's body, Diego had searched in vain for Pedro's helmet but had been unable to find it. The squad urged his return, for it seemed imperative that they leave the base of the mesa before darkness set in. The remains were wrapped in bison robes, placed aboard artillery carts (which the men, in life, would have been disgraced as knights to ride), and taken to the area of the wind-carved sandstone formations to the north of Acoma, where they were to be buried.

Late in the afternoon on 23 January, Godoy relates, the remaining Acome, with offerings of turkeys and blankets, sued for peace. The Spaniards refused these while making plans to enter the Indian village. However, they did not formally enter the Acoma pueblo until 24 January when they established a camp in one of the plazas. Then the Spaniards began to capture the Indians, some of whom had entrenched themselves in the *kivas* and underground passages of the rock that was undermined in every direction. Fire and grapeshot killed many of them, and the pueblo was almost completely laid waste and burned. The loss to the Acome was shocking. Eight hundred were killed in the assault and approximately 500, mostly women and children, were captured.

With the *tampions* replaced in the muzzle of their *pedreros*, the cannons' vent covers secured against the falling snow, the night of 24 January was spent in preparation for a long journey. The 500 prisoners were to be taken to their sister pueblo of Santo Domingo where they were to stand trial. The next day, at first light, the Spaniards would bury their fallen comrades, and as soon as they had accomplished this, they would leave this place.

* * *

After the completion of the burial of his brother and his comrades, and under skies heavy with snow, Diego left Alonso at his brother's gravesite and returned to the base of the mesa. The wind was growing once more; the heavens blackened, and minute flakes of brash as jagged as shards of glass blew from the rock face. Then, in a blizzard of ice crystals, and an unending snowfall, snow and ice began to break away from the top of the massive stone wall to fall on the valley floor.

Diego had gone down into the scrub oak and small *pinon* trees that surrounded the base of the mesa via the identical path he had taken earlier. However, he strayed from the trail, and finally lost it, struggling through massive *satrugus*, or snow waves in fantastic shapes, which had been heaped against the mesa in colossal drifts. The wind did not move through the branches of the trees now as it had on his previous visit. The boughs were too deeply burdened with snow and there was scarcely a sound to be heard except for a thin rivulet of water as it traced a snakelike path along the sandstone wall. Occasionally, a mound of snow slid from the 'crag of sorrow' with the sound of a plaintive wail, or fell at the base of the cliff like a muffled cry. Black trunks and branches of quiescent pine trees separated a little to reveal the white skeletons of denuded scrub oaks, pale and dead against the slate-black sky.

Diego was all but lost, with little chance of finding his brother's helmet, yet he could not return without it, for he had made a promise. He cursed his stupidity for having left the point of muster without informing the captain of the guard, Farfan de los Godos. He also knew, though, that if he had asked for permission to search for the helmet, it would not have been granted. Every man was needed, and he was risking the lives of the entire company by his actions. If he was able to return safely to where the prisoners were being made ready for the trail, he might be subject to a court martial, but he had to find the helmet, and no one, save a member of his family, could possibly appreciate how important this was.

A stout heart, however, breaks bad luck, and Diego's stubborn persistence eventually resulted in success. Dragging his legs through waist-high drifts, he continued with his cull. *Was this not where they had found Pedro's body?* he asked of himself, crying in desperation. It looked so different now in the heavy snowfall, the sandstone blackened in the fading light. He dragged himself back and forth near the cliff face hoping to feel the helmet beneath the snow and then, suddenly, there it was, wedged within the recess of a rock chimney where it would have escaped his notice had he not fallen just outside its entrance. He reached up, freed it from where it was lodged and pressed the cold metal against his face. It was Pedro's helmet, of this he was sure, and God had wanted him to find it.

Preparations for Defense

No sooner had Vicente de Zaldivar and his men left San Juan, than Onate received a frightening report. The surrounding Pueblos, the San Juan Indians told him, recognizing that the greater part of Onate's army had left the area, were planning to mass for an attack. Onate, with his 40 remaining soldiers, made hasty provisions to fortify San Juan's plaza.[1]

Dona Eufemia, wife of Onate's lieutenant governor, Francisco de Sosa Penalosa, told the Spanish women of the village of San Juan, that all, so far, had been "tarts and fancy cakes," and that it was now time for them to show their mettle. In demonstration of this, she had many of the women on the roofs of their homes waiting to defend their village against the impending attack.[2]

With the glow of watch fires ringing their village, the 25 women waited in the blue cold for the attack they considered imminent. Like Marpesia, one of three Amazon Queens of Greek mythology, who had led Amazon forces across Asia Minor to the Aegean Sea, *dona* Eufemia, and the other women, were ready and willing to take up arms to defend their lands. However, the attack did not materialize, and the villagers, on watch and ever ready, returned to relative calm while they continued to wait in breathless anticipation for word from Acoma.

Crime and Punishment

The people of Acoma arrived at Santo Domingo on 9 February 1599 after what must have been a trek to the edge of human endurance. The weather during the 16 days of travel was extremely cold; snow covered much of the ground, and the prisoners, many wearing the poor tabards of their captors, were very poorly dressed against the elements. Many were barefoot for the foot coverings they had worn had been lost in the snow and the women and Spanish soldiers carried many prisoners, especially the small children. It was impossible to envision these defeated people as belligerents, for they could barely walk, much less mount an attack. Nonetheless, they were guarded. During infrequent periods of rest, the few male prisoners in the caravan were roped together while their women, looking for the telltale signs provided by dried stalks and husks, foraged in the snow-covered earth for wild potatoes, nightshade and prickly pear. The Spaniards had learned that they had to proceed as though an attack was imminent and thus they proceeded.

* * *

Vicente de Zaldivar had sent his quartermaster, Diego de Zubia, to San Juan to take a message to Onate who was on the thorns to know. Onate received this message with much joy. After a promise of *albricias* (the reward for good news), the word of the Spanish victory was spread throughout the San Juan villages. Onate then determined that he would ride to Santo Domingo to meet his army and to conduct an *assize* for he understood the necessity for quick and unrelenting justice if order was to be restored to the land.

The trial was held in the enormous *kiva* at Santo Domingo where Onate had first addressed the chiefs of the seven provinces. It was a legal proceeding conducted in complete compliance with Spanish law. Captain Alonso Gomez Montesinos, native of Villanueva de los Infantes in La Mancha, acted as the Indians' guardian and defense attorney, and Tomas, one of the Indians from New Spain, acted as interpreter.

The Acome spoke first with six villagers providing testimony. Caoma and Cat-ticati said that they were not there when Juan de Zaldivar was attacked, but that they had been told that the Spaniards had been killed "because they asked for such large amounts of *maize*, flour and blankets." Excase offered that the Spaniards had been killed "because a soldier either asked for or took a turkey." Caucachi and Xunusta provided more damning testimony. The former said that the Spaniards had been slain because they "had wounded an Acoma Indian," while the latter said that this Indian had been killed. From them, also, it was learned that the Indians had argued amongst themselves about the best way to deal with Vicente's men, but had chosen to battle as a united people rather than to surrender.

Gomez acknowledged that the Acome had no witnesses or defense pleas to offer (beyond those given above), but, many of them were not guilty as they were absent when the Spaniards were killed.

291

"You should acquit them," he pleaded, "set them free, and allow them to go wherever they wish, and order that they be compensated for the expenses resulting from their arrest. Show clemency," he pleaded. "They are uncivilized."

Apart from these protestations, however, neither Gomez nor the Acome could offer much in terms of their defense, and in the end, their fate was sealed. Their punishments were severe.

The Sentence [1]

In the criminal case between the royal court and the Indians of the pueblo and fortress of Acoma, represented by Captain Alonso Gomez Montesinos, their defender, accused of having wantonly killed don Juan de Zaldivar Onate, maese de campo general of this expedition, and Captains Felipe de Escalante and Diego Nunez, eight soldiers, and two servants, and of other crimes; and in addition to this, after Vicente de Zaldivar Mendoza, my sargento mayor, whom I sent for this purpose in my place, had repeatedly called upon them to accept peace, not only did they refuse to do so, but actually received him with hostility. Wherefore, taking into account the merits of the case and the guilt resulting therefrom, I must and do sentence all of the Indian men and women from the pueblo under arrest, as follows:

All of the children under 12 years of age I declare free and innocent of the grave offense for which I punish their parents. And because of my duty to aid, support, and protect both the boys and girls under 12 years of age, I place the girls under the care of the father commissary, Fray Alonso Martinez, in order that he, as a Christian and qualified person, may distribute them in the kingdom or elsewhere in monasteries or other places where he thinks they may attain the knowledge of God and the salvation of their souls.

The boys under 12 years of age I entrust to Vicente de Zaldivar Mendoza, my sargento mayor, (in) order that they may attain the same goal.

The women over 12 years of age I sentence [. . .] to 20 years of personal servitude.

The males between the ages of 12 and 25 I sentence likewise to 20 years of personal servitude.

Two Indians from the province of Moqui (Hopi) *who were present at the pueblo of Acoma and who fought and were apprehended, I sentence to have the right hand cut off and to be set free in order that they may convey to their land the news of this punishment.*

And males who are over 25 years of age (which consisted of 24 individuals), *I sentence to have [the toes {puntos del pie} of] one foot cut off and to 20 years of personal servitude*

The old men and women, disabled in the war, I order freed and entrusted to the Indians of the province of Querechos [2] *that they may support them and may not allow them to leave their pueblos.*

I order that all the Indian men and women who have been sentenced to personal servitude shall be distributed among my captains and soldiers in the manner which I will prescribe and who may hold and keep them as their slaves for the said term of 20 years and no more.

This being a definite and final sentence, I so decree and order, don Juan de Onate."

With cries of anguish resounding throughout the valley the amputations, which were initiated on 12 February 1599, were carried out at Santo Domingo and at a number of nearby pueblos. These were accomplished by the use of a chisel with the foot or arm then thrust into boiling fat to cauterize the wound. Although some stoically suffered this cruelty, most were reduced to writhing and wailing in agony. When the tears of anguish subsided, the sound of peace was heard throughout the kingdom, a peace for which all had paid a horrible price.

* * *

The Spaniards' war against the Acome leaves a number of questions unanswered relative to the identity of the aggressor. These questions have never been answered to anyone's satisfaction. The Spanish colonists were intruders, even as were the Acome who had, at some earlier time, migrated into the area they were found inhabiting in the 16th century. The Spaniards were strangers in a strange land, and although they sought to live peacefully with their Indian neighbors, the Indians were, at best, ambivalent regarding their presence among them.

The Spanish, however, were intent on establishing a new homeland. They were determined to prevent criminal acts against their people and committed to do whatever was required to meet their needs and maintain their values. In addition to their strong devotion to law and to Christian dictates, there was the question of their safety. If they were to secure their colonization, they had to act decisively. Therefore, the severity of their reprisals does not lie in the character of their leaders, nor of their people. The Spaniards acted with deliberation, fully cognizant of how their determinations would be viewed by others. In a letter written by Juan de Onate on 2 March 1599 and sent to the Court of Spain, he puts it this way:

It seemed to me that this offense (the murder of the maese de campo and his men) *should be punished severely as an example, not only for the said pueblo which had already rendered obedience to his Majesty, but also in order that the other Indians who had likewise submitted should know that we had sufficient strength and power to punish such transgression[s] and boldness. I sent my sergeant major with 70 men. And as they refused to submit peacefully when he invited them to do so, he gave them battle, which lasted three days. At the end of this time they surrendered, after losing 800 Indians killed, 500 prisoners, and 80 executed; and the pueblo burned. All this left the land pacified and* intimidated. . .[3]

In the final analysis, the events at Acoma must be seen in the larger context of the world as it existed at the end of the 16th century. It was a cruel world, in which justice, often savage and rapacious, was seen as required to maintain peace and order in the land.

PART II

The Starving Times

Ore

Don Juan made extravagant claims regarding New Mexico in a letter he wrote to his sovereign. He said, regarding New Mexico, that it was "a possession so good that none other of his Majesty in these Indies excels it." He wrote of "the vastness of the settlements [and] the riches of the West." He spoke of its "many wild and ferocious beasts, lions (pumas or cougars), bears, wolves, tigers, *penicas*, ferrets, porcupines, and other animals whose hides they [the Indians] tan and use." He wrote of its "very fine grape vines, rivers, forests of many oaks, and some cork trees, fruits, melons, grapes, watermelons, Castilian plums, *capuli* (a kind of cherry), pine-nuts, acorns, ground-nuts, and *coralejo* (a delicate fruit)." He also spoke of the "many kinds of very rich ores" although those so far discovered, he said, "do not appear so."[1] The rich ores were there, however, of this he was sure. But he had yet to find them.

The purpose of this letter, written to the viceroy and to his king during March of 1599, was to beg for the appanage he felt due him. With God's help, he said, and if his Illustrious Sir would give him "the aid, the protection, and the help which [he] expect[ed] from such a hand," he, *don* Juan de Onate, would give the king "new worlds, new, peaceful, and grand." He said, "I beg that you take note of the great increase which the

295

royal crown and the rents of his Majesty have and will have in this land, with so many and such a variety of things, each one of which promises very great treasures."[2] He cited the wealth from the mines, the proximity of the South Sea, the increase of vassals and tributes, and salt.

The king would not have appreciated New Mexico's beauty, nor would he have been impressed by the wildlife missed by Onate. And he would have found no use for its many beautiful birds. These would not have interested the king. What the king sought, and what Spain needed, were pearls, silver, and gold, and so far they had found none of these in New Mexico.

But the wealth was there, on the edge of the Kingdom, and Farfan had found it. Captain Marcos Farfan de los Godos, Captain Bartolome Romero and Onate's chief page of the buckler (shield bearer), *Sargento* Hernan Martin Serrano the elder, with six additional soldiers, had been dispatched at Hopi to search for the mines of the Cruzados. The Indians for whom they searched were called 'the Cruzados,' because of the crosses they wore suspended from a lock of hair that fell over their forehead. The origin of this custom was not known at the time; however, it has since been learned that the Indians had been instructed to wear these crosses by an unknown Franciscan Friar who had, long ago, visited their land. This Friar, the Cruzados said, had told them "that if, at any time, they should see men, bearded and white, in order that these white men not molest or injure them, they should put on [these] crosses, which is a thing esteemed by them."

To the gambler—as well as to the prospector—a good hope is better than a bad holding. And these Indians, now known as the Yavapai, seemed to have what Onate was looking for. Deep in the mountains, in what is now the State of Arizona, on the eastern slope of the Aquarius Mountains, Farfan's group had found "an old shaft, three *estados* in depth, from which the Indians extracted the ores for their personal adornment and for the coloring of their blankets."[3] The vein of this ancient shaft, like that of the *Sierra de Cabra* south of Cordova, contained ores of many colors. It was wide, seemingly rich, and had many outcroppings. Outside the shaft, the vein ran alongside the hill and crossed over to another hill. The group of nine established many claims for themselves and for their companions who had been unable to accompany them. The small group determined that the veins were "so long and wide that half of the people of New Spain [could] have mines there."[4] And in addition to the seemingly rich ores, the area had a wonderful supply of water, fields of abundant crops, much game, and a great number of birds of all kinds, which, they felt, was an excellent indication of the good climate of the country.

If this was not heaven, then it was close. However, it was a long way from their base camp at San Juan where, on their return, one sample of ore was assayed at 11 ounces of silver per *quintal*. Diego de Zubia, the *proveedor general*, judged the mines to be potentially rich, or at least insofar as 'many littles make a much.' And although the mines did not rival the treasure of Venice or the mines of Potosi, at last, New Mexico appeared to hold something of value.

The Church of San Miguel

Although the mines at Aquarius appeared to hold something of value, value itself is an elusive variable. From the past participle of the Middle English or Old French term *'valoir'* (meaning 'to be strong' or 'to be worth'), value is *'the quality of a thing,'* what is thought of as being desirable, useful, estimable or important. Pedro's helmet was all of these and, although the floor of a church might have been considered an appropriate location for its burial, there was little question where his mother would want it placed. Pedro was a soldier who had demonstrated the values of sacrifice, courage, and commitment, his mother said, and he died defending his new country. His helmet, which retained the essence of him, should be buried in the barracks at San Gabriel where he would be near his brothers.

Catalina, who was a little restored and was now able to dress herself, asked to be left alone with his helmet and carried it into her darkened room. Here, shrouded in black, she knelt in a grieving position, as though bent over a fallen warrior. The men stood with heads bowed in light which filtered in through the open hatchway and listened as their mother intoned an ancient prayer.

Durme, durme ijiko de madre
Durme durme sin ansia i dolor ...

They could make little else of what their mother said, her woeful sobs masking the words:

Sleep, sleep, mother's little boy
Free from worry and pain ...

Then, with little ceremony, and with only Diego, Alonso, Francisco and their brother-in-law, Bartolome Romero, in attendance, Pedro's helmet was placed within a clay cooking vessel, topped with a stone griddle and buried in the earthen floor of their quarters. The men cried as they accomplished this task, the first tears they had collectively shared at Pedro's death. With this burial they achieved a degree of closure. A bit of Pedro remained with his family and Diego knew his father would have approved of the burial arrangements.

* * *

From here forward, there would be many changes. The Spaniards' sense of security had been shaken by the events at Acoma and *don* Juan knew that a number of mistakes had been made. Although the slain Juan de Zaldivar had gone to the mesa village with a fully armored troop, he had not conducted himself as one must in approaching an armed camp. In this, *don* Juan acknowledged to himself, he shared some responsibility. For if he, the captain general, had sent a warning to his *maese de campo* regarding the Acome, perhaps the tragedy might have been avoided. These errors, and other unforgivable oversights, he contended, could never again be allowed to occur; for diligence is the mother of good fortune.

The events at Acoma suggested to the colonists that they had to be ready for a potential attack from the Pueblo Indians, and able to repel it. Therefore, Onate initiated a number of defensive moves. First, he ordered that an outpost be constructed a short distance north of his headquarters at San Juan, to give him a better command of the approaches to the valley from the north and from the east. The outpost, a rude affair, was composed of four rooms and a tower constructed of newly-made adobes and with material reclaimed from a nearby pueblo ruin. The outpost thus consisted of a keep, but without a bailey, or an *albacar*, the space surrounded by a wall and attached to an edifice where the villagers could find refuge with their livestock during an attack. Onate took note of this but planned to provide this protection elsewhere.

In addition to building his northern outpost and '*miradero*,' or 'lookout site,' Onate made plans to move his headquarters and the remainder of his forces, from the pueblo of Okhe (San Juan) to Yungue (San Gabriel). The colonists would wait for spring to arrive before opening doorways and windows at the ancient pueblo, but the fortification of its plaza would begin immediately.

The pueblo of Yungue was the older, and smaller, of the San Juan villages. As the smaller of the two Indian villages, it only had one plaza. This was rectangular, with no exterior means of access or egress. Onate retained the plaza, as an *albacar*, where, following the clanging of bells, his colonists could seek refuge. For purposes of safety from attack, Onate had entrances of fieldstone made in each of the plaza's four corners. These were designed to provide positions from which to fire at an approaching enemy. The plaza, now strengthened by these fortifications, became the villager's *ejido*, or village common, which, in addition to providing a village pound, provided a public area for threshing and winnowing, a community midden, and a slaughter pen.

The 'Spanish section' of the old pueblo was established on the south end of the pueblo's building blocks. Although a number of pueblo rooms were being left intact and unchanged, an equal number were having walls stabilized or replaced, and considerable modifications were being undertaken to construct adjoining rooms, and to create, to the colonists' European tastes, more adequate and appropriate living spaces. Here, too, at the first hint of spring of 1599, the friars began to sketch out along the ground, the outline for their permanent church.

* * *

"I understand you have a plan," *don* Juan said to the friars who were kneeling in the mud of a shallow depression, "*Fray* San Miguel says you have a plan for the church."

Fray Martinez, who was kneeling in the pit with *Fray* Salazar and two of their assistants, appeared to be building a sandcastle, replete with puddled walls and towers. He shaded his eyes against the brilliant sun, and then stood to accept the captain-general who was standing on the earthen embankment.

"Yes!" *Fray* Martinez said, enthusiastically, "We're to build a church, and we have a plan. Come! Come, see what we have," he said, as he led *don* Juan into the mud-spattered hollow.

Don Juan entered the mud hole, and knelt beside *Fray* Salazar, who was building a miniature tower of adobe mud, cupping it this way and that, in his attempt to make it stand. Onate knelt in the mud for some time, studying the outline of the cruciform structure and trying to discern its various dimensions. "It's beautiful, very well built, solid, and of substance," he said laughingly, "but it's size? I can't tell. What's your plan?"

"This part, this part here, *don* Juan," Martinez said, pointing to the length of the miniature structure, "the nave will be 70 feet long and 25 or 30 feet wide at its base."

"Seventy feet long?" *don* Juan questioned. "Is that not enormous?"

"Wait, wait," *Fray* Salazar said. "I beg that you wait until you've heard the entire plan before rendering an opinion." *Don* Juan agreed to reserve his judgment, and the two friars continued with their description and plan for what they hoped would result in an actual church.

"The design will be that of a Latin cross," said *Fray* Salazar, "as a symbol of redemption, signifying Christ's death on the cross for the sins of humanity. The upright will be of 70 feet, with a cross piece of 60 feet," he said. "And here, here at the front, we'll have . . . "

"And the walls?" asked *don* Juan, interrupting the good father. "How high will the walls be?"

"Thirty feet for the nave, and 35 feet for the transept," interjected *Fray* Martinez, who had been allowing Onate's cousin, and personal chaplain, *Fray* Salazar, to present the design. "The transept walls will have to be higher than those of the nave, so that we can have a clearstory window here where the upright and cross piece meet," he said. "The church will face east, although *Fray* Salazar and I have had some disagreement about that," he said, while smiling at his subordinate, Salazar. "He correctly pointed out that altars have long been placed against the east wall of a church. However, an eastward facing church will allow light to directly strike the altar for early morning worship. And I think we're now in agreement about the placement of the front door. Are we not, Father?" he asked of *Fray* Salazar.

"Yes," Father," Salazar replied. "No church may face north,[1] and south is the only other direction which can be considered. The location of the village and the river rules that out. So, yes, we're in agreement. The church must face east."

"May I tell you of the other features?" asked *Fray* Martinez, again speaking to Juan de Onate. "The northern wall will have a door placed midway along its length, while in front, we'll have a balcony flanked by two bell towers. The balcony will also cover the entrance. The church will be built of earth and stone, and we'll start as soon we've gained your approval."

"It's beautiful," *don* Juan said, "but I question whether you have the resources necessary to build such an imposing structure."

"We want it to be seen from Mexico," answered *Fray* Salazar, as he, *Fray* Martinez, and Juan de Onate exited the pit. They climbed the ladder to the roof of *Fray* Martinez's apartment, across which lay an assortment of equipment. "Our brothers in our mother house in Mexico need to know that we've been successful in establishing our ministry," Salazar said.

Don Juan, who thought that such a structure might well be seen from Madrid said, "And the tools?"

"We have what I gave to every friar for building his church," answered *Fray* Martinez, lifting, and pointing out the tools which lay before him. "Ten axes, three adzes, three spades, ten hoes, one saw, one chisel, two augers, and a plane."

"And those other items?" asked *don* Juan.

"Those are the metal objects required to build our church," Martinez said, "a large latch for the door, two small locks, a dozen hinges, some small latches, and the bags contain 6,000 nails of various sizes."

Onate picked up one of the small locks, and, as though contemplating its interior workings, began locking and unlocking it in quiet deliberation. "Have either of you ever built a church?" he asked.

"No! But we think it's not hard," interjected *Fray* Salazar. "Anyhow, we're sure that God will give us the direction we require when we need it."

Juan de Onate looked at the two friars and at the tools they had spread on the roof before them, and then to the edge of the Spanish block where the church was to be built. The priests had no pulley blocks or other hoisting devices, and the many beams the builders would need would have to be hauled to the top of high walls. He blew air from between his pursed lips before continuing.

"The *vigas*," he said, in reference to the beams required for the construction of the roof. "It appears you'll need 30 or 40 of them, of what, 35 or 40 feet in length?"

"We make it be 15 for the nave, and an additional 20 for the transept," said *Fray* Martinez with the precision for which he was noted.

"They'll have to be brought from the high *sierras*, and I can spare few men for this venture," Onate said, to the priests who did not need his permission to embark on the building project. "Anyhow," he added. "I think that very few of our men will volunteer to assist you. They've refused to begin building their own homes and many want Galiana's palace. And Indian men consider the raising of walls to be a disgraceful occupation. You may employ the Pueblo men in the hauling of earth and for the making of *adobes*. Otherwise," he said, "you'll have to make do with women, and with boys and girls, both Indian and Spanish, who may help you."

"We know out limitations, *don* Juan," said *Fray* Martinez, who was about to reveal why he had included Juan de Onate in his planning. "The labor will be voluntary, *don* Juan. But we ask that you request a levy of two individuals from each family to be used in the construction of the church."

"I'll do as you ask," Onate answered, as he grasped the top of the ladder while readying his descent from the roof, "and I have but one request of you. Design your church as if it were to be used for military purposes," he said, "and build it as a fortress. This will require high, impregnable exterior walls which offer no protection to an enemy. Godspeed."

* * *

"Three spits (spades) only! My God! It will take forever to dig the required trenches with only three spits," said *dona* Eufemia. "I want each family to bring a spit to the work site. And don't listen to your husbands," she said while speaking to the Spanish women of the village. "They'll complain that you'll lose it, or that you'll break it, or that you'll throw it away! Do not listen to them! Mark your spit with your name, and bring it with you tomorrow. We'll have it back in your husband's inventory before he finds it gone!"

Shallow trenches, the width of the intended walls, were dug and filled with fieldstone. Upon these foundations, the boys of the village began laying up several courses of cut blocks to a height of one *vara*.

While the work of trenching was being done, many in the village were engaged in the tasks of making adobes. The earth required for this purpose was readily available. The clay soil, which results from the disintegration of rock, by various agencies of erosion, was at the surface of the earth, and was collected with little effort. Dug from a series of pits, which then became the depressions within which the friars, colonists and Indian women worked, the adobe makers kneaded the clay into an even paste. Straw and manure were worked into the mixture to act as a binder and to prevent the bricks from cracking while drying. The mud was then worked into a wooden mold, or *adobero*, which was used to make the clay bricks. In a day or two, the bricks were taken from the ground where they had been made, turned on their edge, and later stacked in piles for final drying. Using this method, the colonists made an incredible 200,000 large bricks, each 50 or 60 pounds in weight, with dimensions of 10 inches by 18 inches by 5 inches. On top of the stone portion of the walls, walls of coursed adobe began to rise, with new adobes being made, seasoned, and brought to the building site.

* * *

Lucia followed her younger sister, Francisca, as they climbed the fragile scaffolding to the top of the adobe wall. "Mama wanted to come," Francisca said, "but I wouldn't let her. I can just see her falling from here. And it would happen, you know" she said to her sister. "She's so frail, and weak . . . I worry about her. She couldn't do anything up here anyway," Francisca continued, while she and Lucia waited for the next level to be set out. "She couldn't scoot one of these bricks into place, much less lift it. No, it's better that she be left at home where she can be safe."

"I agree," Lucia said, as she followed Francisca in pulling the hem of her long skirt between her legs and tying it in front, "that's why I volunteered to take her place. She may think this her duty," Lucia said of her mother, "but we can't have her up here. And as long as I can leave here to feed the children," she said, speaking of her own small children, including her new-born, Ana, "I'll work until this is finished."

To move bricks from the ground to the top of the wide wall, the workers were using a series of ramps. Tugging on the roped ends of a burlap bag on which a large brick had been placed, the sisters pulled the brick up the final ramp to the top level.

"I'm worried about mama," Francisca said, as they worked to move the brick onto a newly laid bed of mud mortar, "she often says things that make no sense. And when I ask her to explain, she says that I'm too young to understand. And then she cries and says that she'll explain it to Alonso. Too young to understand!" Francisca said in exasperation. "I'm almost 18! When will I be old enough to understand?"

"Shh! Don't speak so loudly," Lucia cautioned, while again tying her kerchief around her sun streaked hair. "Don't be too hard on her, Quita," she said, using Francisca's pet name. "She's speaking of things of her childhood, and I don't think she understands them either."

"Well, that's easy for you to say," Francisca said, as she brushed mud from her scraped knees. "You don't have to live with her. She keeps asking Alonso if it's time! If it's time for what? I ask. She wanted him to build her a shed where she could eat and pray. And when he refused, saying that this would call unwanted attention to us, she disappeared. We were worried sick, looking here and there—even in the river. When Alonso found her, she was sitting in one of those little huts, one of those the Indians use when working in their fields. She was praying, and weeping, he thinks. He said he could see her shoulders trembling from her sobs, although she denied crying. Does Alonso tell you of these things?" Francisca asked her sister.

"He told me about that," Lucia said, "but perhaps I don't know everything that has happened. Maybe I can help you understand," Lucia said, while she and Francisca worked to bring a new brick to the top of the wall. "When mama was a little girl," Lucia said, "she and her brother would spend much of the harvest season with their grandparents, our great-grandparents, the Avalos. I didn't know them," Lucia said sadly, "they died long before Diego and I were born. But they had a farm, and mama loved to be there with them. Mama said that when the harvest was over, she and our Uncle Alonso, would help their *abuelo* build a shed in the fields near his home. I think the whole thing was just magical to her— the roof of green branches with leaves intertwined. Mama said that the aroma was wonderful, scented myrtle, fragrant willow, and other leafy twigs and branches. They'd spread yellow sand on the ground, and drape the walls with table clothes and blankets. And when they were finished building it, they'd put tables and benches inside, the table set with candlesticks, and dishes, and silverware. It must have been delightful, especially to a child of what . . . six or seven. Willow branches on the floor and shaken in the air, with prayers of thanksgiving for the good harvest, and singing, and eating. Mama said that from heaven, one would not have been able to see people below, only a small forest of willow trees shaking in the wind."

"But mama says she can't explain these things. How do you know of them?"

"I don't know them. Not really. And it's possible she never understood them either . . . rituals passed down through the ages, with their real meaning lost and forgotten. I only know what she and papa told me, and like you, it wasn't very much."

"I've not told you of mama's behavior, Lucia, because I didn't want you to worry," Francisca said. "You've got enough to worry about with a new baby. But I can't keep this inside any longer," she cried, her green eyes sparkling with tears. "She says Juan de Tapia is not one of us, and you know this breaks my heart, for I truly love him. And she says that it's only Alonso she can trust. Only Alonso? With Diego's devotion to her! She's ill, very ill," Francisca said, "and I fear for her future."

"Mama doesn't mean trust in the way you imagine, Quita, but rather 'entrust,' to place something in Alonso's care. Mama once told me that she'd trust Diego with her life."

The young women continued to work on the walls, while their mother waited with their brother Alonso in their mother's new apartment in the village of San Gabriel.

* * *

"Where are the others?" his mother asked of Alonso, as she struggled to raise herself to a sitting position atop her mat.

"They're at the church, Mama, working on the walls," Alonso answered as he observed the roses of starvation which looked like tattooed flowers upon her ashen skin.

"Did you do as I asked you, *ijiko*?" his mother questioned, looking anxiously at him and at the ladder that leaned against the open hatchway.

"Yes, Mama," Alonso answered. "I took all of the bread outside— Lucia's, too—and burned it, just as you asked."

"And the wind, *ijiko*, which way did the wind blow?" she asked looking for an omen of the coming year.

"It blew from the north, Mama," Alonso responded, knowing that his mother had asked him to burn the bread as a safeguard against another unproductive year.

"Oh," his mother responded quietly as she lay back upon her mat. She knew that if the smoke blew south, it presaged further sadness for them, for it meant there would continue to be a scarcity of food—no strewn bread with its closely guarded recipe.

Alonso watched his mother as she mouthed a wordless prayer and dared not tell her that the smoke had blown from the north but had then turned toward the west. He knew, as his mother would know, that there would be nothing but further sadness, for this foretold another year of famine in which there would be nothing to eat.

The Detachment

Onate needed assistance, and he clearly knew it. The letter of 2 March 1599 in which he had extolled the virtues of the new land was a cry for help. If he was to hold on to his adobe kingdom—with all that was not there, and the nothing that was—he needed more men. Therefore, he began plans to send an embassy south to Mexico City to make this plea for him.

In the composition of his embassy, Onate was sending some of his best men. Led by two of his most trusted captains, Gaspar Perez de Villagra and Marcos Farfan de los Godos, the group also contained *Fray* Alonso Martinez, head of the Franciscan priests and lay brothers, Onate's cousin, *Fray* Cristobal de Salazar, and Brother Joaquin Rodriguez whom *Fray* Martinez had asked to be responsible for the 60 small children of the Acome. In addition to a small trunk of Robledo journals, which had been given Brother Rodriguez by Catalina Lopez, the embassy also carried a document, signed by a number of the leading colonists, constituting a vote of confidence in Onate's leadership.

The embassy set off for the City of Mexico sometime during March of 1599, and none of the principals were fated to return. Onate's cousin, *Fray* Cristobal de Salazar (who would later have a mountain range in New Mexico named after him) would die on the trail. Onate's most trusted captain, Gaspar Perez de Villagra, would later desert. In addition, Captain Marcos Farfan de los Godos would quit the venture, and *Fray* Alonso Martinez would be reassigned. The reason for the defections may be found in the attitude demonstrated toward the small group when it arrived at the viceregal capital sometime during the second week of June 1599. Viceroy Monterrey, hearing the reports regarding New Mexico as given by these men, gave permission for them to begin recruitment for reinforcements. He was visibly troubled, however, by what he heard regarding the events at Acoma. The expedition there, these men had told him, had been led by Vicente de Zaldivar, and not by Onate. Therefore, the viceroy mused, perhaps a portion of the responsibility for this outrage lay elsewhere. However, he could not countenance the cruel treatment of these defeated people at the hands of the expedition's leaders, and someone was going to pay.

Meanwhile, with the loss of the four individuals as noted above, the role of leader of the returning caravan had to be passed to another. Therefore, Onate's nephew, Juan Guerra de Resa, who had been raised in Cain (and who still held the title of lieutenant governor of New Mexico), appointed Bernabe de las Casas to take responsibility for the recruitment effort. Casas would be advanced to the rank of captain, but it would take almost a year and a half before his relief column would reach San Juan.

The Missions

Meanwhile, Onate was not resting on his laurels in San Juan. A few may have been fooled into believing that he had achieved fame, honor, or a victory in the events at Acoma, but, he knew that his victory was hollow, and that his wreath of evergreens retained the faint scent of burned flesh. In any event, he had little choice but to continue the venture, even if this required a degree of duplicity, on his part himself and on the part of others in his command.

First among his quixotic adventures, was the demand that his new *maese de campo*, Vicente de Zaldivar, repair to the Indian village of San Marcos to open the mines. San Marcos, which is located northeast of Cerrillos in the Galisteo Basin, was in the area of the lead and turquoise mines which the Spaniards had found the Indians working in 1598. Here, Onate insisted, was silver of high grade. The mines, however, if they ever had existed, were now nowhere to be found.

Vicente was also sent to the pueblo of *El Tuerto* (The Crooked or Bent), east of the Sandia Mountains, where he was told to construct an ore crusher and smelter in anticipation of the riches they would find there. Zaldivar later tried to pass off a sample of ore from New Spain as having come from these hills, but nothing further is heard of the venture.

As a result of having found no nests where he had thought to find birds, Onate was desperate. He had to find a way to make the land pay, and he could not wait for the arrival of his reinforcements to accomplish this. Therefore, with prayers for success, and in one final push, Onate sent his nephew to California.

* * *

If a soldier is to survive, he must live off the land he occupies, be it friendly or hostile. Therefore, Vicente de Zaldivar, with 25 or 30 horsemen, was first sent to the pueblos of the Jumano to replenish his supplies. It was critical he obtain these before heading west, for the Spaniards had exhausted the stores of their Indian neighbors closer to San Juan. However, the Jumanos, like the Acome, proved recalcitrant. Vicente de Zaldivar sent notice of this snub to his uncle, Juan de Onate, and with neither straw nor hay to fill his belly, he continued his westward journey.

Onate was furious. He could not allow vassals of the king to behave in this manner and to further place his colonists in jeopardy. Therefore, he put a detachment of 50 men together and set off to punish the Jumano. In full armor for the first time—that is with helmet, *bevor*, coat of mail, *cuisses* of mail, sword, and *harquebus*; his horse armored with buckskin, bullhide or calfskin—he set fire to a portion of the pueblo of Cueloze, and a number of the Jumano were shot. In addition, Onate had two of the Pueblo leaders hanged, and, for good measure, and because he believed him to be in collusion with the rebellious Indians, had his own interpreter hanged also.

For the moment the Jumanos were quiet. However, late in 1600, five soldiers from San Gabriel, who were venturing south on their way to New Spain, were attacked by the Jumanos of Cueloze. Vicente de Zaldivar, who had been sent packing by the Jumanos, and who had also been turned back in Arizona by additional hostile Indians, was commanded by Onate to punish them. However, before Zaldivar could leave on this assignment, the long-awaited reinforcement column arrived.

Reinforcements

It was a great Christmas present, one of the best Onate had ever received. On Christmas Eve of 1600 the reinforcement caravan, under command of Captain Bernabe de las Casas, with the assistance of Captain Juan de Vitoria Carvajal, arrived at Onate's headquarters at San Gabriel. With the two leaders were at least 73 officers and men bringing their families with them, six Franciscans, additional livestock, and critical supplies. Among the Spanish soldiers were Cristobal Baca the first, Juan Lopez Holguin, and Bartolome de Montoya.

Baca, who was one of the captains who had come to reinforce the Onate colony, was the son of Juan de Vaca, who had been with Vasquez de Coronado. He was born in Mexico City, and was described as being of good stature, dark-complexioned, well-featured, and 33 years of age. With him was his pregnant wife, *dona* Ana Ortiz, three grown daughters, Juana de Zamora, Isabel de Bohorquez, Maria de Villanueva, and a son, Antonio, all born in the City of Mexico. Also with them was their female servant, Ana Verdugo and their extensive possessions.[1]

With Baca, and his Villanueva/Ortiz family was a second Villanueva/Ortiz family with whom he and his wife appear to have been closely allied. Juan Lopez Holguin, like many of the men in the reinforcement column, was Spanish-born. The son of Juan Lopez Villasana, he had been born in Fuente Ovejuna (Sheep Spring) where the Moslems had built a fortress during the 8th century. It was here, also, that the Christians were later to construct an ill-fated castle. The city of Fuente Ovejuna was later to be made famous in 1619 by Lope de Vega as the village where the cruel tyrant, the *Comendador don* Fernan Gomez de Guzman, was killed by his townsmen. Lopez Holguin, described as of good stature, black-bearded, with a mark on his left eye, and 40 years old, was there with his wife, Catalina de Villanueva, and four children. These were a son, Cristobal, and three daughters, Maria and Ana Ortiz, and Isabel, who was later to marry her escort, Captain Juan de Vitoria Carvajal.

A third member of the reinforcement column, Bartolome de Montoya, was there with his entire family. He was a native of Cantillana, near Seville, the son of Francisco de Montoya, briefly described as being short of stature, blackbearded, and 28-years-old. His wife, Maria de Zamora, was born in Mexico City, at San Sebastian, the daughter of Pedro de Zamora, who was a resident of that city, and former *Alcalde Mayor* of Oaxaca. Her mother's name was Augustina Abarca. Maria had married Montoya at Texcoco, and had, by the time they joined Onate's colony, three boys and two girls, all of whom were under 16 years of age. These children were Francisco, Diego, Jose, Lucia, and an infant named Petronila. With Diego Robledo eyeing the comely Lucia de Montoya, all retired to the Church of San Miguel for midnight Mass, for this, the final Christmas of the millennium.

The Snows of Winter

Despite the arrival of the reinforcement column with its badly needed relief supplies, the year 1600 was ending badly. Severe winter snows and frozen temperatures devastated most of the upper Rio Grande, and the situation for the colonists was desperate. The newly arrived soldier-colonists and their families sought to make a niche for themselves in airless rooms in the village of San Gabriel, and all hunkered down against the cold to await the spring planting.

The colonists had been in New Mexico since mid-August 1598 and had harvested two crops. Planted in this high country, at almost 6,000 feet above sea level, were their *Traidas de Castilla*, the Spanish crops brought from Castile, their barley, cabbage, cantaloupes, garlic, lettuce, onions, radishes, watermelon, and wheat. From New Spain, the colonists had added pinto beans, chile, tobacco, tomato, and a new type of corn, called *Cristolina de Chihuahua*, characterized by a long, large cob and grain that was predominantly white. Other fields contained horsebeans, melons, peas, pumpkins and squash. The wheat, a cold-weather grain, adapted well, but, the remainder lagged behind. Barley also did well, but because, as in Spain, it was to be used mainly as fodder for livestock, it was not intended to add to the colonists' food supply. It now, however, was being used to make bread. This consisted of flour mixed from wheat, beans, lentils, and corn, mixed together to make a loaf, as one would a barley cake. The colonists were attempting to ration this—approximately eight ounces at a time, one meal a day. The barley, therefore, was a godsend. Before the winter of 1601 was over, the colonists were reduced to eating cowhides, which they roasted, and ate, even as the Indians (who, after taking a handful of salt crystals, and placing their breath upon it), were eating twigs, dirt, coal, and ashes. The colonists' greatest woe occurred when they could no longer find a bit of leather to eat, for their livestock was dying off.

The problem was the weather. It was, as one soldier lamented, so cold "that the rivers freeze over, and it snows most of the time." And, he might have added that "it would not be so bad if we ate once in a while, for troubles are less where there is bread." The land was in the throes of a little ice age, an era that would span the period from 1550 to 1700 (and some would say from 1450 to 1850), and the colonists continued to be frighteningly dependent on the Indians.

In response to their plight, many of the colonists just wanted to go home. Although they had sold all of their possessions to get here, many wanted to go back, and, unfortunately, several of their leaders began to echo these sentiments.

Captain Pablo de Aguilar was first—and it was fresh sin, fresh penance, with this pig finally coming to its Martinmas.[1] Twice previously ordered to be executed by Onate (first for entering the pueblo of Cualacu without permission, and then for preaching sedition), this Ganelon[2] was at it again. Although he had proven to be brave and badly needed in the assault at Acoma, he became a catalyst for those wishing to abandon the colony. And although Onate felt that it was better to be praised by a discerning few than scoffed at by the unknowing many, he heard of Aguilar's leadership in the traitorous cause and began to devise a plan. He determined to have his men build a weir of twisted truths, so as to catch, and finally punish, Aguilar.

But trout are not caught with dry breeches, and in the end, Onate had no choice but to become personally immersed in the raging stream. They were looking for mines, Onate told Aguilar, but this was merely a pretext to take him out of the village where the hawk—swift and straight as a falling stone—could better fall upon its prey. A day's journey from San Gabriel, in a miserable tent at their wintry encampment, Juan de Onate, with several servants, met to devise a murderous plan.

* * *

Onate raised the flap of Aguilar's tent and peered inside, the intensity of his gaze and the muscled breadth of his torso giving the impression of barely harnessed power. "We've come for you, *don* Pablo," he said quietly. "We've come, for it's time for you to pay for your transgressions."

"Transgressions?" Aguilar asked as he struggled to remove his *cuero*, his arms manacled behind him by the layered sleeves of his protective garment. "Of what transgressions do you speak, *don* Juan?"

"Disobedience, mutiny, and sedition," Onate responded as he and several servants entered the tent.

312

"Give me a moment, *don* Juan, and we can discuss your accusations. I need only a little help from my servant to free me from my coat."

"You'll find no help here," Onate responded. "Inevitably, servants are paid enemies."

Onate's sword made a clean metallic sound as he drew it from its scabbard and stepped to the middle of the floor. "And of the crime of disobedience," Onate asked of Aguilar who was conveniently dressed in the dark clothes of the condemned, "how do you plead?"

"I could offer much in the way of explanation, *don* Juan, but I'll admit to that."

"And to mutiny?" Onate asked, his voice now becoming louder. "How say you?" he asked as he placed the sword's point in the middle of Aguilar's ribs.

"I didn't abandon the colony, *don* Juan. And as you can see, I'm here, standing weak and defenseless while you yourself are armed."

"And of sedition?" Onate bellowed. "Of your stirring up of discontent, resistance, and rebellion against my authority? How say you of that?"

"We only seek to go home, *don* Juan, for we can't survive another winter." Brushing aside the point of Onate's sword with his shoulder, Aguilar moved even closer to Onate before continuing. "I ask that of you now," he said, his fetid breath now additionally tinged with the scent of numerous emotions. "I ask that I be allowed to go home. I'll leave immediately and take no supplies or horses other than the one I have."

"Let you go?" Onate raged. "I might as well think of turning the wolf loose among the sheep, the fox among the hens, the fly in the honey as to defraud justice and allow you to go home. You've been caught, convicted, and condemned, *don* Pablo, and your sentence is death!"

Aguilar shrugged while still attempting to free his arms. "Well, laws go as kings like," he said with a sneer, "but I'm a man of honor and a gentleman and will not allow you to treat me like a Turk! I'm in sin!" he bellowed, "and I demand that you allow me to go to confession before your sentence is carried out."

This was denied. His pleas were ignored, and he was stabbed repeatedly by his assailants as the small group moved like a living

313

organism upon a cultured dish. However, Aguilar was a physically powerful man, of good stature, and although hampered by his leather bounds, he dragged his assailants here and there throughout the tent, struggling to free his arms. Then, liberating himself momentarily, he staggered through the raised flap of his tent where he stood facing Onate and the servants who had followed him. "You've done your work well, my friends, but God will do better," he said, predicting his death and even further damnation. Then, for a brief moment, he stood alone, his labored breath hanging about his shoulders like a translucent shroud. He took a step forward, looked about him at the snowy heights which backdropped their encampment, and fell in the snow, the soft powder like shredded corn silk swirling in the air. He was finally stabbed to death, with Juan de Onate himself rendering the final thrust.

Next to go was Captain Alonso de Sosa Albornoz, in whose company the elder Pedro Robledo had served. Although he had sold his estate in New Spain to finance the New Mexican venture, he asked to return there with his wife and five children. He was given permission to go, and had even begun packing his carts. However, before he could leave, he was asked to join a group of soldiers who were searching for lost horses for Onate could not allow one of his top officers to abandon the colony. After the group had gone for some distance from the village, he was set upon by Vicente de Zaldivar who stabbed him to death. Zaldivar then hid Sosa's body beneath a mantle of stone, and returned to San Gabriel.

* * *

The pall of these murders cast the colonial venture into an entirely different light. Although Pablo de Aguilar probably did not deserve to die, he had proven to be seditious. But Sosa's only sin, was that he had asked to return to New Spain where he could feed his wife and children. The reality was, however, that anyone asking for such permission, was considered by military law, to have earned the death penalty as a deserter from his captain and his flag. This was the ultimate of the merciless punishments that could be meted out for a breach of discipline under arms. However, the manner in which the Aguilar and Sosa were killed, suggests that Onate, himself, was unsure of his standing in this matter. Had Onate been more secure in his right to execute Aguilar, for example,

314

he would have taken him to a scaffold in the village square, or to his own *Peravillo*[3] where Aguilar would have been beheaded.

From here on in, the colonists would be cowed into silence and would say little. However, these murders were like an interlude, for the seeds of mutiny had been sown and now seemed to spread like sheet lightning across a summer sky.

Spring

Delayed by a number of events that had kept him from carrying out his uncle's command to punish the Jumanos, Vicente de Zaldivar was off again. His treatment at the hands of the Jumanos and their subsequent attack upon a small group of Spaniards who were fleeing down the Camino Real on their way to Santa Barbara, were precursors, the Spaniards had been told, to the Jumanos' planned, general uprising. The Jumano, like the Acome, wanted to throw off the Spanish yoke, and if they were successful, nowhere in New Mexico would the colonists be safe. Therefore, the Jumanos had to be put down.

At their great stone pueblo of Cueloze, located on the crown of a hill east of the pass at Abo, the Jumanos came out to meet Zaldivar. With stones and arrows, they proved to be a formidable force, brave, and as determined to defeat Zaldivar's small army, as he was to defeat theirs. Under quickening clouds, which masked the sun, Zaldivar's men repeatedly attacked the walls of the village, only to be driven away. Again and again, the Spaniards attacked the village, until finally, after six days of repeated assaults, the Spaniards were successful in taking it. Zaldivar's men set fire to the pueblo of Cueloze and to two others that were in the vicinity. They killed more than 800 men, women, and children, and the Jumanos were successfully defeated.

The events at Cueloze, like the events at Acoma, clearly demonstrated that while Onate might have had a firm grip on the villages at San Juan, he did not hold the kingdom. As subsequent events would demonstrate, however, even his seemingly firm grounding at San Juan was an illusion.

315

Quivira

Introduction: At one time, the name 'Quivira' was associated with all of the unknown land west of the Mississippi River, and east or north of the Gulf of California. It has been suggested that the name comes from the French word 'cuivre' meaning 'copper,' and that the Indians got the term from Jacques Cartier, who was on the St Lawrence in 1535. Others have suggested that Quivira may derive from the Arabic word 'quivir,' meaning 'great' (as in Wadi Al-Kabir, or Guadalquivir, 'Great River,' the name of the watercourse that flows through Seville). Still others have suggested that the term may be a compression of the Spanish proverb 'quien vivir para ver' (or more appropriately, 'bueno es vivir para ver,') the equivalent of our 'Live and learn.' This was the motto supposedly used by Francisco Vasquez de Coronado to spur his men on in their search for lands rich in gold, silver, and fabrics which, he assured them, lay over the next horizon. Vasquez de Coronado had searched for Quivira from 1540 to 1542, Francisco Leyva de Bonilla and Antonio Gutierrez de Humana in 1593. None of them, however, was successful in his quest to go beyond the Llanos del Cibolo to plant settlements on the strait of Anian. Now it was Onate's turn to look for better bread than that made of wheat.

Why Juan de Onate decided to go east, in search of Quivira, rather than west, in search of the South Sea, however, remains a mystery. He had first told his men that they were going in search of the South Sea. This was the exploration halted during December of 1598 because of the events at Acoma. But sometime before leaving the village of San Gabriel, Onate decided to go to the plains in search of Quivira.

Onate's reasons for searching for Quivira were manifold. Individuals in positions of power, during the 16th and 17th centuries, were driven by three passions: western and northwestern discovery, conquest, and colonization; the exploration of the South Sea; and the finding of a northern passage by water from the Atlantic to the Pacific. The discovery by Columbus of lands heretofore unknown in what is now South America, caused a great deal of confusion among European scholars. These lands, the literati argued, were much further to the east than could be made to agree with their understanding of the Asian continent. Thus, the aim of subsequent explorations became to determine the extent of this newly discovered 'island' (which they determined lay between Europe and the Asiatic mainland), and to find a passage between these new lands, and the Asiatic coast. Despite repeated explorations from both the north and the south along the coast, no passage could be found. This led to three hypotheses: that the passage existed where they had been searching, but that they had missed it; that the land they coasted was a southeastern projection of the Asiatic mainland and not separated from the continent; or that the passage which would establish the correctness of the old maps and narratives regarding Asia, lay to the north. The third hypothesis became the prevalent view and no little activity was given to its confirmation.

The quest for a Northwest Passage began in earnest in 1524, when Giovanni Verranzano, sailing under the French flag, tried to find it. The Portuguese explorer, Estevao Gomes, quickly followed him. Sailing as Estevan Gomez for Spain rather than Portugal, Gomez reached the coast of Maine during June of 1525. At the mouth of the Penobscot River, which he named the 'Rio de las Gamas' (meaning 'River of the Deer'), Gomez felt he had found the fabled strait. He was unable to ascend the river due to the rapids at Bangor, however, and returned to Spain, with little to show for his efforts beyond the Indians he took home as slaves.

Jacques Cartier, as previously noted, looked for the strait in 1535, and Henry Hudson in 1609-1610. Still others, sailing for Denmark, England, Holland, Russia, Scotland, and, in more modern times, Canada, and the United States, were still looking for it at the beginning of the 19th century. Finding the Northwest Passage had been one of the purposes of the Lewis and Clark expedition of 1804-1806. The passage existed, but not where anyone had been looking.

The much-sought Northwest Passage was finally discovered in 1906, when Roald Amundsen's ship, the Gjoa, accomplished this feat in the Arctic. In 1601, however, the passage, which had become confused with the fabled strait of Anian through which fictitious voyagers and adventurers sailed, was an elusive reality. Thus, the search for Quivira and the Northwest Passage, spurred Onate's exploration.[1]

The preparations for the expedition toward the east were as meticulous as they had been for previous explorations to the South Sea, and to the bison plains. Antonio de Godoy relates:

> *The most necessary things having been arranged for the journey, with the supply of provisions, arms, ammunition, and other requisite military stores, with more than 70 picked men for the expedition, all very well equipped, more than 700 horses and mules, six mule carts, and two carts drawn by oxen conveying four pieces of artillery, and with servants to carry the necessary baggage, the journey was begun this year 1601 . . ."[2]*

Although Godoy places the initiation of the journey in the most favorable light, the *Breve Relacion* describes the number of soldiers involved as 80, "half of whom were rather a hindrance than a help." The later judgment was probably accurate. For Onate—as watchful as a man must be when surrounded by scoundrels—had included in the group those he was afraid to leave behind lest they incite a riot as well as his most trustworthy men. However, to his eternal sorrow, he missed some of the former, and they were to lead to his ruination.

With the winds of rebellion blowing on this spring day, the expedition to Quivira set out from the lush vale and forest of San Juan on 23 June 1601. With Onate on this expedition was his *maese de campo*, Vicente de Zaldivar, and two religious, his cousin, *Fray* Francisco de Velasco, who had joined the colony the previous Christmas, and lay brother, *Fray* Pedro de Vergara. Left behind to mind the meager stores were Onate's lieutenant governor, Francisco de Sosa Penalosa, and his most trusted captain, Geronimo Marquez. Marquez, who had sought to warn the captain general that "there was more mischief in the village than he had heard talk of'," watched with some apprehension as the troop rode out of the basin.

A thick ground fog was beginning to lift as the expedition left the valley, and due to a rare meteorological phenomenon, this caravan of soldiers, cannons, and carts, which extended almost a mile, was ethereally reflected overhead, a vision Godoy described as "a scene of wonder and beauty." Yet Marquez was troubled. The sight of his superior leading his army across the sky left him ill at ease.

And no sooner had Onate's column disappeared over the horizon, than the seeds of rebellion began to sprout among those left behind, skillfully manured by the clerics who had sown these germs of dissension. First, the complaints were heard from little groups who had given Onate hidden figs and innumerable *mamonas*[3] as he rode out of the village. "God, this place!" said the dissident colonists. "We sold all we had to get here, and for what? There's nothing here! What happened to the *encomiendas* and Indian tribute? All they have is *mantas* and bison skins, and they cry when we take them. What good is nobility when we have nothing to eat?"

Regarding the poverty of the land, the friars who heard these complaints from the dissident colonists agreed. The ancient *Fray* Francisco de San Miguel, vice commissary of New Mexico and Onate's confessor, did what he could to hasten the colonists' departure. "Why don't you just go?" he asked, fingering his rosary, which was made up of mere seeds strung on a cord of catgut. "There's nothing here for you, and you're getting in the way of our converting the Indians. If you were not stealing their *mantas* and corn, they'd be better disposed towards us. Go! Go home! No one will blame you."

But they would be blamed, for they were settlers **and** soldiers, and they were subject to military law. Moreover, if they left, they would be branded as traitors and worse. They would be executed!

"We can't go unless all of us go together," many of the villagers said. "We must present a united front. If some remain behind, we'll be asked why we too could not stay. We've reached the point of extreme misery, destitution and poverty," they said. "We'll starve to death here. We can't survive another winter!"

This, too, was what Francisco Robledo was being told regarding his mother who wore the rash of pellagra upon her ashen skin. Most vocal in these pronouncements were *dona* Eufemia, wife of Lieutenant Governor Francisco de Sosa Penalosa, and her daughter, Juana de Trejo, wife of Captain Diego de Zubia.

"*Dona* Catalina will die here," they said of his mother, whose recovery from each relapse of depression was slower and less complete. 'If she doesn't die of starvation, she'll die of a broken heart. You must take her home, Francisco. You must take her home!"

Francisco listened to these pleas regarding the recommended retreat and conferred with Diego who was still the patriarch of the family. At first Diego was appalled by the suggestion, but, as time went on and there was no improvement in his mother's condition, he too began to accept the possibility of taking her back.

It went on like this for two months with the voices of the dissident colonists becoming louder by the day. Onate had left the village on 23 June and his rear guard somewhat later, and through July and August, the call to mutiny ran through the villages he had left behind.

There were many who felt that there was an equal lack of corn and justice, and on 7 September 1601, those seeking to leave met in the church of San Miguel. Its namesake friar who had asked to speak with them regarding their future invited them there. This was the first formal meeting San Miguel had sought although many clandestine and informal meetings had preceded it.

Standing in the cool semi-darkness of the cavernous church following a high Mass as offered by the five friars in attendance, the colonists waited to hear *Fray* San Miguel and to begin the list of complaints that they hoped to take south with them. Before addressing his congregation, San Miguel sought to demonstrate that the words he was about to speak were the truth. He stood in his gray robe, its hood lying flatly on his shoulders, and, in the odd manner of the day, took a cleric's oath of fidelity by placing his right hand on the right side of his worn and rumpled habit which was now further stained by the mud of Pecos. Then, walking stiff-armed with the upper portion of his body seemingly attached to his robes, he paced back and forth in front of the main altar intoning his severe pronouncements. San Miguel's major complaint was that Onate was doing nothing to bring the Indians to the knowledge of God or to assist in their salvation.

"The governor," he said, "is a sinner and a seducer who chatters and prattles but says nothing of worth." He spoke of a governor swollen with pride and grown tyrannical. "While you're starving to death he's

320

grown fat and arrogant and has forsaken the path of equity—for the ox that's loose licks himself well."

"He ordered the execution of Pablo de Aguilar and Alonso de Sosa," said Captain Luis Gasco Velasco. "I was there when they were murdered. They were good and just men," continued Gasco. "They didn't deserve to die."

"He also ordered the execution of Manuel Portugues and Juan Gonzalez," bellowed another. "They only sought to go home."

In addition to the grievous offenses previously cited, Onate was even accused of the sin of arrogance for considering having a mace bearer proceed him as he walked through the villages, for stringing his titles at the beginning of letters, and for including crowns in his coat of arms.

"He treats his nephew, Vicente de Zaldivar, as a king-of-arms," they said, "and even allows Zaldivar to address him, Onate, as 'Your Majesty.' "

"He's built an Augean stable of 3,000 mules," they asserted, "unclean for three years. If he were not here," they assured themselves, "we could divert the great river through it and clean it in a day!"

They continued like this in their mighty church of San Miguel, with the defectors describing a land where liberty was dead and life little more than that of a swarm of midges above a frozen pool.

"Nothing grows here," they said. "The frost has barely left the ground when it begins to snow again!"

"And this Onate," they said, "he's showy and insincere, providing empty talk and writing intended only to get our applause."

"He's a lodestone," they said building themselves to a frenzy, "creating a claptrap of dowsing rods and finding nothing but salt! He's guilty of many sins!"

The obloquy continued with charge after charge being heaped upon Onate and echoing throughout the adobe building. There were many who spoke against him and against the colonial enterprise, including his supply-master, Diego de Zubia, and bookkeeper, Alonso Sanchez. Joining in this forsaking of Onate's standard was his new captain, Bernabe de las Casas, and most of the clergy, for, as the saying goes, 'If the abbot sings well, the acolyte is not far behind.' Those who should have put out the fire were fanning the flames, and the previously small blaze was now becoming an inferno.

"If he were here," said *Fray* Francisco de Zamora, who had been standing behind *Fray* San Miguel, and who now moved centerstage, "I would say to him, 'great is your power, and great is the harm you do.' It's not our intention to have the colony abandoned," he said to the colonists who stood before him. "We only want Juan de Onate replaced."

It continued like this through the month of September with the dissident colonists working feverishly to enlist others in their cause. Then, on 2 October 1601, those loyal to Onate also met in the church of San Miguel where they stood before the blessed box. It contained the silver paten with a small hole drilled through the middle which Onate had found at one of the Towa pueblos. Secured in a trade for hawk bells, the paten had been worn by a *cacique*, or village chieftain, as a *patena*, a large medal somewhat like a locket, that was worn by country women. And it was before this sacred dish, a relic of the ministries of the slain Fathers Rodriguez and Lopez at Puaray, that the loyalists met.

Absent from this second group were the carpet clerics, who, eager to avoid danger and exertion, were in their attached *convento* packing their bags. Most vocal among the loyalists was Cristobal Baca the first, who had only been with the colony for nine months. "It's the priests who are responsible for this debacle," he said. "Without their active support and encouragement, the others would not be going."

Those colonists loyal to Onate could not allow the deserters to present charges of *inimicitia* and *dedecus* against Onate (and New Mexico) without attempting to counter them. They contended that these charges, which were as thick as falling leaves, reflected a malicious intent on the part of the dissident colonists to bring shame, loss of honor, ridicule, and public humiliation in addition to legal charges against Onate.

But the truth always rises above a lie, as oil above water, and within the dissidents' tangle of truths, exaggerations, and lies, tiny globules of verity began to rise to the surface. The loyalists skimmed these from the stew and began to compose their own dispatch. In addition to reiterating their support for Onate and for his leadership, they emphasized the many positive features regarding their beautiful land.

322

The land, they insisted, was fertile and productive. They noted that with only seven *fanegas*[4] of wheat, they had produced a small harvest and a seed crop that they retained for the next year's planting. Of 50 *fanegas* planted the following year, they had achieved a yield of almost a 1,000 *fanegas*, and it was estimated that they had brought in almost 1,500 *fanegas* during the most recent harvest. This was the harvest the retreating colonists were waiting for before abandoning the village. Following the completion of their document, they determined that one among them must go south with the retreating colonists to inform the viceroy "of the present situation" in New Mexico, and also, of their "dire need for aid." The certificate was signed by Bartolome Romero, Cristobal Baca the first, Hernan Martin Serrano, Alonso Varela, Pedro Lucero, Simon Perez de Bustillo, and Ascensio de Arechuleta as secretary. Elected to carry their words to New Spain was, as always, the extremely reliable and trustworthy, Geronimo Marquez.

Betrayal / Cravenness / Treason

Adagietto

On 2 October while the men loyal to Onate were meeting at the church, the women, children, and dissident colonists were busy in their own pursuits. Near the church, in an apartment long abandoned by the Indians of Yungue, Francisca was speaking to her mother.

"Mama," Francisca said to her mother who was out of bed and looking through their window of selenite, "I'm going to look for some *tomatillo*. Do you need anything before I go?"

"*Tomatillo?*" her mother asked of the wild plant, bull nettle. "What are you going to do with it, *ijika?*"

"I'm going to make some cheese, Mama," Francisca responded, referring to the herb which was used to clabber fresh milk. "*Dona* Eufemia promised me some goat's milk if I'd pick some *tomatillo* for her. So, I'm going to get some for both of us. I think I saw some by the mill."

"Do you mind if I go with you?" her mother asked in her soft, sweet voice, now tinged with sadness. "We can take Lucia, too," she said.

323

"Then you won't have to go alone."

"I don't mind going alone, Mama," Francisca responded. "But if you're well enough, I'd love for you to go with me."

"And Lucia?" her mother asked.

"And Lucia, too," Francisca responded. "I'll ask her."

* * *

It was a morning of brilliant sunshine, the day new, and sharp, and clear. Splashes of crimson on brilliant maples set off the bright hillside along which they walked. Catalina, lame from muscles atrophied from lack of exercise, her shoulders stooped and bowed from illness, could scarcely walk, and had to be supported by Lucia who led her by the arm. Francisca, who had placed a loaf of *pan trenzada*[1] inside a wrap of shear muslin, cradled the bread in the roll of a blanket which she carried under her arm. The three women moving slowly along the main irrigation canal, chatted while making an inventory of the useful plants they found growing wild along its shadowy embankments and in the fields below. "*Yerba buena*," one would call. "*Yerba del manzo*," would answer a second. "*Cana agria*," would say a third. "And *amole*,[2] and *tomatillo*" as well.

"I saw some yucca on the other side of the ditch," Lucia called to her sister, Francisca. "For our hair," she said. "We can get some on the way back."

A long journey was very much on Catalina's mind as she looked for *contra yerba*, or caltrap, which was good for infections, *ocha*, which was good for sores, and *trementina*[3] which could be obtained from the pinon trees on the other side of the stream. She placed the medicinal plants in the catch of her apron which she held gathered in front of her, and, with Lucia's assistance, continued walking along the *acequia* in uncertain steps.

The main *acequia*, to which secondary ditches were attached, flowed between grassy ramps and ran concealed underneath soaring stands of majestic cottonwoods and slouching willows. Fed by gravity and running cool and deep it gurgled endlessly as it flowed along its meandering channel. Lesser *acequias*, in an intricate web of even smaller ditches were empty of their life-giving waters, the fields through which they ran, now harvested. Some of the water flowing through the main canal was being directed down a narrow chute to the mill where it was being used to power the mill's grinding stone. Having accomplished its noisy task, the water, gushing through a stone sluice in an aspen grove, returned to the river where it merged with the strong current of the turbulent stream. Golden leaves of aspen, trembling in crisp, still air, clattered about them, as vagrant beams of sunlight filtered though the trees. They spread a blanket in a coppice, its tall grass nearly hiding them from view.

"I'm going to have Bartolo make some," Lucia said to her mother, continuing a conversation in which they had been engaged regarding the frothy gelatin-like delicacy made from the scraped trunk of cottonwood. "Like papa used to make, Mama. It will keep for awhile, and we can eat it on some special occasion."

"A special occasion?" a pale Catalina asked as though contemplating Lucia's words. "That would be nice, *ijika*. We used to do that when I was a little girl, too," she said, taking a bit of the bread offered her by Lucia. Then turning her attention to Francisca, and initiating a conversation for which there was no apparent preface, she asked, "Did I tell you about the snow pits, *ijika*?"

Francisca thought about the question for a moment, but could make no sense of it and did not answer. "Do you remember them?" her mother then asked of Lucia who was only four when they left Spain.

"I don't remember snow pits, Mama," Lucia responded. "What I remember, was getting something like an iced drink when we'd visit my grandfather in Toledo."

"Those were from the snow pits," her mother responded, smiling at the two girls. "Well, not from the snow pits themselves," she said, "but from the *puestos* (centers of sale) where my papa used to buy it. During the winter, Quita," Francisca's mother said, again directing herself to her youngest daughter, "snow would be brought from the high country and put in pits which had been dug to preserve it. Then in the summer, the snow and ice would be used to cool drinks and sherbets. That's what you remember, Lucia," her mother said. "My papa would buy it for special occasions like when we'd come to visit, and he used to buy them for my mama's parties. He was a very practical person, my papa," Catalina said, "but he'd do anything to make my mama happy." She then paused for a long moment before continuing, watching as leaves swirled in the mountain stream, and saying rather absent-mindedly, "I wonder where they're going?" she asked quietly, as though her thoughts were elsewhere.

Looking ashen and exhausted, her long lashes casting a shadow against her soft cheeks, Catalina said in her peculiarly delicate voice, "my memory has faded due to my age and my ill heath, but my mama used to have a little cultural group and they'd meet at our home . . . my mama, and all the ladies, wearing their fake eyeglasses. *Quevedos*, they were called," she said softly. "They'd meet to discuss literature and philosophy, but they'd do a bit of gossiping too, although I was usually sent out of the room when that happened. My papa used to say that he was going to put an end to their nonsense, their reading of books in Latin which he didn't understand. 'Let her learn to embroider, or darn, or sew, and leave study to men,' he'd say to me in my mother's presence, just teasing her.

"I used to sit on my cushion at her feet," she said, "listening to her, eating sherbet, admiring the clothing worn by her guests, but really watching my mama who was one of the most beautiful women I'd ever seen. She had an oval face, with a high forehead, and a neck that was positively swanlike. Her eyes, deep-set and shaped like almonds, were the color of amber. *Dios*, did she have beautiful eyes!" she said before continuing. "And her hair, ash blonde when she was a child, was a shade just lighter than auburn. But what I watched most," she reflected sadly, "were her hands, as my mother held her book or gestured in the air. Her hands were long, with long delicate fingers, and glowingly white. I loved her more than anyone should love their parents," she said, "and when she died, I truthfully thought that I could not live without her. My papa said that I didn't speak for a year." Catalina stopped and appeared to be choking back a tear before continuing. "I don't remember that," she said in her pale voice, "the not speaking, I mean. What I remember, though, is praying that God would allow me to go with her. Thankfully, my prayers weren't answered.

"It was then that my brother and I were sent to live with our grandparents," she said sadly, seemingly contemplating it all. "You know," their mother said, "it's awful. I hardly remember his being there," she said of her brother, Alonso, "so caught up was I in my own grief. He must have been as sick as I was, but I don't remember. My grandparents tried to keep us busy . . . and I think that for your Uncle Alonso, that helped. He spent most of his time with the men, and with the sheep. My papa used to come to visit us when he was able, and I know that he thought he'd made the right decision for us—sending us to live with our grandparents. Parents have to make decisions like that without knowing exactly how things will turn out. But I think that it would have been better if we had remained with him," she said wistfully. "I missed him terribly and spent most of my time alone."

"Doing what Mama," Lucia asked.

"Listening, *ijika*. Just listening," her mother responded. "One of the wells was right near the corrals on my grandfather's farm. I spent hours listening to the *norias*. The mule turning the wheel. The pots dipping the water from the well, and then tipping it into a reservoir from which it flowed to the fields. Maybe it was the sound of the falling water that I found soothing?" she said. "I still hear it in my dreams."

"Hear it in your dreams, Mama?" Lucia asked.

"Yes, in my dreams," her mother responded quietly. "Do you remember it?" she asked of Lucia. "It was kind of like . . .whh . . whh . . whh . . . I don't know," she laughed. "It's impossible to make a sound like that. The sound of water splashing into a still pool. I wonder what it is about water?" she asked. "I've always been fascinated with it. The stones in the bottom of a stream. The sound of it trickling through a brick trough. I don't know," she said, attentive to the sound of the water splashing through the stone sluice at the mill.

The three women sat quietly in the cool, still air, eating their *pan trenzada*, scanning their surroundings, listening to the sounds of the mill and of the rushing stream. "Do you want to go back, Mama?" Francisca asked. "We should have thought to have brought you a *monton* (shawl). It's getting chilly," Francisca said. "When we get back, Mama, I'll make us all some chocolate."

"No, not yet," her mother responded in a voice just above a whisper. "I have something to tell you."

The girls steeled themselves for what they feared was coming, Francisca feeling she could not catch her breath.

"They're going, you know," Catalina said of the dissident colonists. "They're going because there's no silver, and because there's little to eat." She paused for a long time, watching the movement of the delicate leaves in the aspen grove, the riffle of water on rocks in the stream, before continuing. "The land is beautiful here," she said, "your papa would have loved it. And I would have been happy here with him. But now, I doubt I can make it my home," she said quietly, while absentmindedly sorting and arranging the herbs which had spilled from her apron, and seemingly hesitant to speak further.

"I said my goodbyes to Alonso, you know," she finally said, reflecting sadly on her parting visit with her son who had gone with Onate on the expedition to the east. "I said my goodbyes, *ijikas*, because I didn't know if I'd be here when he got back."

"If you go, Mama," Francisca cried, "I don't think I can stay here."

"You must stay, *ijika*," her mother cried. "This is your home. Your place is here with Juan," she cried, while holding her daughter, and stroking her hair. He's a good man, Quita, and will make you a good husband. But for me," she said, "my home is in Spain."

As Catalina held her daughters in the shade of the aspen grove, she realized then that this was the impossible task of parenthood—to love your children with every fiber of your being—and then to let them go. They cried, each knowing that nothing would ever be the same again.

The decision to leave New Mexico had been a tortured one. The four Robledos who were to remain in San Gabriel, Diego, Lucia, Francisca (and Alonso who was with Onate) knew they would never see their mother and brother again, and the pain of this reality was almost too much to bear. They lied and told each other that someday they would "go down the trail." However, all of them knew that this would never happen. New Mexico was like the end of the earth.

* * *

The tormented decision had plunged the Robledo family into frenzied activity, but on the night before Catalina and Francisco were to leave, the entire family gathered to sleep on the mud-packed floor of a now empty room at the village of San Gabriel. Lucia, Francisca, and their mother, Catalina, put the baby Ana among them, all under one cover, and, with the rest of the family, spent most of the night in whispered conversation, in singing cradlesongs, and in tears.

After the others had fallen asleep, Catalina climbed to the roof where she spent the rest of the night staring in the direction Onate had gone, waiting for sunrise, repeating a wordless prayer for the future of her children, and for the strength to do what she knew she must do. At sunrise, weak with weariness and sorrow, she returned to her room. There, she found Francisca staring through the clouded selenite of the southern window while cirrus clouds composed entirely of ice crystals began to form in the eastern sky. These clouds, which Francisca perceived as embodying her troubles and sadness, caused a halo of despair to appear around the rising sun which was just beginning to tip the horizon. Francisca remained there until nighttime in an impossible attempt to catch a glimpse of her mother as the caravan moved slowly down the forested valley.

Andantino

It had been a bad year and a bad month, and with the dawn of 7 October 1601, a bad day had begun. In adobe rooms, in which numbing cold gripped its occupants, the Robledos were, like a third of the villagers, saying their final goodbyes. Although Lucia cried, she had little ambivalence regarding her decision. Her place, she knew, was here with her husband. Even her mother had told her this. Her mother, who was going with the Zubia clan, had said the same to Diego and to Francisco, but Francisco, who now held their Carmenan housekey, had insisted that she could not go alone. Thus, on 7 October 1601, with the fields again harvested at San Gabriel, the renegade caravan was set in ponderous motion. Carts had begun leaving the previous evening, eager, it seemed, to put some distance between themselves and *don* Juan whom they feared might return at any moment. In anxious preparation, scattered groups of colonists had packed their carts with each asking the other for this supply or that. Most sought for the long journey were the almonds, olives, raisins, and walnuts that had been brought by the reinforcement column of 1600. Also desired were the ingredients for their medicine chests, beans, barley and lentils in the form of flour for plasters, and the herbs and spices, anise, coriander, lavender, rosemary and wild marjoram. Many of those remaining gave what they could of amaranth, goosefoot, and purslane, but others among them refused. They were not going to support this treachery. Therefore, some of those who were leaving began looting the stores of their comrades who were on the plains.

* * *

The colonists loyal to Onate had made a decision to have a small group of their number accompany the retreating caravan through the land of the Jumano. With the mobility provided by horses, this small party, which included Diego Robledo, would not be as vulnerable to attack as would the retreating caravan with its slow-moving ox carts. Therefore, the escort party, with Geronimo Marquez acting as its captain, left the village along with the caravan.

Pursuit

November 24, 1601

It was a sad assemblage that watched *don* Juan de Onate and his 80 soldiers as they returned from the bison plains. Apart from the two principals, Lieutenant Governor Francisco de Sosa Penalosa, and *Fray* Juan de Escalona, the village had but 25 soldiers remaining, some with their families and servants. The good father had released the retreating friars from their assignments in New Mexico and Sosa had done nothing to hold the colonists. When Onate received this report from the individuals he had considered his supporters, he could only look at them with disgust. *My God!* he must have thought to himself, *what did I do to deserve these two, this ineffective leader whose own sons, Francisco and Estevan, have abandoned the colony, and this traitorous friar?* It may have occurred to him to have Sosa and Escalona executed, but he obviously thought better of this, for his situation was perilous, and he would only add to the tension by behaving impetuously. But the day was not over yet, and with total knowledge of what he was doing, he began legal proceedings against the mutineers, determining to pursue and arrest them.

Before Onate sent his men after his retreating colonists, however, he retired to his quarters where he sat before his writing table, now heaped with stones, and assaying equipment. His colonists, navigating by a solar compass, by geomagnetic sensors, and by scent, were fleeing south like a flock of migrating pigeons desperately in search of food. The situation required urgency, but he could make no mistake, so while his men readied themselves for the chase, he composed a treatise for them to carry with them.

This *auto*, transcribed by Antonio de Godoy, was prepared so that Onate might give the viceroy an account of all they had discovered in the most recent expedition and to provide justification for the merciless reprisals he intended. Then, after sanding it, he ordered it read to all the individuals who had gone with him to the plains, so they might swear to its truthfulness. After the reading, all that were able signed it. For those who could not write, a witness was provided. One of the three witnesses was Captain Bartolome Romero. Vicente de Zaldivar, Juan de Vitoria Carvajal, Gaspar Lopez de Tabora, *don* Cristobal de Onate, Juan de la Cruz, Rodrigo Zapata, and Alonso Robledo signed the document.

*   *   *

Vicente de Zaldivar was put in charge of the small group that was being sent to arrest the retreating colonists who had more than a month's headstart. He chose his best men and the finest horses—good sound creatures with a thirty-league wind, superb beasts with magnificent chests. With three horses for each man the *posse comitatus*, the body armed with legal authority to carry out Onate's orders, was readied for its pursuit. With the words of his uncle still ringing in his ears, that it would be better not to know how to write, then one would not have to sign death sentences, Vicente boarded his horse. With little in their panniers, and nothing in their stomachs, the group set out.

Along the banks of the Great River, majestic cottonwoods loomed into the sky, the river itself a kaleidoscope of leaves and lichen and moss.

They first rode through the pueblos of Santa Clara, San Ildefonso, and Cochiti, the beauty of the rose trail, water gap, and stone *kiva* masking the urgency of their journey.

They then passed through the pueblos of Santo Domingo, San Felipe and Santa Ana. During these periods, they kept to the sticky earth of the river, departing from it only to blaze a new trail when a shortcut presented itself. At Sandia they received news of the retreating colonists, and at Isleta a little more information. The people of the Southern Tiwa, who spoke the language of the San Juan, lived on an island with the river flowing on each side. They said, regarding the retreating colonists, "Yes they passed by here, perhaps four weeks ago, and stayed but one night."

In the *sierras* from which the posse had ridden, the cottonwoods, maples, and aspen were aglow with the radiance of the season. In the intersections of canyons, and along their glittering streams, groves of flaming red maples blazed like dying embers, while along mountain ridges the aspens' elegant green leaves had been transformed to glimmering gold. Purple asters lined the wagon ruts they followed, while throughout the valley, low-lying groves of golden *chamisa* were everywhere ablaze.

Under the small cottonwoods at Alamillo the trail started to become warm, and at Socorro, even warmer. It was evident, however, that the dissident colonists were moving as fast as their ox carts would allow. Moreover, although they were doing nothing to hide themselves, they remained beyond sight and sound, with neither a dust cloud nor the frightful wail of their pinioned wheels to betray their presence.

An Incredible Tangle

Pickets established at the northern perimeter of the dissidents' encampment below Teipana were the first to see him: a lone rider coming from the north with an urgent message.

"We sighted the flickering glow of a watch fire last night," this courier of their rear guard said breathlessly, as he hurriedly dismounted from his lathered horse. "We thought it to be one of the Indians, but this morning we saw a dust cloud and believe it to be riders."

332

"How far back?" asked Diego de Zubia.

"Four, maybe six hours, maybe less."

"Goddamn it!" Zubia said, betraying the anger and anxiety he experienced at receiving this report. "I was hoping we'd have more time before we had to deal with them, maybe getting even as far as the marsh of *Mesilla de Guinea*. But I guess this place is as good as any to confront them," he said in resignation.

"We need to move our camp," he said to Francisco and Estevan Sosa who happened to be with him when he received this news. "Get the carts and everyone into the woods."

In preparation against the attack, the retreating colonists set their camp within the cottonwood forest where they enclosed themselves inside a snarl of rotting logs and branches. Here, beneath a cathedral-like canopy sheltering a cool, dark wood, they set their lines awaiting an attack as forewarned by the member of their rear guard. Their rear guard, a squad of cavalry and some *harquebusiers*, remained at their post a mile or so back up the trail while the main body retreated into the forest.

Their position, they felt, was invulnerable to cavalry and a stand here might be accomplished with little effort. However, to achieve this they had to align themselves along the northern and eastern perimeters of their encampment with *harquebusiers* stretched out along a front of many hundreds of yards. Although their desire was to establish their formation in what the French would have referred to as *en haye*, there were not enough of them to form one long, unbroken double line. And, in spite of their feeling that they had chosen a good position, their field was cramped and broken by rotting trees and cat claw whose sharp and strong thorns snagged at their every step, making movement along the front very difficult.

There was the realization among a number of the embattled colonists that they were enclosing themselves within a cocoon of decaying wood, earth, and grains of sand. If they were unsuccessful at repelling the attack, there was little chance they could break out of the warren. Onate had only to keep them pinned down there until they starved to death. Under cover of confusion and an early autumn dusk, their formation was snarled, their ranks scattered and undressed. Yet with little alternative means for defending themselves, they continued.

If some seemed delighted at the prospect of a fight, it was merely a show of bravado, for although they believed they outnumbered their pursuers, they didn't know what strength might be brought against them. And Onate had the cannons.

A scratch force, which had been required to slog through silt and mud, took up a position on a sandy hummock on the left of their line. It was an unexceptional elevation in an incredible tangle of flood debris that their horses could not penetrate. Therefore, holding their weapons above their heads, they trudged through the waist-high sludge and muck of a sizeable rivulet to take their position on one of the river's many cottonwood islands. Whatever the difficulty in establishing their defensive position there, they could not allow Onate or his cannons to occupy this high ground or to encircle their left flank. They had reckoned upon the willingness of their pursuers to ride night and day in order to force a battle, and now they were here.

* * *

"You may have to choose sides, Diego," Francisco whispered. "They can't tell in the darkness who wears white and who wears black, and you may have to fight just to save yourself."

"It won't come to that," Diego responded. "They're our own people. They may urge you to go back, but they won't bring arms against you."

"You're fooling yourself, Diego," Francisco said. "You've got to see the world as it is, rather than the way you'd like it to be. Onate killed the Portuguese for this same crime, and he won't hesitate to kill us. Perhaps, Diego," Francisco said emphatically, "you could even say that he'll be required to kill us, for he can't allow us to take our report south. It will ruin him!"

"You're wrong, Francisco," Diego replied as he leaned his *harquebus* and that of his father against the fallen tree behind which they crouched. "If I must shoulder my weapon to protect you and mama, I will, but it won't come to that. It will be talk only, Francisco," he said. "It will just be talk."

* * *

Kneeling behind their arboreal barricades, the retreating soldiers waited through the soggy night, their *cuero* and their coat and *bevor* of mail sagging on tired shoulders. The sun was just rising over the distant mountains to the east when they spied a second rider of their rear guard riding alongside a marshy brook, and steeled themselves to hear his report.

"The fire was Indians only," he shouted, "the dust, bison. Light your fires and eat!"

The breakaway colonists continued, moving as quickly as they were able. If an ox cart broke, they abandoned it and incorporated its occupants and supplies into other vehicles. They rode through a world of forest, grassland, wetland, desert, and river, snapping at their oxen and urging greater speed.

Below Teipana, they began to detect the essence of marshland in the air and see the wash of sky and clouds mirrored in a vast expanse of water. They were soon surrounded by a cacophony of birdsong: cowbirds, ring-necked pheasants, sandhill cranes and a swarm of red-winged blackbirds that filled the sky. To the west lay Chupadera Peak that rises 6,195 feet over the Rio Grande Valley. The dark and heavily shaded old lava beds and undergrowth of the Oscuras lay to the east, while the yet-to-be-named Manzanos and Ladrones lay behind them from the direction they had come.[1]

The landscape, pitted and strewn with boulders, was replete with four-wing saltbush, mesquite and creosote whose round, white fruit filled the air with the scent of balsam. Heaps of rubble inside clumps of cactus and beneath sumac bushes marked the homes of wood rats, while cane and Christmas *cholla*, bladderpod, and Indian figs were strewn across the land. Many of the nopal or prickly pear bore the teeth marks of the rabbits and collared peccaries that devour them for their moisture. Lizards scurried across the trail and jackrabbits and mule deer could be seen in the *bosque*.

* * *

Anxiously, they rode through the *Jornada del Muerto*. This was the essentially waterless stretch of nearly 90 miles first traversed by Juan de Onate in 1598; it would save them a day or more of travel. With the San Andres Mountains on the east, and the *Fray* Cristobal Range on the west, they moved down the high, wide valley amid shrubs of mesquite whose yellow flowers of ten stamen, paired thorns and long straight pods provided fodder for their beasts. They were unable to stop, however, because their beasts could not survive for more than three days without water when they were on the move. Therefore, when they emerged from the *Jornada*, and again encountered the river, they had to stop since their beasts were crazed with thirst. The place of this encampment was immediately north of the *Sepulcro de Robledo* (Robledo Gravesite).

* * *

Their campsite looked toward the Dona Ana Mountains that hugged the horizon to the east. It lay beneath the canopy of a brilliant turquoise sky, and the incessant honking of enormous flocks of snow geese crossing and crisscrossing the valley in their flight south searching for food. Further in, ashen bluffs, replete with rock wren and cliff swallows, ran along the Rio Grande. These provided a backdrop for the multicolored cluster of cottonwoods that curved and twisted along the margins of the river with its velvety scent of moss and mud. Riders were sent back to support their rear guard and pickets were set around their encampment. The air was brisk this late October and campfires were lit to ward off the chill.

* * *

Diego had come as far as he intended, much farther, in fact, than others in the escort party had wanted. The caravan would remain here but two days. This would only allow them time to catch their breath, and then they would have to be on their way again.

The time Diego spent with Francisco and his mother during this retreat was the most painful he had ever experienced. He had not anticipated the deaths of his father or of his younger brother and had, therefore, only dealt with death's extremely painful consequences. However, in parting from Francisco and his mother, a parting he was to experience "as the nail from the flesh," there was the realization that

336

every word and every breath were among the last they would experience together. Diego and his mother spoke of *Sobradisa* and Diego voiced his sorrow that his mother would never see this fabled land.

"I'll see it, Diego," his mother promised. "As it is in your dreams, it will be in mine. You go there, Diego," she said. "Plant our seed and make our garden grow. It'll be our land and your papa's dreams will be fulfilled."

On the trip south Diego had begun to realize that he had never truly come to know or to appreciate his brother Francisco. Now 21-years-old, and fully recovered from the injuries he had suffered at Acoma, Francisco had grown before his eyes into a very intelligent and handsome young man—a youngster no longer, and someone who could ably care for their mother.

Francisco asked Diego about Carmena and about their Castilian *meseta* which he, unlike Diego and Lucia, had never seen. He mused that should his mother return to Spain, as was her intention, he would go with her. There, he would retrieve Diego's white stone, unearth his father's treasures, and become known as a *Gachupin*.[2] Once he became a rich man, he said, he would send for Diego. They laughed at this reversal of roles, for Diego was no longer the patriarch of the family.

* * *

Before dawn, on the second day of their encampment below the *Jornada*, Diego, Franciso and their mother left their camp and rode down the broad valley a short distance to the burial site. The sun was just tipping the horizon to the east laying a wash of gold upon the trees and casting an ethereal glow to it all. The river was a gloomy, sullen thing with none of the glint or glitter of its waters in the North. Running cold and dark beneath obscure cottonwoods, its color that of the earth from which it seemed to have sprung, it was further darkened by the crush of overhanging foliage. They dismounted.

Each had marked the spot in his or her mind by what they had considered permanent terrain features, but they now wished they had blazed a tree or made a marking on a stone as a guide for relocating the site. Without such a marking, however, they could not find the burial site which lay hidden among the tattered remains of a field of *Anil del Muerto*

(Sunflower of the Dead) identified only with the two fossilized stones. They had successfully located Onate's cairn and knew they had the right field, but, although they had carefully searched the area, they couldn't find the spot and now had to face the prospect that they might have to leave without ever locating it.

As they made their third sweep of the extensive field among what had been bright yellow sunflowers whose silvery green and gray foliage hid the ground at their feet, they were startled by an enormous covey of quail that scattered before them. These strange birds of perhaps a thousand or more appeared to have come up from the river in small groups and now congregated together seeking safety in numbers.

Diego watched as the birds skittered through the bush of yucca, mariposa, and wild tomatoes, their chunky, blue-gray bodies and powerful legs beating the ground before them. Black-bellied and crowned by outrageous topknots, they were comical as they chattered and ran through the shrub. Then, unaccountably, these ground-dwelling birds, which had run so wildly before them, suddenly turned. In apparent confusion and agitation, the birds raced directly toward them and, with an enormous explosion of wing-beats, burst into the air.

"My God," Francisco said as the birds flew directly over him, "what was that about?"

"I don't know," Diego responded as he raised his *harquebus* to his shoulder, reaching behind him with his left arm. "Something scared them," he said, "something even worse than us."

"Get down, Mama," he commanded as he pushed his mother to the ground with his left hand. "Get down!"

As Diego knelt beside Francisco, their mother behind them holding onto the edge of their leather jackets, his father's words raced through his mind:

'It's all about birds, Diego, you've only to read their signs.'

He and Francisco sighted along the barrel of their weapons, hoping to see what the quail had seen. They swept the ground before them with their eyes peering close through shafts of light, imprinting without effort the terrain ahead. They waited like this for many minutes listening to the

338

wind move through the crown of the trees as the quail fluttered and cackled in nearby trees, sitting sentry and waiting to renew their browse.

"Cover me while I check," Diego demanded of Francisco as he reviewed the remnants of desert buckeye and paintbrush before them. "I'll see what scared them."

"Hell, no!" Francisco said. "If you're going, I'm going with you."

"You can't, damn it," Diego responded while silently picking his route. "You have to stay with mama."

Without waiting for a reply, Diego rechecked the load of his father's old weapon which he carried rather than his own. Then, bent over double, he began to work his way toward the southern edge of the broad field. Francisco strained to hear Diego as he moved through the bush. Suddenly, he heard what he believed was the sound of the flash of powder in a pan, but no explosion. Francisco tensed but heard nothing more.

They stood in a glen alongside a small black pool, its water stained by the leaves that steeped within it. The leaves, leaflets and catkins of this incredible tangle, were triangular and toothed, soft and scaly, and lay thickly at the bottom of the pool and in the brook that fed it. The brook, with its small waterfall, was covered with moss and lichen and now, also, with a plethora of leaves in gold and sienna and burnt umber.

The pool had begun to freeze about its edges. Still, the racing water remained open and full of sound. They stood looking at the water in the murky grove of cottonwood, listening to it and to the sound of their footsteps as they walked in the bracken and remained woodless. A small breeze came up, rustled the leaves about them with a sound like falling rain, and took a few from their branches, even many that seemed reluctant to fall.

As Francisco and his mother watched, they observed Diego as he moved noiselessly through the trees gathering a bouquet of flowers as a parting gift for his mother. The gravesite, which had been located for them by the quail—and the coyote that had scared them—lay between them and the track the wagons would follow as they moved south through the valley.

They had rebuilt the cairn there as a memorial, a grave marker, and as an indicator of where something of value lay, adding a stone in prayer for each member of the family.

And then the hour of parting came, the day beautiful and crisp as only New Mexico can provide. Under a blue and cloudless sky, and with a sun that startled the Robledos with its brightness, the caravan, which had been at its encampment behind them, slowly began to move through the undulating hills to the east of the river. Troubled with the duty that now lay on his shoulders, Francisco held the reins of their horses and watched the caravan until he determined it was time to go.

Diego, with a deep pain in his heart, was unable to put his feelings into words. For it would be, for Diego, a rending loss that would be re-experienced at each waking, with each kindled light, each leaf as it spun away into a riffled pool. Choking back his tears he hugged his brother and then his mother who held him one long last time. "*De lo caro*, Diego," she whispered, "*mi sangre y mi corazon*. Remember, Diego," his mother added as she held him, "as long as we're in your dreams and in your memories, we'll always be with you."

As Diego's mother moved to mount her horse, he grasped her wrist crying, "Wait, Mama!" Although his mother attempted to look away from him, he could see her eyes like red stains against her ashen skin. Neither spoke as Diego kissed his mother for the final time. She then held his face in her hands trying to embed the memory of him into her mind: the red hair and beard, his square shoulders, his large strong hands; he was so much like his father. With Francisco's assistance, she climbed aboard her palfrey, the one she would ride until transferred to one of the springless carts. Sitting there with Diego's bouquet in her hand, she noted that the breeze had come up again revealing the golden splendor of the cottonwood grove, the squawbush and mountain spray presenting themselves as remnants of a brilliant blaze. She turned in her saddle for a final look at Diego who appeared heartbroken and abandoned in the brilliant light, a cascade of color now falling at his feet.

Diego stayed one additional night at the site of his father's burial. On the last night, with his saddle bags packed—and wearing a lone silver spur—he rode Babieca a short distance toward the bank of the silver stream which shone in the moonlight with a glaze like burnished ice. A great horned owl made known its presence. He drank in the indefinable scent of cottonwood and fresh water and dismounted.

The October grass was blanched and withered, black against the furrowed bore of cottonwoods, noisy underfoot. Here, he looked once more at the huge bluff, bleak, darkly gray, remote, and silent that marked where his father had been buried. In the moonlight, he could clearly see shells which were embedded within the stones which lay at his feet. He picked one up, ran his thumbnail noisily across the matrix, extracted one and placed it within his leather jacket. He then walked down to the river where he sat astride a once-regal cottonwood that had fallen along its banks. And as he sat there in the darkness, with the moonlight shielded from view, he thought how similar this great river was to the rivers of his parents, the Tagus and the Alberche. They elicited in him a state of mind that joined him to the experiences of the people who had lived and died along their waters of beauty and mystery. Atop his furrowed perch, focusing on the old and unknown world of this ancient ocean, he thought of his father and of the distance his father had come to this gray monolith and to the end of his dream. It was a dream, Diego thought, which must have seemed so close that he could not fail to grasp it. Yet he knew that his father's dream was multifaceted and that an important part of it lay behind him in Spain, buried somewhere in the vast obscurity of their Castilian *meseta*.

More importantly, however, Diego understood that his father had believed in the future and in their quest for a newer world—newer, more peaceful, and grander. It had eluded him, his father had felt, but, in fact, it had not, for Diego and his progeny would continue his father's quest: to strive, to seek, to find, and not to yield.

EPILOGUE

He Who Deserts for the First Time is a Novice

The retreating colonists eventually reached the safety of Santa Barbara where they placed themselves under the protection of *Nueva Vizcayan* authorities. Vicente de Zaldivar and his troop arrived a short time later. He had only missed them by 12 days. As he had no authority in *Nueva Vizcaya*, he could not carry out his promise to execute its leaders and compel the remainder to return.

Although it was determined that the retreating colonists had set a bad example by their "boldness and impudence," it was concluded that they "were not exactly soldiers organized with all the formality of an army" since "the main and principal object of their going was as settlers." In addition, many had sold their estates and had gone "at their own expense, taking their sons, daughters and families, which is not done in military expeditions." It was determined, therefore, that they were not and could not "be considered as deserting soldiers, especially when [one] consider[s] the cause—want and privation—which they set forth as sufficient to justify their return." They had acted "with the advice, approval, and attendance of their prelates and spiritual fathers" and for all of these reasons were not subject to military law. Therefore, the retreating colonists were not required to return to San Gabriel.[1]

The colony managed to survive without them with a number of steadfast colonists remaining behind. Among these were Lucia Lopez Robledo, her husband Bartolome Romero and child Ana; Hernan Martin Serrano the elder, his wife Juana Rodriguez and son Hernan II; Juan Perez de Bustillo, his wife Maria de la Cruz and daughters Ana, Yumar, Beatriz and Catalina; Geronimo Marquez and son Diego; Juan de Vitoria Carvajal; Alonso Varela Jaramillo and his brother Pedro Varela de Losada; Ascencio de Arechuleta; Hernando Ruiz de Hinojos; Cristobal Baca the first, his wife Ana Ortiz and children Maria de Villanueva and Alonso; and Bartolome de Montoya, his wife Maria de Zamora, and children Diego and Petronila. They would become common ancestors for many present-day New Mexicans among whom there remains a praiseworthy memory of them as the first settlers. Their descendants remain a rugged people with common geographical origins, a long shared history of which they are conscious as distinguishing them from other groups, and a memory that keeps it alive.

Whether the Carvajals, Robledos, Romeros, and/or, others, with the New Mexico expedition, were descendants of Jewish converts, remains an open and enduring question. That there were Jewish *conversos* and *convertidos* in New Spain is beyond question, and their presence among the Onate colonists was likely. Yet, if descendants of New Christians were in New Mexico, whether as crypto-Jews or practicing Catholics, their presence there was illegal (the king even having gone as far as issuing a special decree, that "no one named Carvajal"[2] was to be allowed to lead or to participate in the conquest). If the descendants of Jewish converts were in New Mexico, they would have worked to keep their presence there a secret, for had the authorities become aware of their existence, their land grants, and titles as *hidalgos*, would likely have been nullified. Positive evidence for their existence, therefore, is understandably lacking, and is likely to remain absent, until someone finds the records of an Inquisitional investigation for one of New Mexico's colonial ancestors.

The subjective evidence for the presence of *marranos*[3] among the Onate colonists, however, is tantalizing, and relates to the way they married and built their families—for if they were retain the essence of who they were, they could only trust others of their stock. As Cecil Roth notes in his *A History of the Marranos*, "As a matter of course, alliances were contracted as far as possible amongst themselves." The evidence for one of these alliances may be found among the third generation of these early colonists.

Lucia Robledo was married to Bartolome Romero. Their daughter, Ana, who took her surname from her mother, married Francisco Gomez. Gomez was from Portugal, which, at one point in history, as the result of the General Conversion of Portuguese Jews in 1497, was almost synonymous with being Jewish. Although labeled a Jew by his political dissenters, he was to hold every office of importance in New Mexico, including those of governor and *alguacil mayor* of the Inquisition.[4]

The first son of Francisco Gomez and Ana Robledo was Francisco Gomez Robledo. On May 4, 1652, the Inquisition arrested Gomez Robledo, one of only 35 *encomenderos*[5] in New Mexico. Arrested with him were two individuals, one of whom was *encomendero* Diego Romero. Romero was the son of Gaspar Perez and Maria Romero. Maria Romero, who was the daughter of Bartolome Romero and Lucia Robledo, had taken her surname from her father. Therefore, Francisco Gomez Robledo and Diego Romero, were first cousins on their mothers' side.

First jailed at the Santo Domingo pueblo, where they were to be held for five long months, Gomez Robledo and Romero were eventually taken to the City of Mexico for trial. They were to remain in jail there for a year before they were even to learn the charges against them: the accusation of Judaism against Gomez Robledo, and apostasy and heresy against Romero. As John Kessell notes in his incredible study, *Kiva, Cross, and Crown*, the charges against Gomez Robledo "proved to be based mainly on hearsay." Yet, the Holy Office continued with its procedures:

> Bodily examination by physicians showed that *don* Francisco had no "little tail," as one of his brothers was alleged to have, nor could the scars on his penis be positively identified as an attempt at circumcision. In audience after audience, answering forcefully and directly, and utilizing to the best advantage the long and loyal Christian service of his father (Francisco Gomez), Gomez Robledo earned himself a verdict of unqualified acquittal.[6]

Romero, also tried by the Holy Office, was condemned as an apostate and heretic. He was required to appear in penitential clothing in an *auto de fe*, the public procession of Inquisition prisoners. He was sentenced to service in the Philippine galleys. This sentence was later commuted and he was banished from New Mexico. Later, however, after it was determined that he was a polygamist, he was sentenced to 200 lashes, and to six years' of manual labor as a galley slave. He died in jail in Vera Cruz while awaiting his first bark.

France Scholes, leading historian of colonial New Mexico, was not impressed with the qualifications of the accused Gomez Robledo as a Jew, and I would guess, he would not have been impressed with Romero's qualification either. But none of the studies undertaken thus far, notes Henry Tobias, author of *A History of the Jews in New Mexico*, "rule[s] out the possibility that crypto-Jews did enter the province . . ." He continues by saying that Seymour Liebman and Martin Cohen, both modern scholars regarding Jews in Spanish America, concede

> *that the ability of crypto-Jews to hide their beliefs and customs exceeded the capacity of the Inquisition . . . to root them out.* [7]

Whether more can be gleaned from Spanish records regarding the presence of crypto-Jews in New Mexico remains an open question. The sobriquet of crypto-Jew, however, leveled against the Romero/Robledo clan, has stuck to these families like a historic burr on a dog's coat, giving us what may be a glimpse into their religious past.

As early as 1599 the brave and tenacious Acome began to slip their bounds and return to their stone mesa. Early in 1604, *don* Juan de Onate sent a peace mission there and was successful at reestablishing a working relationship between the two peoples. The Acome now welcomed the Spaniards "with festivity and rejoicing," giving them *maize* and many blankets, deerskins, and turkeys. Eventually, the Acome completely rebuilt their village and it remains occupied today.

On October 7, 1604, *don* Juan de Onate finally set out on horseback, traveling overland from the *villa* of San Gabriel to find the South Sea. Accompanied by Geronimo Marquez and 30 additional soldiers, the explorers went west through Arizona and down the Colorado to where it emptied into the Gulf of California. Thinking it to be the ocean, Onate took possession of it "for the king, our lord," and after determining that it was one of the best sites he had ever seen for a port, began his long march home. He had discovered nothing new, however, and with not a man missing, returned to San Gabriel on April 25, 1605. On August 24, 1607, Onate renounced his office. Two years later, during the first part of 1609, Viceroy Luis de Velasco the younger, finally notified him that he was being replaced.

In renouncing his office, *don* Juan de Onate passed on to others the labor of leading the steadfast colonists into the future. The major task for the new leader, whoever he might be, was, as Tennyson was later to state in speaking of a people under similar circumstances, to "labor, by slow prudence to make mild a rugged people, and through soft degrees subdue them to the useful and the good."

Onate—whose snows were coming—reached the City of Mexico on April 30, 1610, exactly 12 years from the date he had first entered New Mexico. On June 1, 1613, the crown instructed the new viceroy, Diego Fernandez de Cordoba, Marques de Guadalcasar, to bring charges against him and to carry his trial to its inevitable conclusion. We may imagine that a number of secretaries of the viceroy's tribunal worked in relays to describe the many crimes of which he was accused, and to read the depositions and statements made regarding his service in New Mexico. Onate was arraigned on 30 separate charges linked to his governorship. He was found guilty of 12, among which were the use of excessive force in putting down the rebellion of the Acome, the murders of Pablo de Aguilar and Alonso de Sosa Albornoz, and the ordering of the deaths of the two Portuguese deserters. He was fined, condemned to perpetual exile from New Mexico, banned from the City of Mexico for four years, and deprived of his honor, position and personal dignity.

Onate spent much of the remainder of his life attempting to clear his name. Although he was later successful in being reimbursed for his fine, the complete restoration of his honor eluded him. For good service, it was an ill reward. However, in 1624, the king made him mining inspector for all of Spain, a position that gave him a degree of prestige and authority. It was in 1626, while conducting his work in a mine near Guadalcanal, Spain, that Onate collapsed and died as the result of an illness he had contracted several months earlier. Despite his many failures, he had successfully established the foundation for a new kingdom.

The colonists remaining at San Gabriel began drifting away from the site as early as 1607. They began to reassemble in a narrow valley some 20 miles south of the pueblos of San Juan where they established a new *villa* and provincial capital. They called their new village Santa Fe.

After his return to New Spain in 1601, Francisco Robledo disappears from view. However, by 1604 Alonso had apparently followed him to New Spain. In that year Alonso Robledo was living at *El Real de San Antonio de Padua* in Cuencame. He was a miner there and had a wife and small son.

Diego eventually married Lucia de Zamora, daughter of Bartolome de Montoya, who had joined the colony that Christmas of 1600. In 1607 they were still living at San Gabriel.

Decades later, in 1663, Francisco Gomez Robledo, great-grandson of old Pedro Robledo and Catalina Lopez, referring to them as his maternal great-grandparents, said that his great-grandmother, Catalina Lopez, had returned to Spain.

The Robledo girls remained in New Mexico with their husbands, *Alferez* and Captain Bartolome Romero, and *Alferez*, Captain, and *Encomendero*, Juan de Tapia. The family name, assumed by Ana, daughter of Bartolome Romero and Lucia Lopez Robledo, survived as Gomez Robledo when she married Francisco Gomez and bore him a large family. Francisco Gomez became interim governor of New Mexico in 1641. Ana Robledo, an individual reported to have been outstanding for her charity and good deeds, died in 1680 during the Spanish retreat from New Mexico following the Pueblo Indian revolt. Her gravesite was referred to as 'the place of *Dona* Ana,' and the village of Dona Ana, the Dona Ana Mountains and Dona Ana County in southern New Mexico all take their names from her.

The village of Robledo, the Robledo Mountains, and Mt. Robledo, the latter located 10 miles south of Radium Springs, take their names from *El Sepulcro* and *Paraje de Robledo* (the Robledo sepulcher and campsite) named for Pedro Robledo. He was buried near the present village of Robledo on the east bank of the Rio Grande between Dona Ana and Radium Springs. These became important landmarks along the *Camino Real.*

The area of bounty, *Las Dispensas*, first discovered by Vasquez de Coronado in 1541, and later rediscovered by Vicente de Zaldivar in 1598, would remain unsettled for over two centuries. First driven from the land by Indians in 1823, and by hail in 1835, a third group would finally return in 1836 to make it their permanent home. A portion of their grant of almost half-a-million acres, would eventually be set aside as a game preserve. A haven for wildlife, 8,750 acres of the enormous grant including Middle Marsh and Wigeon Pond, has become the Las Vegas National Wildlife Refuge. First known as *Las Vegas Grandes en el Rio de Las Gallinas* (The Great Meadows on the Gallinas River) and later as Las Vegas, the city of Las Vegas eventually became the home for a number of Robledo descendants.

Because of the interest of Adolf Bandelier, who walked into the pueblo of San Juan sometime between 1880 and 1885, San Gabriel finally came under the archaeologist's trowel. Found among many hundreds of other artifacts in digs conducted during 1944, and later in 1959, 1960 and 1962, were a gilt cord hair net and an inlay decoration for a gun stock. The latter was a piece of animal bone (substituted for the ivory customarily used in Europe) which had been used as the base on which the depiction of a walled medieval city had been incised.

And finally, in 1951, an elderly leader of the San Juan Indians, while digging clay to make adobe bricks, "found that he had struck and broken a native-type stone griddle at the bottom of his pit. Beneath the stone had been a cooking vessel, now likewise broken. Nestled inside that vessel" lay "what he thought must be 'an old hat.' " This was sent to an authority on armor who determined "that it had been a flat type archer's helmet and was not only the oldest piece of armor ever found in the United States, but had been fashioned in Europe a century before Onate . . . brought his colony into New Mexico."[8]

ACKNOWLEDGMENTS

I would like to offer my thanks to Gloria Trujillo and Charles Martinez y Vigil who discovered among the archives in Seville, records, dated 1574, pertaining to the request for license by Pedro Robledo and Catalina Lopez to travel to the New World.

To Mary Viera whose thoughtful and sensitive editing contributed greatly to the completed manuscript.

And to my parents, Ed and Sinnie Lucero, who provided a loving and wonder-filled home in Las Vegas where much of this book was researched and written. The long views from our beautiful porch towards Hermit's Peak on the north, and the National Wildlife Refuge to the east, will forever live in my heart.

A number of books were helpful in developing the avifaunal, cultural and historical background for the novel. These in particular were indispensable: Herbert Eugene Bolton (Editor), *Spanish Explorations in the Southwest, 1542-1706* (1908); Miguel A. Cervantes Saavedra, *The Ingenious Gentleman Don Quixote de la Mancha, Volume 1 & 2* (Translated by Samuel Putnam) (1949); *Fray* Angelico Chavez, *Origins of New Mexico Families: In the Spanish Colonial Period* (1973); George P. Hammond and Agapito Rey, *Don Juan de Onate, Colonizer of New Mexico, Volumes 5 & 6 of the Coronado Historical Series* (1942); John T. Nichols and William Davis, *If Mountains Die: A New Mexico Memoir* (1994); Cecil Roth, *A History of the Marranos* (1932); *When Cultures Meet: Remembering San Gabriel del Yunge Oweenge. Papers from the October 20, 1984 Conference held at the San Juan Pueblo, New Mexico* (1987); (Mrs.) William T. Sedgwick, *Acoma, the Sky City* (1926); Marc Simmons, *The Last Conquistador: Juan de Onate and the Settling of the Far Southwest* (1991).

I would like to offer my apologies for the great liberties I have taken with the lives of the members of the Robledo family and with the geography of the Chama River Valley.

350

NOTES

PERIOD I: THE KINGDOM OF CASTILE

The Tribunal

1. An invitation to those persons conscious of having committed heretical actions in the past to come forward and confess their crimes, on the understanding that they would receive merciful treatment.

2. A time limit, generally of 30 or 40 days, within which one was to respond to an Edict of Grace. After the lapse of this period, guilty persons were liable to be proceeded against with all the rigor of the Inquisition.

3. A horrible torture in which a wet cloth was laid over a prisoner's mouth and nostrils, and a small stream of water slowly poured upon it. This caused the prisoner to suck the cloth into his throat. Before strangulation occurred, the cloth was suddenly pulled away, taking water and blood with it.

To Newer Lands

1. A title, roughly equivalent to the English squire.

2. The measures for ridding the country of gypsies were not then as repressive in Spain as they were in Germany where there was, in 1577, a public order which "forbade all electoral princes and governments to allow gypsies to travel or do business in their states or to give them safe-conduct, escorts or passports, and any such documents, current or future, were declared null and void."

In England, in 1577, eight persons at Aylesbury, Buckinghamshire, apparently English-born gypsies, were hanged for no other crime than "feloniously keeping company with Egyptians and adopting their dress, language and behavior."

3. Literally, 'solid earth,' but named here for the 'Firm Island' of the famous Spanish romance of chivalry, the Amadis of Gaul, 1508.

4. During the five-year period between 1576 and 1580, approximately 9,919,300 English pounds of gold and silver entered this port. These numbers were second to those compiled during the greatest period of imports, 1591-1595,

351

when approximately 20,231,000 English pounds of precious metals were off-loaded at Seville.

5. The tower, 75 feet in width and 300 feet in height, once one of the tallest towers in the world, is in reality two towers, one built inside the other. It was so well-designed (by the man who invented algebra, it is said) in terms of its 35 ramps, that the *muezzin* could go up on horseback.

The Passage

1. Although notorious for their pirating, both of these corsairs who sailed under the English flag would later become even more famous. Fame would come to Drake when he circumnavigated the globe between 1577 to 1580, and to Hawkins when he commanded a squadron in the fleet that defeated the Spanish Armada in 1588. However, before achieving the notoriety that would forever place them in history, they almost had their boats shot out from under them. This occurred during the previous decade, in 1567, when their vessels were the only two to escape a fleet of Spanish ships when attacked at the fortification of San Juan Ulua in the harbor of Vera Cruz. Thereafter, they waged a private war against Philip of Spain and wanted revenge.

2. These events would precede by 11 years one of the major weaknesses of the Spanish Armada where many of the casks for both food and water were made of green rather than seasoned staves. The results would be the same—rotten food, spoiled water and many sick and desperate people.

3. It is the glow accompanying the brush-like discharges of atmospheric electricity that appears as a tip of light the masts of ships during stormy weather. The light, also called St. Elmo's fire, is romantically associated with St. Erasmus, one of the patron saints of sailors, as the visible sign of his guardianship over them.

PERIOD II: THE KINGDOM OF NEW SPAIN

Vera Cruz

1. The name applied to the territory conquered by Hernando Cortes.

2. Forty-five miles north of present-day Vera Cruz.

3. Their fears were not without foundation. Only two years before, in 1575, a ship carrying religious relics donated by the pope to the Jesuits in New Spain had been split open on the rocks at Vera Cruz. Some of these relics may have been those assembled from various places at Toledo at the time of the Islamic invasion and transferred for safekeeping to Oviedo, capital of Spain's first northern Christian kingdom (791). The chest within which these relics had been placed was first opened in 1025. It was found to contain an unbelievable treasure of sacred objects which had been dug up, traded, stolen, fragmented, and multiplied among which were: 11 relics of apostles; 57 of martyrs; 14 of doctors

of the church, one of which was a bone of St. Thomas Aquinas; 24 of holy confessors; and 27 of other saints. Besides the above, Pope Gregory XIII (father of the Gregorian calendar), former legate of Spain, made a gift to the college of St. Peter and St. Paul of two bones of those saints; a good-sized piece of the Holy Cross; one thorn from the crown of Jesus; two relics of St. Anne, mother of the Virgin Mary; and one bone of New Spain's patron saint, St. Hippolytus (170 ? – 235 ?), considered to be the most important 3rd century theologian of the Roman church. Also found in the chest, but not given to the Jesuits, were artifacts which were reported to be fragments of the *matzo* of the Last Supper and phials (broad, shallow drinking vessels) of the blood of Jesus and of the Virgin Mary's milk. (King Alfonso VI commissioned a sumptuous silver reliquary to contain these latter remains that are still to be seen in the cathedral treasury of Oviedo.) After the relics were taken away from the sailors who had rescued them from the tortured seas, they were finally placed in their reliquaries at the *Colegio Maximo de San Pedro y San Pablo* in 1576 and 1578.

Early in 1588, another fleet would also meet with untoward conditions at the port of Vera Cruz. That fleet as anxiously awaited as the one on which the Robledos arrived, would be dashed to pieces on the reefs at the mouth of the harbor. Over 138 persons would perish in sight of the town for lack of boats on shore to save them.

Texcoco

1. A blue corn mush and a thin gruel of the same.

La Carrera: Direct Commerce with the New World

1. Literally, 'to walk the stations.' The term may refer to the Stations of the Cross, a series of 14 pictures or carvings which depict incidents in the last journey of Christ from Pilate's house to His entombment. They are commonly arranged round the walls of a church. It is a popular devotion to visit the stations in order, reciting prayers and meditating on each incident. The term may instead refer to so-called Station Days or Station Churches. Station Days were those on which the pope formerly celebrated Mass in one of the so-called Station Churches in Rome. The Papal Station Masses fell into disuse, especially during the exile of the popes at Avignon, but traces of the custom survive in the indulgences attached to visits to the Station Churches, and, by extension, to a church new to the penitent. The meaning here may be understood as attending church for a private devotion at an hour other than for the celebration of the Mass.

The Beyond

1. This decree may have been prompted by Sir Humphrey Gilbert's plan for a series of English voyages for the exploration and settlement of eastern North America. It suggests that there was a sense of urgency in extending Spanish hegemony north and eastward from New Spain.

2. While these events were coming to their conclusion on the bison plains, important explorations were also being conducted along the east coast of North America. These forays, which occurred between 1584 and 1590, under the command of Sir Walter Raleigh, centered on Roanoke Island in the modern states of North Carolina and Virginia. Their purpose was to protect English privateering by establishing mainland bases in North America from which they might attack the Spanish West Indies, as well as the fleets sailing from them, more successfully. These explorations, which were to become known as the 'Roanoke Voyages,' represented the first English attempts to plant fortified places and permanent colonies on North American soil. Although they eventually failed, they are what drove Spain to continue in its drive north from New Spain.

3. "Sleeves are good after Easter," says Cervantes in his masterpiece *Don Quixote*, for sleeves were originally given as presents and hence came to signify a gift. It is noted that Queen Isabel made Ferdinand's shirts and that he complained that she replaced the sleeves many times before making him a new shirt. Red sleeves, to be worn at the time of her execution, were given to Mary Queen of Scots by one of her attendants.

4. This Spanish word means pumpkin. It is also used in the expression *dar calabazas*, literally to 'give the pumpkin to,' referring to the rejection of a man's marriage proposal or similar jilting.

5. In the seven-year period, 1565 through 1572, an incredible 66 Jesuits alone were added to the company of martyrs in missions from Japan to Brazil. An additional 36 died while nursing those suffering from the plague in epidemics in Lithuania, Rome, and Spain.

New Horizons

1. This was the *sambenito* or *saco bendito* (sacred sack) which was often referred to as an *abito* in official records. An innovation of the Spanish Inquisition, it was a yellow linen garment painted over with devils and flames. If the condemned individual was to be burned at the stake notes Cecil Roth in *A History of the Marranos*, his *abito* "bore a representation of devils thrusting heretics into the fires of hell." If the condemned person had escaped the stake by confession, "the flames pointed downwards," and as punishment, the *abito* "had to be worn in public, particularly on Sundays and festivals, even after the release of the prisoner, exposing him to universal scorn and derision. After its immediate utility had passed," the *abito* "was generally hung up in the parish church . . . accompanied by a fitting inscription: the wearer and his family being thus marked out for lasting humiliation. These memorials of shame were destroyed only with the abolition of the Inquisition in the early years of the 19th century." p. 131.

2. One of the functions of the Inquisition was that of giving certificates of *limpieza de sangre* to persons who had no traceable Jewish or Moslem ancestor

to contaminate their linage. Participation in some entities—for example, commissions in the army or entrance into the faculty or even the student body at some universities—were confined to persons who could fulfill this condition. *A History of the Marranos*, p. 75.

3. This expression was employed to advise the rowers of a bark to make ready, and used when they had to row lustily.

Caxco

1. The Robledo and Romero inventories are as they appear in the official records as reported in, *Don Juan de Onate, Colonizer of New Mexico*, pages 245 & 265.

Honor and Pride

1. The siege lasted three years, three months, and thirteen days.

2. This phenomenon, the killing of body lice, is said to be observable immediately after passing the Azores. *Don Quixote de la Mancha*, p. 1005, Chapter XXIX, note 7.

Santa Barbara

1. A individual charged with the administration and defense of a given region as, in this case, the *adelantado's* deputy.

The Initiation

1. Dubbed the 'Apostle of the Indies,' the Sevillian, Bartolome de Las Casas, was the first priest ordained in the New World. Twice himself an *encomendero* (in Hispaniola and Cuba), he denounced Spanish exploitation of the Indians. After renouncing his *encomiendas*, he spent the rest of his life crusading against the *encomienda* system and the military conquest of the New World peoples.

2. It was probably 17-year-old Ana, and perhaps Catalina, who may have also been in her teens, who caught their eye. Some of these flirtations and courtships were eventually successful. Alonso Varela married Catalina Perez de Bustillo. Hernando de Hinojos married Beatriz Perez de Bustillo. Asencio de Arechuleta, also with the expedition but not among the brothers mentioned above, eventually married Ana Perez de Bustillo. A fourth Perez de Bustillo girl, Yumar, married Antonio Baca who, with his parents and several siblings, joined the colony in 1600.

3. A dependent administrative district.

4. A mendicant's certificate which allowed students to ask for alms under license from the rector of the university, or, failing that, from the ecclesiastical court of their diocese.

The Trail

1. Water was also found at the *Sierrezuela de las Ogeras* and especially at the *Ojos Milagrossos*, so-named because when a horse stepped in a bog near a

large spring, a waterspout about the thickness of an orange shot into the air nearly to the height of a man and then continued gushing about a span high.

The Taking

1. The description of the fish the colonists provided speaks to how different today's river is from the one they encountered. They took *bagre, machote, robalo* (a fish like bream), *armado, apujas, matelote,* and a white fish almost half a yard long that resembles *jurel* a spiny sea fish of the mackerel family.

2. *Conquistadors in North America,* p. 225.

PERIOD III: THE KINGDOM OF NEW MEXICO

PART I: The Year of Two Seasons

Cualacu

1. This was also the approach used by Meriwether Lewis during June of 1805 while accomplishing 'the great portage' on his trek up the Missouri River to the Pacific Ocean. Lewis had spotted a single cottonwood tree of some 22 inches in diameter just below the entrance of a creek, the only tree of such size within 20 miles. He put six men to work cutting it down. Then, sawing it crosswise, his men made wheels for the 'trucks' or wagons they constructed for transporting the canoes and baggage around the Great Falls of the Missouri.

2. Even before Vasquez de Coronado, who entered the region in 1540, the crown issued many *cedulas* and ordinances to safeguard the Indians' communal land and water rights. The basic decree of 1533 said in part: "They [the governors and viceroy] shall leave to the Indians their lands, patrimony and pastures in such a way that the Indians may not lack what they need and that they may have all the relief and repose possible for the support of their home and families." This was followed by the *Ordinances of His Majesty for the New Discoveries, Conquests and Pacifications* issued by King Philip II at *Bosque de Segovia* on July 13, 1573. These ordinances stated in part that the Indians who lived in permanent communities "shall have advantages of water, land and wood, entrances and exits and lands for cultivation, and an *ejido* [common land] of a league in length where the Indians can have their stock without their mixing with those of the Spaniards."

3. He had been previously sent ahead to explore the road on April 26th and had traveled 16 leagues.

4. Onate's fourth great-grandmother, Maria Nunez ha Levi, was the sister of Rabbi Salamon ha Levi who, as Pablo de Santa Maria, became a convert. His conversion, which was apparently sincere, was followed by those of his mother, his sister, and his five children, two sons of whom became priests. All three of

the clerics, Rabbi Salamon ha Levi included, later became bishops of the Catholic Church. *A History of the Marranos*, pages 19 and 24.

5. Decree of 28 October 1480.

6. A mounted soldier or knight who enjoyed the status of a nobleman.

7. A bed on wheels that may be pushed under another bed.

8. A relay of horses.

9. Although the Inquisition was especially concerned with those who on their death-bed reverted to this practice, this reflected a vague biblical rather than Jewish reminiscence lost in the dust of time.

10. Place or spot.

11. This rite was a survival from classical mythology in which a piece of gold or a jewel was to be used as toll payment for the boatman, Charon, who carried the souls of the dead across the River Styx to the Lower World.

The Diary

1. Often erroneously referred to as an antelope.

2. The trail the colonists followed, possibly the trace of the so-called 'turquoise trade route,' may have been one of those by which the Indians of Mesoamerica influenced the Pueblos' religion and culture. These trade routes, one of which was more than 1,100 miles in length, were used by trade missions of the Aztec, Maya, Toltec and other ancient Mexican and Central American peoples, as they came northward in search of the precious mineral turquoise. The nomads these Mesoamerican traders encountered eventually adopted certain aspects of the Mesoamerican culture including the domestication of *maize* and established permanent villages. As a result of the contact between these various peoples, the Pueblo Indian culture flourished on an unparalleled scale in North America.

Antecedents

1. *Spanish Exploration in the Southwest, 1542-1706*, p. 220.

The First Village

1. A ritual using flour for divination.

2. 1.85 yards, a unit equivalent to the height of an average man.

3. *Spanish Exploration in the Southwest, 1542-1706*, pp. 216-17.

The Necessary Water

1. The river takes its name from the Tewa word, '*tzama*,' reaning 'red.' Rising in the mountains of present-day southern Colorado, it flows into the Rio Ojo Caliente below Okhe.

2. From the Arabic *as-saqiyah*, for canal.

Chapel and Kiva

1. A coarse goatskin cloth, so rough that it pricked one when he touched it.

2. The gathering up of wandering natives and placing them under the guidance of friars from one of the missionary orders.

3. *Spanish Exploration in the Southwest, 1542-1706*, p. 177.

Hunting

1. In reference to their high ratio of noise, and lightning to the low level of moisture produced.

New Promises

1. Although the United States has the richest temperate zone assemblage in the world—some 200,000 species, many of which are found in New Mexico— some of these fish appear to be misidentified. The site, however, is not. It is the Gallinas River near present-day Las Vegas, but Vicente was not the first to be there. The spot first known as *Las Dispensas*, which refers to a storehouse for food, was called that by Pedro de Castaneda, chronicler of the Vasquez de Coronado expedition. One of the soldiers in this expedition said regarding the place: "There we found something we prized more than gold or silver, namely, much *maize*, beans, and chickens larger than those in New Spain, and all better and whiter than I have seen in my whole life." *Restored Towns and Historic Districts of America*, p. 308. The river, whose name refers to the *gallina de la tierra*, or chicken of the region, may describe prairie chickens, pheasants or other wild fowl. The stream, which includes the Beaver and Hollinger creeks, flows southeast to join the Pecos River six miles northwest of Colonias.

2. *Spanish Exploration in the Southwest, 1542-1706*, pp. 223-24.

3. *Spanish Exploration in the Southwest, 1542-1706*, p. 226.

4. That is, the Asiatic buffalo, or wild ox.

5. *Spanish Exploration in the Southwest, 1542-1706*, pp. 228-29.

6. His surname refers to a grove in the meadow where cattle pasture.

Mills and Creatures

1. This creature, a Coelophysis, was discovered, or perhaps rediscovered, by George Whitaker at Ghost Ranch, near Abiquiu, New Mexico, in 1947.

The Bitter Season

1. An old word used by peasants to denote food (meat) prepared to be eaten with bread.

2. A structure made of three sticks tied together in the form of a cross. The upright member is left long, so that it can be used as a handle for holding the meat over a fire.

3. A kind of cold broth made with bread, olive oil, water, vinegar, garlic, onions, etc.

4. Literally, 'rotten pot,' a highly seasoned dish of meat and vegetables cooked in a bulging, wide-mouthed pot or jar known as an *olla*.

5. Getting oneself into a position where he cannot regain his feet.

6. A pony that readily allows himself to be handled and subdued.

7. Tame oxen employed in driving bulls from pasture.

8. A legendary character who prophesized the obvious. Sample: It is certain that if you go to the mirror you will see your face.

Home and Hearth

1. Leather wall hangings were employed by the Spanish as a wall covering in summer, especially in Andalusia, where their winter place was taken by tapestries. Tapestries, however, were an expensive luxury for the poor, who in place of them, and in all seasons, made use of silk serges or twill. The serge and twill were made into a kind of coarse frieze adorned with painted or embroidered figures or landscapes.

2. The so-called 'Fast of Esther,' a *marrano* feast that rivaled that of the Day of Atonement itself.

Acoma

1. The native name of the town is Aco and that of the people, the Acome. Footnote 4, pp. 182-83, *Spanish Exploration in the Southwest, 1542-1706*. The names may derive from the Keresan work *hak'u* meaning 'to prepare or to plan.' At least two alternate meanings are given: 'the place where the echo returned clearest,' and 'people of the white rock.'

2. *Spanish Exploration in the Southwest, 1542-1706*, pp. 183-84.

3. *The Last Conquistador, Juan de Onate and the Settling of the Far Southwest*, p. 128.

4. Perez, writing in his 1610 *History of New Mexico* about the 1598 expedition, said of his ordeal: "At last I arrived at a great cliff [El Morro] at whose foot flowed a crystalline stream. I threw myself into its water, blinded and burning with thirst, and drank long of its cool waters."

5. An *estado* was approximately five feet, seven inches, the height of an average man. The Spaniards estimated the height of the mesa to be more than 279 feet. It was 367.

6. A kind of blood baptism symbolizing capturing a strong animal's blood through contact.

We Meant Them No Harm

1. Aquinas's three conditions for a just war were the authority of the ruler, a just cause, and a right intention.

A Rage of Cannonballs

1. They had been using the sunflower for many purposes for at least 8,000 years. Roasted hulls were steeped in boiling water to make a coffee-like beverage, while white dye was extracted from hulls and petals. Face paint was made from dried petals and pollen. Oil, extracted from the ground-up seeds by boiling, was used for cooking.

2. Literally, "Saint James and close in up them." The sense is 'close in upon them' or 'attack.'

3. *Acoma the Sky City*, p. 87.

Preparations for Defense

1. Involved in this defensive move, among others, were Francisco Robledo, "Esteban, [the] noble, well-loved son of [the] great [Juan de Vitoria] Carvajal." Juan Perez de Bustillo, Geronimo Marquez, and his sons Juan Diaz, Pedro Hernandez and Francisco Marquez; Hernan Martin Serrano the elder, and his son of the same name, "the good [Francisco] Cadimo;" and Juan de Herrera.

2. With her, and bearing arms were, among others, her daughter, *dona* Juana de Trejo, wife of Captain Diego de Zubia; *dona* Isabel Sanchez, daughter of Captain Alonso Sanchez, and wife of the slain Diego Nunez de Chaves; *dona* Beatriz Navarro, wife of Captain Alonso de Sosa Albornoz; *dona* Ana Perez de Bustillo, daughter of Juan Perez de Bustillo, later to become the wife of Asencio de Arechuleta; *dona* Lucia Lopez Robledo, daughter of the deceased Pedro Robledo, and wife of Bartolome Romero; *dona* Maria de la Cruz, wife of Juan Perez de Bustillo; and *dona* Pascuala Bernal, wife of Juan Griego.

Crime and Punishment

1. *Don Juan de Onate, Colonizer of New Mexico*, pp. 477-78.

2. This was a Pueblo name for the bison-hunting Apache Indians who lived on the eastern plains.

3. *Spanish Exploration in the Southwest, 1542-1706*, p. 218.

PART II: The Starving Times

Ore

1. *Spanish Exploration in the Southwest, 1542-1706*, p. 217

2. *Spanish Exploration in the Southwest, 1542-1706*, p. 219.

3. *Spanish Exploration in the Southwest, 1542-1706*, p. 244.

4. *Spanish Exploration in the Southwest, 1542-1706*, p. 246.

The Church of San Miguel

1. Forbidden by the Council of Trent (1545-63) except in special cases when no other solution was possible. The prohibition may derive from a medieval belief that the apocalyptic peoples of Gog and Magog will at the Last Judgment come from the north.

Reinforcements

1. Among his possessions were a coat of mail; *cuisse*; *bevor*; *harquebus*, with accessories; leather jacket; lance; leather shield; eight cavalry horses; one cart with 12 oxen; six suits of clothes of coarse cloth and silk for his wife; one dozen shirts; six sheets; two doublets (a close fitting jacket, with or without sleeves, usually worn by men); and two shawls. For his daughters, he had four sets of

clothes for each one; 32 shirts for his children; four doublets for each; three mattresses and accessories; and one box of shoes. For himself, he brought six suits of wool and silk; 12 shirts; and one piece of Rouen linen.

The Snows of Winter

1. It was the custom to kill pigs on St. Martin's Day. Thus the proverb: 'To every pig comes its Martinmas.'

2. The traitor of *Roncesvalles* in the Charlemagne legend.

3. A place near Ciudad Real where the Holy Brotherhood executed its prisoners.

Quivira

1. Bancroft, *History of North Mexican States*, supports the Introduction.

2. *Spanish Exploration in the Southwest, 1542-1706*, p. 251, text and second footnote.

3. The fig: a gesture of contempt made by closing the fist and inserting the thumb between the index and middle fingers. *Mamona*: a gesture that consists of laying five fingers on ones beard as a sign of contempt.

4. An amount equal to 1.6 bushels.

Betrayal / Cravenness / Treason

1. Braided bread which resembles *challa*, the Sabbath bread of the Jews.

2. *Yerba Buena* or spearmint herbs, and *yerba del manzo*, or lizard's tail, both of which were used for a hand pomade. *Cana agria* for one's teeth. *Amole*, for shampoo.

3. The pitch from a pinon tree, used to remove boils or deep splinters from under the skin.

Pursuit

1. The Manzanos later took their name from old apple orchards in the vicinity that are reputed to be among the oldest in the United States. The Ladrones, which attained legendary status for the difficulty of their terrain, later became the hideout for Navajo, Apache, and American cattle rustlers and horse thieves.

2. A Spaniard living in, or returned from the colonies.

EPILOGUE

1. Quotations are from the Spanish record as presented in *Don Juan de Onate, Colonizer of New Mexico.*

2. Antonio Fernando Carvajal, native of Fundao and one of the most prominent merchants in London, was the founder of English Jewry. Luis de Carvajal the younger, considered to be the most learned of Judaizers, was martyred in New Spain in 1596. His uncle, also named Luis de Carvajal, was governor of *Nuevo Leon.* Juan de Vitoria Carvajal was one of Onate's colonists.

3. An old Spanish term dating back to the early Middle Ages and meaning swine. It was applied to recent Jewish converts in reference to their aversion to the flesh of the animal in question. (Roth)

4. The Holy Office had attempted to establish the Inquisition in New Mexico in 1598 but did not succeed in doing so until 1625. Francisco Gomez is also one of only two individuals (the other being Gaspar Perez de Villagra) for whom we have documentary evidence of his receipt of the title of *hidalgo.*

5. In return for the privilege of collecting tribute from specified Indian pueblos, the *encomenderos*, the backbone of colonial defense, maintained horses and weapons, and responded to the governor's call to arms when needed.

6. *Kiva, Cross and Crown*, pp. 191-92.

7. *A History of the Jews in New Mexico*, p. 18.

8. *When Cultures Meet: Remembering San Gabriel del Yunge Oweenge (Papers from the October 20, 1984 Conference held at San Juan Pueblo, New Mexico.*